1957

A TOAST TO LADY MARY

"A blessed companion is a book"—JERROLD

Also by

DORIS LESLIE

Novels

FULL FLAVOUR

FAIR COMPANY

CONCORD IN JEOPARDY

HOUSE IN THE DUST

FOLLY'S END

THE PEVERILLS

ANOTHER CYNTHIA: *A Fantasy*

Biographical Studies

THAT ENCHANTRESS: *Life of Abigail Hill, Lady Masham*

POLONAISE: *A Romance of Chopin*

ROYAL WILLIAM: *Life of William IV*

WREATH FOR ARABELLA: *Life of Lady Arabella Stuart*

THE GREAT CORINTHIAN: *Portrait of the Prince Regent*

A TOAST
TO
LADY MARY

★

DORIS LESLIE

THE COMPANION BOOK CLUB
LONDON

FOR
SHANE LESLIE
direct descendant
of
LADY MARY

THIS edition, issued in 1955, is for members of The Companion Book Club, 8 Long Acre, London, W.C.2, from which address particulars of membership may be obtained. The book is published by arrangement with the original publishers, Hutchinson & Co. (Publishers) Ltd.

FOREWORD

IN THIS portrait of Lady Mary Wortley Montagu, presented in narrative form, I have endeavoured implicitly to follow the main events of her life. All letters and verses quoted are authentic; no character is fictitious. Those familiar with Lady Mary's correspondence will perhaps recognize that, wherever possible, I have used her own words in the dialogue.

I am gratefully indebted to the Earl of Harrowby and to Messrs. Methuen for permission to quote certain excerpts from the letters collected by 'George Paston', and first published in her biography of Lady Mary Wortley Montagu. These include the letter initialed M.P. on page 96.

A list of authorities consulted will be found at the end of the book.

DORIS LESLIE

'Where are people matched!—I suppose we
shall all come right in Heaven; as in a country
dance the hands are strangely given and
taken . . . and at last all meet their partners
when the jig is done.'

Lady Mary Wortley Montagu

Great George Street, London, August 21, 1762.

Propped on her pillows she lay in the sweet tranquillity of deadened pain. They had been dosing her with hemlock. "My head," she said, "feels light."

From her bed she could see roof-tops darkly shining after recent rain; a smoke spiral drifted upward from a chimney-stack, soft against a rose-flushed sky. The room closed in with shadows gliding formless and uncoloured amid the soft confusion of her mind. Swift glimpses of the vanished years, unfolding from the veiled mists of memory, were revealed, fresh as a primrose, or the mossy path her steps retraced through forest ways to Thoresby. . . .

She was at her writing-desk that overlooked the park where fallow deer, motionless as carven bronze, grazed beneath the elms. It was one of those clear April days that steal June's warmth from summer, with the blue above, the green below, and bird-song rioting in thickets.

Her strayed glance fell on the unfinished page before her and, dipping her quill in the inkpot, she wrote:

'I have trusted my reputation in your hands. Perhaps I have been indiscreet. Would any woman but me renounce all the world for one, or would any man but you be insensible of . . .'

Her pen spluttered, made a blot; then, as she seized the sandcaster to sprinkle it, pandemonium below drove the colour from her cheeks and brought her in a flurry to her feet.

A jingle of harness, a scraping of wheels, a hammering upon the door, and her father's voice, loud-raised, shouting at a footman. "Her ladyship? Where is she?"

A mort of trouble brewing now, and he, un-named, the cause of it!

She snatched her letter, thrust it in the bosom of her gown, composed her face and went to meet her father. Her head was high, her little body held erect. None should guess she trembled.

7

Straddling the hearth-rug before the blazing logs in the great oaken hall he stood, his heavy jowl sunk in a cascade of lace, his hands beneath the tails of his corbeau velvet coat.

"So, for all your cunning you've been catched!" roared her father. "Creeping like a trollop up backstairs to go a-courting. What! My daughter to disgrace my name in the house of a Grub Street hack—I say you did!" With his clenched fist he smote the air as if to crush her bleating protest. "You were seen. You borrowed my coach. I took you for a girl o' sense—as much sense as'll sit on a farthing. My liveries are known in all London, you fool. Why didn't you hire a chair?"

His concern, it would seem, was less for her lack of propriety than for the blow to his pride.

She bit back the hot words that leapt to the thought, standing meek as butter there before him with eyelids lowered and hate seething.

"Well?" bellowed her father, "and what have you to say?"

She had nothing to say. This, then, was the end of it, or maybe the beginning. Let him shout!

"And if you dare defy me, sending messages and letters under cover of a mopsy, picked from the gutter to act as go-between, I'll——"

Yet there had been a time when she had worshipped him, this large, full-blooded, noisy man, whose rageful threats rose up to hit the rafters for every peeping maidservant to hear. . . . That time, unforgotten, when on a summer's evening she had been awakened from first sleep to see her old nurse bending over and the dazzle of a candle in her eyes.

"Why, what's to do?"

"There's all to do, and no good in the doing. Up with you. Hurry now! We're to be dressed and be gone. His lordship's orders."

"Why?"

"Who's to ask his lordship why and wherefore? The coach is come and we must go."

Nurse dragged the bedclothes from her, stripped her of her shift, dressed her in her best gold broidered taffety, wrapped her in a hooded cloak and walked her down the stairs.

It was darkening. High above a tree-top one lonely ice-

8

green star winked at her through the window-glass when she sat, with Nurse beside her, in the coach that bumped and rattled on its way to the speed of its six Flemish horses. Bouncing on the springless seat till she felt bruised all over, she asked:

"Is my father taken sick?"

"Maybe; though if he is, I'll lay that he's more sick than sorry." Which left her none the wiser, and in some quick alarm.

With her nose pressed to the breath-fogged pane, she saw dim fields give place to cottage windows glowing lemon-coloured in the twilight. Nurse, plucking at her prickly chin, was full of sombre forebodings.

"Last night a weasel crossed my path for warning. And now comes this commandment from his lordship. I knew how it would be. Odso! A bad night's work."

The coach swept into a broad high-road, and stopped at a turnpike for toll; then on again, passing great houses lit by flambeaux and the torches of link-boys waiting to guide chance pedestrians home through the grim murky ways of the town. Soon the coach slackened pace, threading in and out the traffic—never had been seen so many chaises, chairs, and horsemen; and strolling gentlemen in fine array of velvet laced with gold and silver flashed upon her vision as pictures in a fire under the crazy gleam of lanthorns swinging. Ladies, too, there were, in masks that hid their eyes, and gowns that sparkled, shimmering, like flowers in the sunshine after rain. But Nurse drew close the curtain to hide the lovely sight of them—"for I'll not have you looking upon sin."

"Where are we now?" she wished to know.

"At Hell's gate," was the comfortless reply.

The coach halted with a scraping of hooves and wheels on cobbles. A footman came to hand her out. Nurse, wheezing, followed after.

An open doorway flung a path of candleshine across the narrow street, and in that flood of light, as if called there by magic, stood her father.

"Here she is—God bless her!" His winey breath was on her lips as he stooped to brush away a lock of hair that fell upon her forehead. Then he took her by the hand and led

9

her through a passage lined with portraits of gentlemen in attitudes.

"So let them see," her father said, "and let them judge. I've laid my shirt on you tonight, my darling. Stay you here——" he bade the nurse, who urged him:

"I beseech your lordship—have a care."

"A pox on your croaking. Hold your mouth! Let's off with this."

He unfastened and flung aside his daughter's cloak, and with one of his comical looks at her, said: "Make a bold entrance, sweet, an you love me. Lift your chin and show a smile."

Pattering beside him on the rush-matted floor she laughed to find him jovial and friendly, scarcely to be recognized in the monstrous furbelow that fell in glossy curls about his shoulders. How white his teeth, how ruddy his face, how handsome he, and loving-kind. . . . She must be dreaming.

There was a sound of song, a clapping of hands, a stamping of feet; a boisterous welcome for somebody. Who?

She stood with her father in the entrance to a room filled to over-crowding with gentlemen: no ladies. A myriad candles in crystal lustres shone through a haze of tobacco smoke, lighting a table loaded with eatables, flagons of wine, dishes of all sorts—a feast, to make her aware of a hole in her stomach. Some hours had passed since she had supped.

Releasing her hand, her father pushed her forward and addressed the company. "Your Grace, my lords and fellow members, allow me to present you to . . ."

They rose and yelled for her; lifted brimming bumpers and drank to her; they pressed around her, fingering her hair, praising her eyes, her eyelashes. "An inch long, ecod! You could hang rings on 'em!"

A jaunty dark man in the tallest of wigs knelt to encircle her waist with his arm. His face was on a level with hers, and he smelt of wine-drenched violets.

"O, admirable!" he declared:

> 'Would I were free from this restraint,
> Or else had hopes to win her.
> Would she could make a saint of me,
> Or I of her a sinner!'

10

Through the tempest of applause that followed, someone called:

"She conquers Congreve!" And the whole room voiced an echo, "To conquer all of us!"

Then they sat her at the table and plied her with syllabub, muscatels, and sweetmeats; and when she had eaten as much as she could, till her belly was tight as a drum, they lifted her and stood her there among the bowls of fruit and steaming punch and empty bottles; and one man brought a drinking-glass and placed it at her feet. In his right hand something glinted, brighter than the jewels on his fingers or a rainbow in the sky.

"Now see," he cried, "your name inscribed hereon for all posterity!"

Amid the buzz of talk and shouting laughter she watched, and watching, marvelled how with a diamond he scratched that brittle surface till letters formed for her to read as clear as copperplate.

The Lady Mary Pierrepont
Toast of the Kit-Cat Club

And to those passing shades of remembrance she whispered: "Never in my future life was I to know such happiness as on that distant summer's night when I was . . . eight years old."

THE YEARS BETWEEN
(1703-1739)

★ I ★

SHE WAS the eldest daughter of Evelyn Pierrepont, fifth Earl of Kingston, of Thoresby in Nottinghamshire. The death of his wife, after nine years of marriage, had left Lord Kingston with four children on his hands, to mourn his loss six merry months at most.

Of her mother Mary could remember nothing more than a blurred face, small and white, and a little thin voice like a broken bird's; and that when Papa was present she seemed smaller still and whiter than a crocus in the grass at eventide.

But although totally eclipsed by her husband, Lady Kingston, whose maiden name was Feilding, daughter of the third Earl of Denbigh, may have passed to her first-born in latent heritage, that love of learning and of letters not manifest in her or any other of her kin, with exception of one: Henry Fielding.

When asked by a relative, Lord Denbigh, why he chose to write his name with the 'ei' in reverse, he answered because he was the only member of his family who knew how to spell. In that he would appear to be mistaken. Lady Mary Pierrepont, his cousin once removed, could spell, could read, and was writing Latin verse before the author of *Tom Jones* had been conceived. Yet her education, admittedly, was wanting, in that she declares she was entirely self-taught. The old nurse who had nursed her mother and was beset with superstition, filled her head with tales of witches and hobgoblins, led her through the alphabet and left her at the end of it to discover the meaning of words. She soon did. Her father's library supplied her with romances. She read all she could lay hands on, devoured the novels of D'Urfé and Mademoiselle Scudéry, 'Englished by a Person of Honour', and wrote her first poem—in imitation of Ovid's

Epistles—at the ripe age of twelve. Attentively she sat through her brother William's lessons while he laboured with his tutor at his Latin, that she might be, she modestly confesses, 'not a Master but a Mistress of the Arts.' In short the Lady Mary was a prodigy.

Her father, who had earlier inclined to look upon his daughter's thirst for knowledge as a novelty, came later to regard it in the light of a hare-lip, or any other blemish on her beauty, which would not, he considered, be improved by brains. As a child, however, she delighted him. The success of his whimsical suggestion that she be displayed at the Kit-Cat Club, and unanimously voted the Toast of the Year, was, he believed, a happy omen for her future.

In common with every other gentleman of quality, Lord Kingston was convinced that the purpose of a female lay wholly in the capture of a mate. Suitably endowed with the huntress's equipment, she should prove herself a worthy participator in the chase which must inevitably lead her to the altar. Judge, therefore, of Lord Kingston's disappointment and dismay to find his pretty Mary did not conform to pattern. While outwardly a model of filial devotion it was evident that, for all her tractability, she possessed a will to clash with his. Obstinacy and determination lay in the set of her square little jaw, belied by the dimple in her chin. Delicately formed and small for her age—she never grew after fourteen—she epitomized the essence of engaging femininity, and conversed like an Oxford Don!

Greatly did Lord Kingston deplore the bitter fate that had left him the sole parent of three daughters, two of whom were passably attractive and one of them exceptionally so. Yet he fully realized that Mary's charmful assets might prove a liability. An eligible *parti* lured on by her good looks would doubtless be warned off by her keen wit. The other two presented no problem to their father. He had shirked responsibility of one—Evelyn, the youngest; her he had placed with his sister, Lady Cheyne, of Cheyne Manor at Chelsea. But he could not so readily rid himself of Mary. It was necessary his house should have a hostess when he entertained his guests, and no sooner was she old enough to act in that capacity than he insisted she should learn the art of carving; a formidable undertaking in those days when dinner began with a baron of beef, a boar's head and a dozen ducks or capons.

On such occasions Mary had to eat her meal alone, an hour or so beforehand, in order to perform her functions at the board. The rowdy trenchermen who sat around it, when liberally spiced with wine, were anything but dainty in their speech. Mary must have shrunk from their loud swearing, their red drink-sodden faces, their leering looks at her. And it may be that her young association with unbridled masculinity impelled her to re-create in his image not Man, as she knew him, but a demigod austere and gently spoken.

An approximate approach to her youthful ideal is envisioned in her 'Autobiography,' written as a novel but in which we are assured that not one 'sillable', except the names, is fiction.

And in this, supposedly, true account of herself, 'Laetitia', alias Mary Pierrepont, is first introduced to 'Sebastian'.

Who was 'Sebastian'? Where did 'Laetitia', daughter of the 'Duke of Regiavilla', meet this elegant and personable gentleman, the reputed lover of a certain 'Mademoiselle'? A fictitious name for this young lady is withheld from the romance, yet the part she plays in its first chapter is not without significance to the story of that strangest courtship ever told.

The prototype of 'Sebastian', thinly disguised, was the son of Sidney Wortley Montagu of Wharncliffe Lodge in Yorkshire, between whom and Lord Kingston a certain similarity of circumstance existed. Both were widowers; both had been bereft of their wives while their children were still in the nursery, and both had inherited considerable estates.

The Honourable Sidney Montagu, a younger son of the Earl of Sandwich, had married Anne Newcomen, the greatly loved illegitimate daughter of Sir Francis Wortley, under whose Will and at whose death her husband assumed his name, and with it the Wortley fortune.

The father of 'Sebastian' belonged to a generation that had imbibed to its depths the gaieties offered at the Court of the second Charles. Raffish, hard-drinking, bucolic, his reputation in the county was scarcely unequivocal. His amorous adventures were a by-word. He kept a mistress in state at a neighbouring establishment, liberally entertained his cronies at her table, and was lugged to bed drunk every night. He cared nothing for his person, and wore habitually in the house and out of it a dilapidated wide-brimmed, low-crowned hat in the style of a Spanish sombrero.

Seated in a high-backed chair with a flagon of wine at his elbow, he would receive his brother, the venerable mild Dean of Durham, who, notwithstanding he professed profoundest shock at the Squire's bawdy, declined no invitation to attend the saturnalia at Wharncliffe Lodge.

What more natural, therefore, than that Anne Wortley Montagu, the Squire's elder daughter, and the Lady Mary Pierrepont, should be drawn together by a common source of grievance? The father of each, while feared for his rude temper, was—they had to face it—a disreputable rake. On the contrary, Anne's brother, young Mr. Wortley Montagu, was polished and pure and unsullied as old Mr. Wortley Montagu was not. A master of the classics and a graduate, with honours, of Trinity College, Cambridge, he had made the Grand Tour and returned from it an ardent Whig of fastidious taste and political ambitions. This paragon, then, was the exquisite 'Sebastian' who laid siege to 'Laetitia's' heart.

His sister Anne, a lively, large-bosomed, rollicking girl, was diametrically opposed in character to Mary, whom she regarded as possessed of all the virtues. To be sure there were occasions when Mary was inclined to be high-handed, a trifle sharp with one less gifted, less in every way outstanding than herself. But if Mary accepted Anne's homage as her due she was always ready to allow for Anne's deficiencies, and obligingly attempted to instruct.

The nameless 'Mademoiselle' of 'Laetitia's' narrative may have been one of several young ladies who lived in the neighbourhood of Thoresby; or despite 'Laetitia's' declaration that the story she begins to tell and never finishes is true, 'Mademoiselle' may not have lived at all. Since, however, Laetitia-Mary Pierrepont is insistent on veracity, we can believe 'Mademoiselle' to have been a young person

15

much given to brag, for, according to her own account, every gentleman with whom she came in contact fell a helpless victim to her charms.

The exploits of this lady, some three or four years older than 'Laetitia', were the envy of all who cared to hear how she had been presented in Coronation Year to Her Majesty Queen Anne; of her modish gowns, her jewels, and the many offers for her hand and heart, none of which, it seems, she had accepted. Her heart was given, her hand promised to the elegant and scholarly 'Sebastian'; most galling to 'Laetitia', whose Papa, the redoubtable 'Duke of Regiavilla', kept her in his castle under strictest supervision. And so it came about that 'Laetitia', exceedingly vexed by—one would hesitate to say jealous of—the vainglorious 'Mademoiselle', planned to bring pride to its fall. A party for this purpose was contrived at the house of a willing accomplice: none other, we surmise, than Mistress Anne. A company of ladies, all of whom were under seventeen, sat around the card-table to play Bassette. Only one gentleman had been invited to the gathering, 'Sebastian', the guest of honour, 'who', we are told, 'did not expect much conversation among a set of romps'.

He was mistaken.

While the hostess busied herself with the tea, 'Laetitia' took the opportunity to criticize and discuss a new play then being acted in London, and 'in a manner so just and so knowing he was as much amazed as if he had heard a piece of waxwork talk'. . . . Which is the more surprising, since at that time 'Laetitia' had never visited the Playhouse in her life . . . 'From thence the discourse turned to poetry, in which she showed herself to be so well versed in the moderns and classics,' that the gentleman was positively stupefied by the youthful Laetitia's erudition. Cards were forgotten, the tea stood untasted, and Mademoiselle, 'forced to be silent while they talked about what she could never understand', turned scarlet with mortification.

Sebastian, who had agreed to mark the score, was called sharply to attention by Mademoiselle, whose nails, we take it, were itching to get at Laetitia. She, as if unconscious of the storm she had brewed around the tea-cups, innocently continued her discussion, to the crushing defeat of her rival. 'This day,' the narrative proceeds, 'put an end to his interest in the lady . . .' Indeed his admiration for Laetitia was visible for all to see.

It is not certain how much fiction is mingled here with fact, but that Mary first became acquainted with Edward Wortley Montagu in some such fashion, and that she did show off her knowledge for his benefit is likely. From that time forth the friendship between the Lady Mary and Edward's sister Anne progressed with fervour. Confidences may have been delightedly exchanged when the two young ladies met to gloat over and giggle at the downfall of Mademoiselle.

Alone in Anne's company Mary was never the earnest young pedant discussing the classics and plays. She could condescend, when she chose, to girlish chat. Anne, a few months older than herself, was in one respect more fortunately placed, in that her Papa had allowed her a season in Town. From her Mary learned something of the latest modes, the newest caps, called 'fontanges', vastly unbecoming and starched to tower high in pleated folds above the forehead; of Queen Anne's affection for the beautiful Duchess of Marlborough, wife of the great General who— Anne had it pat—was hen-pecked by his lady and shockingly close-fisted. And her temper! A proper shrew. But no denying the Queen doated on her madly. Yes, they called each other by pet names! 'Mrs. Morley', 'Mrs. Freeman'. Only think! How droll. And everyone in London, or the London that Anne knew, spoke of Her Majesty's liking for 'cold tea', offered by the Duchess to make her drowsy and to stop her drooling.

"Cold tea?" echoed Mary, widening her eyes. "Why should cold tea make her drowsy?"

"Because, my dear, it isn't tea at all." Anne hushed her voice. " 'Tis brandy."

"You mean," said Mary, horrified, "that Her Majesty dr——"

"I mean," Anne deftly interposed, "that I haven't said a word to be repeated. Let's forget it. When will your Papa be bringing you to Court?"

"Never," Mary dismally replied. "He's too fond of himself and the ladies to care about me. I'm kept, as it were," she sighed, "in purdah."

"Never mind," Anne consoled, not daring to ask what was 'purdah'. "You are yet young."

"In years," Mary corrected gently, "but older in my thoughts than you could ever be though you lived till you was ninety."

"You look no more, if as much, as your age," returned Anne, huffed by Mary's supercilious smirk, "and you dress like a child o' ten."

Mary's cheeks pinkened. She set down her cup and glared at her hostess. "That is a misfortune I am powerless to check. 'Tis my father who orders my gowns. True, his taste is odious, but he cannot treat me," she declared, "so childish and guarded all my life. I am fourteen, and some girls of my age are mothers—or wives."

"Yes," Anne commiserated. "Pity 'tis that nature is so backward in obliging you."

At which unwarranted cut Mary kindled. A sore point this, and one where Anne invariably scored, in that she had undergone her transformation, an enviable state of being which Mary had not yet achieved. During the last few months Anne had grown apace, was generously moulded, and wore dresses chosen for her by Lady Halifax, wife of an ex-Chancellor of the Exchequer, and Sidney Wortley Montagu's most distinguished relative. Anne went decked in taffety that rustled, in stockings of green silk, in buckled shoes with high red heels, and rings and things—and of all most to be coveted—a 'modesty tucker' to her low square-necked bodice. But Mary, breastless as a boy in simple ginghams, had nothing for a tucker to conceal, yet:

"I should be thankful," she sweetly commented, "that nature has not overburdened me with flesh."

It was Anne's turn to redden.

"If 'tis my figure your ladyship's pleased to deride, let me tell you I'd sooner be shapely than lean as a lath."

"Some advantage, however, is to be gained from my meagre proportions," cooed Mary, "for at least I don't carry so much to my front that you can't tell it from my behind."

18

But Anne's reply, hot to pounce on this impertinence, halted at her lips, when she perceived in Mary's attitude a metamorphosis. From her eyes, that were neither blue nor grey but of that colour mistakenly called violet, all rancour faded. She sat as one lost in pensive trance to gaze, not at her hostess but over her head at the long window that opened on the lawn. There strolled a gentleman leisurely advancing toward the house, with a spaniel at his heels and a gun beneath his arm.

Mary's eyelids fluttered; she raised one hand as if to enjoin silence while voicelessly, alarmingly, she mouthed.

"Lord, Mary!" cried the startled Anne, "what's taken you?"

" '*Este procul lites, et amaræ prœlia linguæ; Dulcibus est verbis mollis alendus amor*'," quoth Mary, her tone rising ever higher, to end upon a squeak—"which is to say—hem— 'Get hence, contentions and battles of the bitter tongue. Soft love——' " her voice faltered, and was prompted crisply from the window——

" '—is fostered on sweet words.' "

"Mercy on us!" With a stifled shriek Mary laid a hand upon her heart; her lovely lashes lifted till they touched her eyebrows, tilted up and slantwise like the wings of a bird in flight. "Mr. Wortley Montagu! How dreadfully you scared me."

A sober, dignified, elderly young man with a trifle more austerity than humour in his countenance, was Edward Wortley Montagu. Swinging a careful leg across the low-embrasured window-sill, he stepped into the room and bowed apology to Mary for "this ill-timed interruption."

"I thought," Anne told him sulkily—her pout implied his presence was superfluous—"that you were still out shooting with Papa."

"I have left our father under an oak, sleeping off the effect of the refreshment he took to sustain his exertions. Am I not to be allowed a dish of tea?"

"Certainly. I will ring for a cup."

A cup was brought; cakes were passed, and Mary, who had already eaten more than her fill of the dainties supplied, was persuaded to accept and demolished, in rapid succession, three almond pasties and four macaroons. Thereafter conversation, languishing, turned upon the weather. Mr. Wortley Montagu remarked on the likelihood of rain. The munching Lady Mary said she hoped not. She had a long journey before her and if rain were threatening she had best be gone.

Anne ran to her side to press her down into her chair, saying, "But you've only just arrived!" Edward drained his cup, bestowed a piercing glance upon the blushful Mary, and confessed himself surprised to hear her ladyship quote Ovid.

"Oh, that!" With a modest shrug Mary deprecated 'that'. "I have studied Ovid since my infancy."

"Prodigious!" ejaculated Edward in the liveliest amaze. "What other of the Masters do you know?"

"Well, sir," she drooped her lashes, "I doat upon Epictetus, and I've learned most of Horace by heart. I find solace in a stoical philosophy."

"But you told me you much prefer novels," blurted Anne. "And what of the romance you are writing?"

"Do you write romances?" inquired Mr. Wortley Montagu, increasingly impressed.

"Anne!" Mary's colour deepened. "You should not betray a secret."

"You have never said it is a secret. You read a whole chapter to my sister Katharine and me, and I've heard from Mistress Banks and half a dozen others that you've read it to *them*, all about Laetitia and Seb——"

"Sir! I beg you will not heed her foolish prattle," interrupted Mary, crimson to the ears. "Believe me, 'tis Anne, not I, who romances."

"O—ooh, Mary!" Anne's eyes and lips were spherical. "How can you deny it? We saw your handwriting."

"I *can* deny it! You've never seen——"

She was in greatest trouble now, and hideously conscious that Mr. Wortley Montagu, for all he was solemn as a crow, regarded her achievements as unconformable and freakish; a young lady who spoke fluent Latin, who had as good a knowledge of the classics as himself and could, were she put to it, write English prose as well as Mr. Addison, or so she had confessed to Anne—would she repeat that too?—was side-splitting as a sawney at a Fair. And again, more determinedly, she rose.

"There's a heavy black cloud in the sky, sir. Your prophecy of rain, I fear, will shortly be fulfilled. I must not delay my departure."

"Your father," queried Edward, "is at Thoresby?"

"No, he is in London, and that is further reason why I dursn't be from home. In my father's absence," she was proudly careful to inform him, "I am the head of his house."

"Then if you will not stay, at least you will allow me to escort you on your road."

"My maid attends me," she said faintly: a mild fabrication. No maid attended Mary; she was in care of old Nurse, who even as she spoke had come to the door and stood there, over-laden with shawls.

"How now, poppet! 'Tis time we were away, saving your pardon, sir." Creakingly Nurse bobbed. "We must be off betimes to avoid the night air. Here, chuck, let me cover your chest."

As if unaware of her ladyship's abasement, Mr. Wortley Montagu offered his assistance.

"She's always been one to take cold," explained Nurse while she muffled her lady in wool.

"I must commend your precaution," Mr. Wortley Montagu concurred. "In such treacherous weather and with so rare a plant as Lady Mary——"

She dropped a glove; he dived to pick it up. "Say thank you kindly, sir," prompted Nurse to Mary's silence, and—"rare plant indeed!" she snorted. "That's to say—to some. To others, for their sins, a plague. Self-willed and hoity-toity, I can't tell you! Always was from a babe, and so sickly —you'd never believe. Not a drop could it keep down, though we tried everything from a wet-nurse to a mare. Yes, sir, may I be drawn and quartered if I lie. We reared it on mare's milk and then it all but died o' the green sickness. So there it is." Nurse tied the strings of Mary's hood beneath her chin. "And here we are. And it'll always be my baby—" with wheezing sentiment she added, "contrariwise or no. Now, lovey, bid goodbye to Mistress Anne and thank her for

21

the handsome tea, and God send that you don't vomit what you've eaten in the coach."

Heavenly Grace, prayed Mary, forgive me for the murder in my heart. And:

"Thank you, Mistress Anne," she meekly said. "Obleeged, I'm sure . . . Sir," much deflated, she curtsied to the bowing Edward, but was somewhat cheered when he told her gravely:

"We must meet again to discuss the classics and stoical philosophy. Meantime, I suggest for your reading Quintus Curtius. Or perhaps he is no stranger to you?"

She shook her head, chapfallen, to admit: "Yes, sir, he is."

"Then he must not be a stranger to you long."

A week later a parcel was delivered at Thoresby addressed to the Lady Mary Pierrepont. Her sister Frances, all agog, stood over her while she unfastened the wrappings to disclose an impressive leather-bound edition of the very book that he had recommended: *Quintus Curtius*. And on the title page a verse inscribed to her.

> '*Beauty like this had vanquis. ed Persia shown,*
> *The Macedon had laid his empire down,*
> *And polished Greece obeyed a barbarous throne.*
> *Had wit so bright adorned a Grecian dame,*
> *The am'rous youth had lost his thirst of fame,*
> *Nor distant Indus sought through Syria's plain;*
> *But to the Muses' stream with her had run*
> *And thought her lover more than Ammon's son.*'

* * *

Mr. Wortley Montagu might have been immensely flattered had he known with what rapture his gift, to say nothing of his first and last attempt at poetic composition, had been received by Mary had he bestowed on her or it a second thought. But he did not. He went back to London and, absorbed in political activities, forgot the young lady's existence.

The struggle against French domination which had resulted in a war that shook the whole of Europe and was to ring the name of Marlborough down the ages, had brought with it hostility at home. Parliament was now become a tilting ground where the champions of two conflicting Parties, Whig and Tory, were to fight their bitter battle to its end.

The Queen's High Church and High Tory predilections had gained for Anne's first Parliament of 1702 a majority of a hundred Tories in the Commons, with a determined Opposition in the House of Lords. Almost all the young intelligentsia, of whom Edward Wortley Montagu was representative, were Whiggishly inclined. Edward, however, put his theories into practice when, in 1705, he contested and secured the seat for Huntingdon. In this he had been well supported by his kinsman, Lord Halifax, and his friends in the literary world: Addison, Congreve, and Steele, all of whom encouraged him to think himself to be an indispensable addition to their Party.

While 'Laetitia', at each brief encounter with 'Sebastian', hopefully embellished her romance, little did he guess that every word he spoke to her was endowed with subtle meaning; that the doggerel he had composed in a moment of bored leisure was engraved upon her heart and interpreted to signify his passion, unconfessed.

She had arrived, at last, at that mysterious borderline between childhood and adolescence when the monotony of daily life, hemmed in by petty barriers, fades before a lifted new horizon; when quickened consciousness responds to every fleeting impulse; when known familiar things assume a visionary splendour; the springing green of grass, the note of a thrush in the ivy, an outflung spray of cherry blossom, a miracle of white against an April sky; the smell of moist rich earth, a leaf unfolding, or the startled grace of antlered deer, these and all such trivia were suddenly illumined as the brightly coloured text in some grave monastic missal; or conversely, with sense attuned to penetrative suggestion, the glow and vehemence would vanish, dissolved in melancholy, wholly irrational, induced by a harsh word, a Latin verse forgotten, or—'even greater ills than what I feel, I fear,' we have her word for it; 'my fame—my Ovid—both for ever fled, what evil is there left for me to dread?'

IT NEEDED the perception of 'Aunt Cheyne' to detect the ready flush in cheeks too pale, the too frequent laughter, the sullen moods that followed; the symptomatic restlessness between youth's bud and blossom.

An indomitable woman, parrot-nosed and raucous-voiced, was this sister of Lord Kingston, whom he heartily detested. Magnificent in salmon plush that ill became her ultra-pink complexion, Lady Cheyne on a morning in the spring of 1706, called upon her brother at his Arlington Street house, to be told he was at breakfast. Bidding the footman, "Do not disturb his lordship. I will go to him," she went.

His lordship, who had passed the early night in gaming, the later night in wine, and the dawning hours in the arms of a highly priced young person from Old Drury, was not in the best of good humours. He had lost a thousand guineas at the tables, had drunk too much of a shocking bad vintage that had sadly turned his stomach, and had found his charmer not improved by close acquaintance. A malodorous bitch, he sourly reflected, a discredit to whoredom and his taste.

His man brought a tray with rusks and chocolate, and announced the approach of Lady Cheyne.

"God rot her!" was his lordship's amiable response. "Go tell her I am sick or dead—or what you will, and keep her out."

But she was in, and bearing down upon him in his bed where, unwigged, he sat, with the tray on his knees, a blue stubble on his chin and no expression save repugnance on his face.

"Good morning, Kingston," quacked Lady Cheyne, "you're as yellow as a guinea. Are you sick?"

Lord Kingston shared a look of hate between his cup of chocolate and his sister.

"Hi, you!" he called to his departing man, "take this filth away and fetch me brandy."

"A hair of the dog?" heartily inquired Lady Cheyne; and she settled herself in a chair with a hissing of silks that suggested she nursed a brood of snakes beneath her petticoats.

"As you know," stated her ladyship, "I have been recently

at Thoresby, and I regret to observe in my niece Mary, a change—a very marked change—for the worse. The time is come that she be taken firmly in hand. She spends her days mooning and moping and reading and writing. She is full of the fantods, giggles for nothing and cries for less. Were she mine I would give her the birch. As she's yours, I suggest you present her."

"Present her?" hollowly echoed Lord Kingston. "What d'ye mean, present her? To whom?"

"To the Queen, naturally. At Court. I myself will——"

The servant entered with a flagon on a salver, filled a crystal goblet, and handed it to his parched lordship who drank it in one draught.

Disdaining interruption — "I myself," repeated Lady Cheyne, "will present her. I advise that you bring her and Frances to London and that they stay here for the season. I will superintend their wardrobes. Their gowns are a disgrace."

Holding out his empty glass Kingston beckoned his man and said: "Fill it again."

"You'll burn up your bowels," cheerfully remarked Lady Cheyne. "And what is this I hear, that you have been appointed a Commissioner for the Union with Scotland; I confess I am astonished."

Lord Kingston fixed his aching eyes upon his sister's massive bosom and asked, "Why?"

"The inference is obvious," cackled Lady Cheyne.

"But too obtuse for one of my low persick—" he sucked his furred tongue, tried again and carefully achieved, "perspackicity. How'ver Her Majesty is graciously pleased to nom'nate me for that office and to con——"

"An office I presume that is purely complimentary," broke in her ladyship. "Yes?"

"To carry with it," rejoined her brother, glowering, "the hon'rovamarquisate."

"A *what*?"

"T'ser Majesty's intention to con—confer on me the marquisate of Dorch-'m—chester," explained Lord Kingston, belching.

"Of Dorchester?" incredulously echoed Lady Cheyne. "And why—in Heaven's name—a marquis?"

25

"Presumably because," she was loftily assured, "my servishes've merited reward."

"Crumbs," rasped Lady Cheyne, "from the rich Freeman's table! Honours and dukedoms and marquisates and whatnot are handed out with lavish indiscrimination, but—" she smiled dreadfully—"I have yet to learn in which direction lies your service to the Queen, unless by proxy to her Duchess—or her Junto."

Lord Kingston's bilious countenance assumed a reddish tinge. "I can disregar' your pleasantries at myess'pense," he blustered, "but m'licious i'plication pointed at my friends I cannot pass."

"Lickspittle!" retorted her ladyship obscurely, "take it how you like it. I'm not here to carp. Be a marquis an it suits you, *or* the Lady Marlborough. I could weep for the poor Queen, with Mrs. Freeman at the Privy Purse pulling thousands out of it, to say nothing of the dowries purloined for her daughters. And speaking of daughters and dowries— what settlements do you propose for yours?"

Lord Kingston's gloom visibly lightened. Daughters and dowries, unpleasant topics though they were, required less concentration to evade; so he evaded.

"Find 'em husbands first. Too young to think o' marriage."

"Ptchah!" or some such sound emitted Lady Cheyne. "Too young at seventeen?"

"Seventeen?" Fixing his bulbous eyes in some alarm upon his sister, Kingston bestirred himself to hazy calculation. "Sev'teen, sixteen, fourteen, an' the boy—a pox on my forgetting—is he twelve?"

Her ladyship removed her stately person from the chair. "As I perceive you to be more than usually raddled this morning, Kingston, I will take my leave. You were saying——?"

He was not saying, he was thinking: How Cheyne or any other man could bring himself to bed with this bandy-legged pelican God alone knew. But: "I will ring for your coach," he hastened to tell her, stretching an arm to the bell-rope.

"Then all is now arranged," magisterially pronounced her ladyship, moving toward the door. "I am glad you agree with my decision. You will at once send for my nieces from

Thoresby. They will stay here in London for the season. I shall thus be enabled to keep an eye on them and——" with ghastly playfulness she wagged a finger at him—"and on you! As for your liver, I advise a dose of calomel and senna after meals, and *bar*ley-water last thing at night."

A few days later the Pierrepont sisters received from their father his summons to Town. Little time was allowed for the journey's preparation since his letter desired that they should depart within the next twenty-four hours.

While Frances inspected their gowns, of which neither possessed more than two fit to wear, so patched and mended were the rest of them, Mary, on her knees before a chest, was packing books.

"And what," asked Frances, pointing, "do you want with all of those?"

"Yes, Ladybird," Nurse, darning stockings, glanced up over her spectacles, "you'll not require to read in London Town. Better leave your book-learning behind you. We've small room for your baggage in the wagon as it is."

"I intend to take my books," said Mary, flat.

"She's crazed," jeered Frances in a loud aside. "She'll make herself a laughing-stock among the gentlemen when she starts speechifying Latin verse to 'em. If she thinks to get a husband with her bookishness she'll find herself a maiden still, at fifty—Ooh—*ow*! You filth!"

This pained ejaculation was wrung from Frances in a shriek as Mary, adder-swift, was on her toes to claw and to receive a vicious thumping in return.

"Good-lack-a-day!" groaned Nurse, abandoning her stocking to interpose her bulk between the pair of them, "Heaven save you both from burning for your godless ways. Lady Mary, leave her be! You've set your mark upon her face—Oh, no, you don't!" Intercepting another lunge from Frances, Nurse seized her hands and held them fast.

"She's drawn bloood with her nails," yelled Frances. "I'll be poisoned!"

" 'Tis your own fault if you are," said Nurse. "You should know better than to rile her. Come with me, I'll bathe it. A pretty tale this to tell his lordship."

By which it might be thought that between the Ladies Pierrepont little love was lost; but not at all. They were devoted to each other. True, Frances was inclined to despise her sister for her learning and to loathe her for her looks, which in everything of dainty form and feature were all that Frances lacked and greatly envied. Dark-eyed and gipsy-haired, she favoured her father; was tall, well-built, and longed to be little—not swarthy, but pink as a fondant, with dimples, and teeth white as almonds. No girl had any right, considered Frances, to be so very prettyish and gentle-seeming, with the temper of a tigress and the wisdom of a witch.

"One of these days," she sombrely confided, while Nurse dabbed lotion to the scratch upon her cheek, "I'll *kill* my sister Mary. I hate her worse than beetles. She's so monstrous vain you'd think to hear her talk she was the Queen o' Sheba. And the way she flaps those eyelashes of hers makes me retch. I wish she'd take the pox and die—I do!"

"Shame on you!" wheezed Nurse, aghast. "Go fetch a glass o' water and rinse your mouth clean of those blistering words lest they turn and reflect on yourself—and pray God for His forgiveness."

"I won't," rejoined Frances, "I mean it. Why should *she* have long eyelashes that curl up the tips and me—hog's bristles? 'Tisn't fair!"

"She sickened o' the rheum when a babe," Nurse doatingly recalled. "Its eyelids were glued together with the pus and wouldn't open, and so I cut its lashes, and that's why they grew."

"Well, I'm sure I wish you'd cut her throat instead," retorted Frances, "then I'd ha' been spared her wild beastliness." Darting away from Nurse's ministrations she ran to the mirror on the wall. "See my face! I'll wager she tore it a' purpose to disfigure me—the hell-cat!—so's I'll look a sight when I go to a ball." She swung round. "I suppose we *will* go to a ball?"

"Every night, I shouldn't wonder," lied Nurse comfortably, well satisfied at this return to norm. "And now, lovey, go fetch me your night-shifts that I may overlook and mend 'em, and then we'll get on with your packing."

"*Yes!* On with the packing!" cried Frances in high glee.

28

"On with the packing and off with the spleen." And all smiles she rushed from the room, singing a small tuneless song as she went, of: 'Misery-misery-*mee*, and a dying duck called from the willows a wee-*eep*, O misery-misery-mee-*ee-ee*!'

Over the nurse's red full-moon face passed a cloud, and shaking her head as she rummaged in a drawer, a strangely unaccountable young lady, she reflected, was this second daughter of his lordship, and one whom she believed to be a changeling. Nurse could have told, and often did, the tale of how she had seen a green, very small, glimmering man with squirrel's eyes, standing by the child's cot the night that it was born. And she had cried with fear—to wake the sleeping babe and its mother, poor soul. And when she looked again for the little green man he had gone; yet his sign was left on the infant's brow in the shape of a smutty fingermark that had never been there at the birth; nor for all the washing could she move it, and there it was still, to this day. Which singular occurrence would point to fairy's work and a replacement in the cot of Lady Frances.

But despite her avowed aversion for her sister, Frances was at peace with her and all the world when, attended by Nurse, they started out upon their journey south; no light undertaking after rain with the roads hock-deep in mud. They entered London after four days' hard going and three nights spent in none too cleanly inns. Bone-weary and itching all over from bug-bites, the girls, who upon arrival asked nothing but to tumble into bed, were at once commanded to their father's presence.

The prospect of housing his two elder daughters at Arlington Street for the season was reviewed with little joy by Lord Kingston. He foresaw an end, or at least a hindrance, to his personal pursuits, and his greeting accorded with his humour.

Throughout her life her father was the only man whom Mary feared, to drain her heart of love and breed dislike. To her he represented the antithesis of all that she demanded of his sex, personified in her englamoured portrait of 'Sebastian'. She saw her magnificent parent as she believed him to be: the gross male, supremely self-satisfied, sole ruler of her destiny, her very right to live and have her being in any world or any thought but his. With the merciless intolerance of youth she could neither perceive nor allow for those integral compulsions, implicit to the squirearchy of ownership, inherent from a line of forebears whose wives and daughters were as much their property as the lands they overlorded.

Yet, standing humbly there before him, she was bound to concede him his charm—that fatal charm which made slaves of all his women—but not a slave of her. Shrewdly observant she stripped him of veneer to explore the omnivorous pursuant of desire, idolized by those whom he pursued. The sybarite and sensualist were proclaimed in the loose-lipped mouth, the heavy jaw, and those turgid indolent brown eyes bequeathed to Frances; withal a splendid figure of a man, shown to advantage in the elegant foppery of gold-laced velvet and rare Mechlin at wrists and throat.

"I trust," said his glum lordship, " that you had a pleasant journey here?"

"We did not," ventured Mary, suddenly emboldened, "have a pleasant journey here at all. The beds were frightful, and we shared them with a host of fleas—or worse."

"You nauseate me," shuddered Lord Kingston.

"I'm not bitten," Frances hastened to assure him. "I washed myself in vinegar and changed my shift, but Mary went to bed in her clothes."

"And such clothes," remarked his lordship, taking snuff, "as would put to shame a pair of Wapping fish-fags!"

It was on the tip of Mary's tongue to ask "whose fault is that?" But she restrained herself and smiled. There was something in that smile to cause her father's pompous face to flush with irritation. A saucy piece this one, agad! and he boiled with an unconscionable urge to box her ears. "Your Aunt Cheyne," he cleared his catarrhal voice to say, "has undertaken to present you. Modistes and milliners are waiting in attendance with their fal-lals. I pay the piper— and a pretty penny too. A coach-and-four will be placed at your disposal, and your aunt has engaged the service of a maid experienced in waiting upon ladies, though by your looks—" he inhaled a spicy pinch of Bergamot—"neither one nor t'other can be described as such. For the rest, that you are not seen nor heard by me about the house is all that I insist upon. Now go."

They curtsied, backed, and submissively they went. But once fairly out of ear-shot with the door closed behind them, Frances let forth in a fury. "The beast! How hateful, cold, unkindly—what a way to greet us! Scoffing at our dress. 'Tis his disgrace, not ours, that we go so poorly clad. He's mean as dirt, and him so rich and grand. I loathe him to his guts—the sneering swine! It's nigh upon twelve months since he set eyes on us, and all he can say is keep out of his sight. *I'll* keep out of his sight, and welcome! Wish I'd stayed at Thoresby and never come to Town. The only one of us he cares about is William."

And the only one of you I care about, said Mary secretly, is William. Deep within her heart she sheltered this love for her brother who, though still in the schoolroom, was more akin to her in spirit than any other being, save 'Sebastian'. True, familiarity with the youngest of the family had not yet bred contempt. William, strictly guarded by his tutor, Mr. Franklin, a gentleman of German origin who had replaced his first and more lenient instructor, shared his noble employer's belief that woman's rightful place was in the stillroom or his bed, and nowhere else. So marked indeed had been his disapproval of Mary's attendance, book in hand, as silent witness to the knowledge he imparted to his pupil, that she took the hint and unwillingly retired. Her attempt, with an ear to the keyhole, to acquire a smattering of Greek, was a lamentable failure. Long afterwards she confessed that although well-versed in Latin, she regretted she had never been allowed to master more than the alphabet in Greek. And now that she had come to London to be launched upon Society, her higher interests were distracted by more mundane affairs.

The selection and fittings for gowns ordered by Aunt Cheyne and supervised by Madams with mouths full of smiles and pins; the spread of coloured taffeties laid out for inspection; the rich glowing velvets for cloaks, the fairy gauze and lace for scarves; the caps, the hoods, the coquettish flowered headgear, the false curls and—most intriguing—the powder-puffs of swansdown, the carmine salve for lips, the

31

rouge for cheeks—these and the intricacies of dressing-up and making-up were, if truth be told, a happy substitute for booklore.

The excellent young woman, Grace, whom Lady Cheyne had engaged to wait upon the sisters, was received by Nurse with ill-concealed contumely, for all she professed relief to be rid of her charges. "Since," she told them acidly, "I don't aspire to turn you into painted Jezebels. Your mother, poor simple soul, God rest her, whom I nursed from the cradle, ne'er touched her skin with worse nor a soap-ball in her life. Beauty from a roodge-pot is only skin-deep. Health and happiness rise from the innards. Brimstone and treacle," declared Nurse, "has done more for your complexions than this muck with which that mincing hussy plasters you. Harlots, nothing less, is what you'll pass for when you curtsy to the Queen. And I only hope and pray you won't be driven from the Court as having walked in by mistake—from the streets."

But neither Nurse's wet-blanketings nor the series of lectures delivered by their aunt on their way to the Palace could dim anticipatory delight. Dusk had fallen, and the torch-flares, held aloft by link-boys, lit the gaudy liveries of coachmen and postilions to offer passing glimpses from each gilded equipage, of wondrous ladies, bejewelled, powdered, patched, and of their cavaliers in gold lace, furbelows, and glittering with Orders.

Mary, in a gown chosen by Aunt Cheyne, had emerged from the hands of her maid, a stranger to herself. The reflection revealed in her looking-glass had been that of a modish princess with two inches added to her stature by the high red heels of her cloth of silver shoes. Was this regal personage in turquoise satin, pearl-bestrewn, the shabbily dressed and almost always untidy Mary Pierrepont, despised of her father and mocked for her learning—was this indeed she—this beautiful high-coloured creature, whose dusky hair fell in a redundancy of curls, not entirely her own, about her shoulders? Whose small figure was so tightly-boned in its corset that every breath she drew she deemed her last; whose bodice, artfully padded, left so much of her uncovered that her mirrored image blushed?

She scrutinized her face; a flawless skin that, despite Nurse's bemoanings, owed almost nothing to the 'roodge-pot'. And what heavenly eyes! The maid Grace had worked wonders to those greatly-prized lashes with a brush dipped in dark oily liquid. Her left cheek, rose-shaded, carried a patch—in the shape of all things curious!—a little coach and horses. Then, as she leaned nearer to the looking-glass as if she would have kissed herself for love, Frances, coming up behind her, had jabbed a spiteful elbow in her tight-laced ribs. "Have done staring at yourself, conceited pea-hen! I want to see how *I* look. Get away."

Mary got away, and Frances took her place. She too had undergone bewitchment. Her gown of peach satin gleamed with gold thread; its bodice, Mary was chagrined to see, needed no padding; Frances looked to be bursting from her stays. She wore a rose in her hair and a necklace of rubies lent by Aunt Cheyne. Grace, stepping back to review her handi-work, declared: "There'll not be two such beauteous sights at this Court as your ladyships, I'll say."

Nurse, at the door, overhearing Grace's rapture, wither-ingly capped it: "Sights is likely. Never truer spoken. Little did I think I'd live to see these two I reared from sucklings rigged out in finery more befitting to play-actresses than virgins. Shameless, I call it, to bare your bosoms to the gentle-men as if you went a-begging to be raped."

"I doubt," sparkled Mary, "that we'd go begging long." And at the shock on Nurse's face she rippled into laughter. "Faith, 'tis a marvel we aren't turned Dissenters or nuns the way you preach at pleasure. I'll warrant me your father was a Roundhead."

"So, and if he were—better be that than the Lord o' Misrule as is some I could mention that dwell in this sink of iniquity," rasped Nurse. "I'll to my prayers for your saving, lest the devil claim you for his own tonight."

And recalling that ominous pronouncement while she sat in the coach on her way to Court, Mary giggled—and she giggled till she shook. Aunt Cheyne, beside her, turned her towering head, fearsomely adorned in stiffened lace, to ask: "Why do you shiver? Are you cold?"

"No, Aunt, I am hot. May I open the window?"

"And be smothered in dust and grit? Certainly not. And now one last word to you both on deportment. So soon as the presentations are done there will be dancing, and——"

"What will they dance?" Frances dared to interrupt. "I only know the jig. Supposing——"

"You will follow in your partner's steps."

"But what if I don't have a partner?"

"That would be a sad disgrace," said Lady Cheyne. "And pray will you allow me to put a word in edgeways?"

"Yes, Aunt." Frances closed her mouth, and in an unheard whisper uttered: "Sow!"

"When you are led out to dance," said Lady Cheyne, "you do not speak to your gentleman unless he speaks to you, when you will answer him becomingly—and do not air your views. Let him air his. You—" she revived Mary's faint attention with a nudge, "you must agree with all he says, and on no account be drawn into a discussion upon literature or politics. There's nothing a man so mortally dislikes as a learned woman. 'Tis as unseemly and unnatural as a hen that crows. And you, my girl, are far too fond of crowing. Hold your tongue. Be modest. Mind your manners. Here we are."

Here they were, indeed.

Their excitement increasing every moment the girls alighted from the coach, and, conducted by bowing officials along a maze of passages, they followed in the wake of Lady Cheyne. Before, behind, thronged guests in a colourful motley of brocade, velvet, satin, plush, with Orders glinting, jewels flashing, as if all the wealth of the Indies was about to be poured at the feet of Queen Anne. In slow-moving massed formation on they went, their exquisite gowns, their uniforms, hidden in the crush of surging bodies.

Half-suffocated from the stench of sweat, perfume and fading flowers, the aching scent of lilies, the corpse-sweet sickly smell of tuberoses, the pungent aromatic odour of strewn herbs, Mary, conscious only of a longing for fresh air, was pressed forward as if without volition. In her struggle to retain her place and balance in the crowd she had lost her aunt; but Frances, whose hand clung stickily to hers, was wedged beside her hissing in her ear: "God send that we come out of here alive!"

34

It must have been near upon an hour before they reached the State Apartments; and, as if with one accord, that pushing, struggling, hard-breathing, soft-swearing assembly spread outward and fanwise with a long-drawn congregational sigh of relief.

From vast vacancies of distance the voice of the Lord Chamberlain announced the names of those to be presented; and still moving on, but now with more agility, Mary heard her own name called.

Propelled by the herd she had come to the arched entrance of the Throne Room, guarded by two pages in cloth of gold and silver . . . She stood alone, her sight bemused by the radiance of a thousand candles, of an infinite expanse of polished floor, of tier upon tier of seats filled with privileged spectators, and, on either side, a sentinel row of red-coated bodyguards whose breastplates shone like brazen suns.

Her aunt, in the rear of her faltering steps, whispered a warning: "Don't stand and look about you, girl! Go on." And Mary was seized with sudden panic to find herself a solitary unit in that watching multitude. Go on she must. There could be no turning back, no hand to aid or guide her; no consciousness save that of awful fear. With a prayer unuttered, "Save me!" she summoned all her will to fix her gaze upon her goal.

There, enormously enthroned upon a dais, with her Consort beside her, grouped around with halberdiers in gold and scarlet tunics and Elizabethan trunks, sat Her Majesty, the Queen.

Immobile gentlemen, splendidly attired, sprang to life and ceremoniously bowed.

A lady, very lovely, with hair like ripest corn, clothed in purple, strung with pearls, and much in evidence about the Royal pair, smiled with a great display of teeth.

As Mary billowed to the ground—she had been practising her curtsy for a week—all terror fled. Confidence restored, assured her that this remarkably stout and, but for her regal surroundings, decidedly commonplace middle-aged woman, England's Queen, might well inspire love but never fear.

Heavily upholstered in ruby plush, with the blue ribbon

of the Garter and the Star upon her chest, her crowned head tremendously curled, Queen Anne appeared—Mary shockingly acknowledged—less like the Sovereign and Defender of the Faith than the Fat Lady at Nottingham Fair.

Her Majesty spoke: her voice was surprisingly young and clear; her large bovine eyes, as they rested upon Mary, beamed kindliest approval.

"We are delighted to receive the Lady Mary Pierrepont. We are well acquainted with your father, the—" An almost imperceptible pause was instantly prompted by the ubiquitous lady in purple.

"The Marquis of Dorchester, Madam."

"Your father, the Marquis of Dorchester," the Queen dutifully intoned.

"Pass!" in a penetrating whisper commanded the lady in purple.

Mary passed; she had been drilled by her aunt. She must curtsy again—to the Consort.

Prince George of Denmark, in a blond full-bottomed furbelow and the uniform of Lord High Admiral of the Fleet—an office that for him carried with it no more than its name—was a martyr to gout, over-indulgent to food and to wine, a great-hearted simpleton, and, to the wonder of his gentlemen, still faithfully devoted to his wife.

His eyes, embedded in pouches of mauvish pink flesh, glanced hazily at Mary as she sank to the bob, then away to see who would come next.

Frances came next; while Mary, thankfully released from her ordeal, waited in an ante-room adjoining where the several young ladies who had preceded her were assembled and chattering like magpies. Almost all were strangers, but here and there she recognized a face she knew. Mrs. Banks,[1] from Scofton near Thoresby, a plump little partridge of a girl who professed for the Lady Mary the greatest admiration, fluttered, chirping, to her side.

"I declare! I never hoped to have the joy of encountering your ladyship. A friend from home, if I may dare to name myself in that capacity. It is my first presentation, and your

[1] The abbreviation 'Mrs.' for Mistress was used in the reign of Queen Anne for single and married women alike.

ladyship's, too, I believe. What a wonderful gown—how sweetly it becomes you."

And, said Mary, how sourly does yours; but she did not say it aloud. What she did say, with the gentlest of smiles, was: "Lemon and cerise could not more deliciously fadge with your complexion, Mrs. Banks."

Which caused the young lady a blush of delight. Praise from Lady Mary, so very far above her, so pretty and so clever, and of such high estate, was praise indeed. But Mary had no time to waste on Mrs. Banks, who was pouring out a tale of her journey south, and of a highwayman who held them up at Barnet, "—gallop, gallop after us to overtake our horses, and halt our postilions, commanding them to stand. Such an adventure! I have had the vapours ever since. And whatever do you think?"

"I can't conceive," said Mary, edging off as Mrs. Banks edged nearer.

"'Twas no highwayman at all, but a gentleman who had seen me drop my handkercher at the last posting-inn. He picked it up and rode a race to catch me——"

"And," smiled Mary, "did he catch you?"

"Te-he!" tittered Mrs. Banks, "was there ever such a quiz as your ladyship! But I'll acknowledge him a personable gentleman, and he rode behind us all the way to London, and Mamma has never ceased to scold, accusing me of——"

"Mary! I've been searching for you everywhere. I was told that you were here."

She turned to see Anne Wortley Montagu beside her, very finely dressed in green and gold, with a chaplet of white flowers on her fawn-gilt hair.

"Here comes Frances," Anne caught at Mary's hand. "Quick! We must dodge her. I die to talk to you alone. Let's find a seat."

They found a seat in a secluded corner, and had all to tell each other of their doings here in London, of which Mistress Anne had more to say than Mary. She, who had been in Town for near upon a month, had as yet seen nothing of the city's sights. Her drives in her father's coach, attended by Aunt Cheyne, had given her but briefest glimpses of that fashionable life with which Anne was entirely familiar. Anne had attended the Playhouse and the Opera. She had heard the famous Signora Francesca Margaretta de L'Epine sing divinely in Italian; she had visited Mrs. Salmon's waxworks, where she had seen the image of Margaret, Countess of Heninberg, lying on a bed of state with three hundred and sixty-five children around her, all born at one birth—"a miracle of wonder! How beautiful you look. Did the Queen speak to you? Isn't she fat? The Prince yawned in my face. What do you think of the Duchess?"

"Which Duchess?" Mary unguardedly inquired.

"Lud, Mary!" Anne was swift to seize on that. "Is it possible you cannot know? There is only one Duchess to be reckoned with at Court. Mrs. Duchess Freeman, to be sure. Did you observe her pearls? Crown jewels—borrowed. Hush my tongue!" Anne clapped a hand to her mouth. "I'll be hanged if I'm heard. But it's true."

The two girls had not met for some months, and as Mary now saw Anne she was struck to see her slender. Gone were her curves; her creamy neck showed hollows at its base; her eyes were very bright, her cheeks flushed as if with fever.

"Dearest Anne! I trust you are not ill?"

"Ill? Never better, save for a tickling cough that followed a rheum I catched last Christmas."

"But Anne, you've grown so thin!"

"The Lord be thanked for that. You've always been abusive of my figure. Have you supped? I'm mortal hungry."

Mary too was hungry. "I trust we'll have a meal."

"I hopefully trust so indeed," said Anne, "but past experience of Courtly functions teaches me to think that we'll get naught but citron water while Mrs. Freeman holds the Privy Purse. Mean? My dear, she'd rob the dead of the pence on their eyelids—and as for the Duke—I've heard tell that after battle when his leggings are so swollen with rain and mud that they have to be cut off him with a knife he—can you believe it!—orders his servant to sew them up that he may wear them again, for economy's sake. Yet he'll waste the nation's money in prolongation of the war."

"Anne," Mary eyed her straightly, "I'm surprised you can

talk scandal of our country's hero. The Duke and his Duchess are sans peur et sans reproche."

"Still," Anne nodded sagely, "there's many that they fear, and who reproach them too. You'll soon glean all the gossip of the town, my dear. What I let fall is food for sparrows merely."

"That when scattered may take root and grow a crop of food for vultures. You've no right to speak so bold—I might say foolish—when your brother," Mary blushed, "stands for Parliament—a Whig."

"Yes," Anne retorted, "and Lord Halifax, my father's kinsman, too, is a strong Whig, a member of the Junto, whatever that may signify. But I've no Party preference, nor interest in such tedious affairs. I only know," she shrugged her shoulders, "what I know."

"Which very little knowledge," rejoined Mary, sugarsweet, "can be dangerous if little understood."

Her remark went unheeded. Anne's eyes were straying. "The room is over-crowded. The bobbings must be over soon. The names are alphabetical—they've reached the Y's. I can hear him calling 'Yarborough'. That will be one of those long-nosed Yarboroughs from Haslington in Yorkshire. Do you know them?"

Mary shook her head. Vexing to admit she did not know them; and still more vexing not to have known the beautiful Duchess of Marlborough, whom everybody who was anybody knew; nor to have been on more than nodding acquaintance with any soul present save that vapid Mrs. Banks. It was on the tip of her tongue to ask: "And is your brother with you?" but Anne, full of chatter, gave her not a chance.

And now the last presentation was done, and Mrs. Yarborough in puce—"she must have matched her gown to her complexion," giggled Anne—had come from the Throne Room and was hailed by a cluster of vestals. Frances, flouncing up to Mary, asked, "We surely will not stay in this stuffy room all night? Aunt Cheyne said there would be dancing."

Even as she spoke, and as if in answer, could be heard the squeak of fiddles; and like a breeze-swept garland, that flowery assemblage turned toward the music to follow where it led.

Later, in the dawning, when Mary, sleep-forsaken in the bed she shared with Frances, watched the febrile recurrence of that evening's pageantry, one figure only was predominant; all the rest no more than supers in the scene.

To the strains of flute and harpsichord the brilliant pattern of the dancers had joined, converged and parted, to join, converge, again. There had been one shaming interval when it seemed she must go partnerless; not any of those gilded youths, the paint upon their faces melting in pink rivulets, who had asked her once to dance, had asked her twice. Mary dismissed them with contempt as 'pretty fellows'; yet, even so, it was bitter to acknowledge that while she sat ignored beside Aunt Cheyne, Frances had been led out by Lord Mar, the prettiest of fellows in silver-laced velvet and a flaxen periwig. Certainly extenuation might have been considered, since Frances looked the elder of the two. Still, the slight had rankled and was not to be assuaged by the marked attention of a 'fellow', nothing like so 'pretty' as the Earl of Mar.

This was a gentleman, lavishly attired, frilled, beruffled, furbelowed, with jewels on every finger and sparkling in his steinkerk; whose heels were so high he looked to be walking on his toes; whose calves were stupendously padded, and whose teeth were large and yellow as an old grey mare's.

Somewhat to Mary's wonder, Aunt Cheyne received him with a grace she had denied to the pretty Earl of Mar.

"My dear, allow me to present—" The music crashed upon a chord to drown more of his name than its first syllable, beginning with a K.

And always, ever after, when despite herself he was remembered, Mary never spoke of him except as 'Mr. K.'

It mattered nothing that she could not dance the latest steps; he danced them for her: the Contretemps, the Coupée, the Bourée, the Pirouette—he named them as he pranced— the Bound or Tac.

She was breathless, half hysterical; he held her hand to crush it, lifted high above her head, bowing, scraping, dreadful! Puffing with exertion, breathing down his nose.

"Sir!" she gasped, "you—tread the measure so—peripatetic—I'll wager you have studied at the feet of Aristotle."

"Not at all!" protested Mr. K. "Faix, your ladyship has kissed the Blarney Stone. Sure, I learned to cut me capers at the French King's Court before you were cutting your teeth."

His accent verified his cast of feature; the long upper lip and the button of a nose.

" 'Tis an art, sir, none the less, that is engrained in you, I'll warrant. The Irish are noted for their jigs," said she, demurely.

"Now how in the world did you guess me for an Irishman? I'm amazed at your perception, Lady Mary. Do you know the Entrechat?"

"I do not, sir, know the Entrechat. And I beseech you, of your mercy, to reflect—I am a tyro where you excel."

"Och, you dance," said he, perspiring, "as to the manner born, to outrival Terpsichore, daughter of Mnemosyne and Jupiter, begar!"

"Sir, you're kind to flatter me, but this is my first Ball."

"Impair me vigour! 'Tisn't true! I'll not believe ut!" gallantly incredulous ejaculated Mr. K. And so abruptly did he halt upon the point of a Fleuret, that the following couple directly behind him were brought into instant collision.

Profuse apologies were offered on the part of Mr. K., and accepted with frigidity by the gentleman whose corns had suffered torture from the impact.

The music sang and sighed, to end on one last expanding sob of violins. The dance was done, and Mary, much the worse for it, hot, exasperated, turned a shoulder icily on Mr. K. For the gentleman he so clumsily had injured was Sebastian-cum-Edward Wortley Montagu.

His partner, Dolly Walpole, sister of the future Sir Robert, a pretty feather-brained young lady, and one of Mary's least loved friends, accosted her in laughter tinged with malice. "La, Lady Mary! One would think you'd learned to dance at Hockley-in-the-Hole, for I declared you and your gentleman—" she eyed him saucily—"look about to qualify between you for a sparring match."

"Ah! Destroy me, and is it your sweet self I've offended, Mistress Walpole? May I never stir alive from here," Mr. K. submitted with Hibernian intensity, "if I'd have dared impose me heel upon your slippered daintiness to trouble one thread of your shoe! I'll eat dirt from this minute for a week as penance, an you'll forgive the unforgivable—my arrant *ark*wardness. Madam, may I claim you for the next— a Rigadoon?"

Dolly, full of dimples, curtsied, glancing up beneath her lashes at the diamonds that oozed from Mr. K.

"May I too have that honour, Lady Mary?" Edward murmured. "Although I've not a notion what a Rigadoon may be."

"Nor I, sir, neither," rippled Mary in a tremble.

"Madam, have you supped?"

No, she had not supped.

He led her to the supper-room. . . .

Wakefully recalling, while Frances snored beside her, the design of that intricate gala display, it was as if she were reviewing a portraiture in tapestry, brilliantly coloured and entirely unreal. She had dwelled so often on this myth-like 'Sebastian' that his material substance, facing her across a table in the room where other couples drifted back and forth was, strangely, less remarkable than any dream of him; still more strange that his words, and their clear-clipped intonation, were as elusive to recapture as those of the loved dead.

She, who confessedly had prayed for this meeting, hoped beyond hope he would accompany his sister, had adored her mirrored image for him alone, was now tongue-tied in his presence; shy as a dairymaid, devoid of wit or sparkle, a country-girl, a bumpkin: and he so poised, assured.

A flunkey set a dish of sweetmeats on the table, poor substitute for supper; offered wine. She tasted hers and asked him, hiding desperation, for surely it was he should lead the talk? "And do your Parliamentary duties much engage you, sir?"

"No," he answered curtly, "they do not."

A bad beginning. Expressly had Aunt Cheyne tabooed that topic, and she needs must introduce it; still, it served to save a pause from lengthy silence.

Mary tried again. "Have you visited the Playhouse, sir, this season?"

"The Playhouse?"

With a palpable effort he had roused himself from reverie. Anxiously she scanned his face, seeking there the cause of his abstraction. His eyes were lowered; the shield of his austerity encompassed him to raise an impenetrable barrier between them . . . And, unromantically, she was in need of food; she had been too excited to eat before she left. Should she dare intrude on his reflections to ask him to fetch her a something to eat? Then even while she uttered faintly, "Sir, I have a fancy for—" a chicken-pasty, she had almost said—a diversion unexpected intervened; but not from him. It was doubtful he had heard her speak. Among the latest visitants to the supper-room, a newcomer had entered, a young man who, although a shade too plump, too pink, was possessed of remarkably good looks and an air of self-assurance that distinguished him from other 'pretty fellows' in search of refreshment at the board. Having secured a bumper of wine, the gentleman gaily directed his greeting to Edward; but his bow and the smile that went with it were for Mary.

"So, sir, despite the ruling of your august kinsman, 'Maecenus', I see you are inveigled from the faithful, your constituents, to taste the levities of Court . . . My duty, madam."

Scarcely waiting for his formal presentation—"Mr. St. John, the Lady Mary Pierrepont"—he rattled on, deliberately ignoring Edward's stiffening resentment. This Mary had been quick to note, and wondered at its cause. It was clearly apparent that between these two, the one an earnest Whig and politician in the bud, the other a High Tory in the bloom, antagonism rankled. The spark of animosity in St. John's careless gambit was reflected in the flare of Wortley Montagu's reply.

"It were better for the State if Lord Halifax, or 'Maecenus', as you are pleased to dub him, should continue to retain the influence he has acquired in the service of Her Majesty than, like his namesake of old, he should strive against those who seek to destroy the roots of constitutional authority."

Well!

Although Mary had followed as little of this speech as if it had been said in Hindustani, its purport seemed not to have escaped the gentleman to whom it was addressed. Slightly swaying where he stood, his silk-stockinged legs planted a trifle too widely apart for perfect elegance, St. John drained his glass and quizzically eyed the pinch-lipped Wortley Montagu.

"Your classical allusions, my dear sir, overwhelm me. Is it possible that you prognosticate disaster, when yet another victory for our unconquerable Duke is imminent—at Ramillies?"

"I speak not of present war, but of future peace," retorted Edward, "should peace be held in honour."

"Yes, ecod! My sentiments exactly. Mars in alliance with Venus." St. John bowed again to Mary, his face suffused with a glow that might have equally been caused by wine or admiration. . . .

Then, so soon as St. John had left them, Mr. Wortley Montagu pompously addressed her: "Madam, I regret I am forced to curtail the delight of your society. I am pledged to an appointment of some urgency. May I conduct you to your father or your——?"

His glance toward the doorway implied unflattering haste to be gone.

"I am brought here by my aunt, Lady Cheyne. Will you have the goodness to conduct me to her now."

She had striven to keep her voice as cool as his; yet, mortified and hating him for his indifference, she hated herself more for the besotted fancy that he held her in esteem. He esteemed her as much, she declared to her pillow, as she esteemed the handkerchief she dropped on her way out. He had picked it up and returned it, politely. So *that* ruse, borrowed from Mrs. Banks, had failed. She had hoped, at least, he would have asked to keep it, but—"This is your ladyship's, I think," was all he said; then he crooked his arm and walked her thence to Lady Cheyne.

The Queen retired early: the Duchess of Marlborough, Mistress of the Ceremonies, sped departing guests with one eye on the clock. Before the stroke of midnight all was over.

But to whom, Mary asked herself as, hot-eyed, she turned

and twisted, was Mr. Wortley Montagu pledged for an appointment, and at such an hour? The answer was obvious, his hurry too conclusive, her idol fallen, her dream shattered by his feet of clay. . . .

Thumping her creased pillow, that to her burning cheek felt as it were stuffed with flint, not feathers, she relaid her head upon it with a prayer. "May he enjoy his light o' love more than he enjoyed *my* company tonight—and that would not be difficult. So let him stew!"

Then she got out of bed and went to forage in the larder, to soothe her empty belly and herself with chicken-pie.

Edward, who had hired a chaise to come to the Palace, left it before the first of the guests had departed. And being of a thrifty mind he chose to walk the short distance to his destination.

The night was moonless, cloudy, with a slight wind risen that set the gaily painted signs creaking above the bow-windowed shops of St. James's Street. The cobbled road and narrow right of way swarmed with loiterers waiting to watch the return of coaches carrying beaux and belles from the Palace. In shadowed alleys footpads lurked, in readiness to fall upon some drunken fop staggering to or from his club or favoured ordinary. But it was not toward one of these that Edward turned his steps, with fastidious care for his shoes on the mud-greased paving-stones.

Accepting the offer of a link-boy to lead him on his path, he trailed the orange blaze of the torch to Bennett Street, nearby. At a door, over which hung the sign of an apothecary, Edward halted his guide and flung him a coin. The boy, on all fours in the gutter to find it, hurled abuse at its donor for a 'skew-eyed punk who squeezed a groat from his guts as sticky as blood from an oyster!'

Disdaining these and further choice remarks, Edward beat a sharp rat-tat on the door with a brass knocker in the shape of a serpent coiling a rod. After a moment's interval, employed by the link-boy in making obscene gestures at his lordly patron's back, the door was opened by a thick-set gentleman with a face like a bun, three chins, and a military bearing. A black peruque fell in shining curls about his shoulders; his scarlet sword-knot dangled to his knees; ruffles of lace adorned his wrists and steinkerk: but if his dress were a trifle too flamboyant for good taste, his greeting lacked nothing of jovial sincerity.

"Welcome, sir! Come in! I'm delighted to see ye, and honoured, i' faith, that you discard the pleasures of a Palace Ball to pleasure me. Speak softly, will ye? Margaret, poor soul, has the megrims. She's retired early and begs you to excuse—mind that loose board—'twill trip you up. I'm for ever plaguing Keen, my landlord, to mend it, but he waits for me to make the first move, as if the rent I pay him for two rooms were not enough and more than the whole house with the rot and the rats in ut is worth."

Yet, despite his injunction to speak softly, this speech was delivered at the top of his voice, a deep-toned mellow voice in which still lingered a trace of the Dublin accent acquired when its owner was a small boy in St. Bride's.

While he talked, this merry gentleman urged Edward up the stairs and into a room laden with the fumes of wine, and heavy with tobacco smoke.

"D'ye care for Frontiniac?" he asked his guest. "I've the last of a case left behind by a parcel of smugglers I put to rout off Landguard. Joe! Here's Mr. Wortley Montagu hot from the Ball at the Palace, and bursting full o' likely news by the looks of um."

He who had been addressed as Joe languidly rose from the table, on which, among other dishes, were the carcass of a broiled fowl, a leg of ham, several empty wine bottles and two glasses, filled. One of these Joe lifted and drank, "Good health and good fortune to Mr. Wortley Montagu . . . And so let's have your news, sir, if Dick gives you half a chance to tell it."

"Wait now, Joe, will you? Mr. Wortley Montague can't answer your toast nor loosen his news till he's wetted his gullet. Pray sit down, sir. There's a dish o' walnuts before you. These bottles are dead. I'll uncork another."

Edward sat, and, with his flicker of a smile, said: "I can answer Addison's toast in words, so, Captain Steele, spare your wine. My news is scurvy and my health, Joe, is better than my fortune."

46

"Pity 'tis—" their host reflected, digging a corkscrew in the neck of a cobwebbed flagon he had fetched from a corner cupboard—"pize take me, but these French frogs know how to clamp a cork! Pity 'tis, as I was saying, that a Parliament man of Mr. Wortley Montagu's integrity should go unpaid for service rendered to his country."

"I was under the impression," said the suave Mr. Addison, "that the service of a member of Parliament is rendered to none but himself."

"Which might equally apply to all governmental policy, including that of—hey! ye devil, now I've got ye!"

The cork came out of the bottle with a pop, and was triumphantly displayed by Captain Steele.

"Take a look at um, will ye? A beauty of a cork! Stuck fast in the years of his vintage as if loth to part from the sweetest wine that ever came out o' the South. As I was telling ye—what now was I telling ye? Wait, I know!" he quenched Addison's reply with a wave of the corkscrew—"a policy which can be equally applied to that of Under Secretary of State."

"Touché, Dick," Addison laughed softly, took a candle from the table and relit his churchwarden pipe. His addiction to tobacco was a habit that Edward, despite his admiration for Joe's elegant hexameters, considered to be barbarous.

Although Addison and Steele were of one age, Joe appeared to be years younger than the Captain. They had been schoolmates at Charterhouse together, and fellow undergraduates at Oxford; and a more ill-assorted pair could scarcely have been found among those ancient cloisters; the one short, stoutish, beetle-browed, bubbling over with good-nature and high spirits; the other studious, tall, spare of figure, soft-eyed and gentle as a doe; yet possessed of a rapier wit that could cut to the quick, or cajole and charm where he chose. He had charmed Wortley Montagu when he first came to know him in Paris at the house of the British Ambassador, Lord Manchester. Edward's relationship, though distant, to this distinguished peer, may have somewhat influenced Addison's regard for him, 'whose acquaintance,' he wrote in a subsequent letter, 'is the

47

luckiest adventure I could possibly have met with on my travels'.

A still luckier adventure than that meeting was in store for Addison when he commemorated Marlborough and Blenheim in a poem that made him famous overnight, to strike its highest note among the Higher Whigs. No matter that Addison's political opinions were evanescent as his Muse; he had arrived with his *Campaign* amid the clamour of popular ovation, to be acknowledged by the chiefs of both Parties as a literary giant, and to end by marrying a Countess.

While Steele filled the glasses, Addison, who however deep he drank never soused his sense, had observed that Edward was preoccupied. The frown on his forehead, discerned by Lady Mary, had deepened to a furrow. He sipped at the wine his host extolled, and which Edward's mild palate could not thoroughly appreciate; and every now and then during Steele's incessant chatter, he cracked a nut between his fingers, picked at its skin, but did not eat.

Presently, when the loquacious Steele had exhausted a variety of topics, from the price he paid his barber for a periwig —'thirty guineas as I live, and made of horsehair'— to his recent appointment as Groom of the Chamber to Prince George, a post that might have been more correctly, but less high-soundingly styled 'Gentleman-waiter', Addison, from behind a smoke-wreath, cut him short.

" 'Tis a wonder, Dick, that your vocabulary does not run dry at the point of your pen, so much wear and tear does it give to your tongue. Our friend here, I can see, is simmering to tell us—what have you to tell us, Edward? 'Confirm the tidings as they roll, and spread the truth from Pole to Pole!' "

"H'm." Edward's smile slipped. "I could answer you, Joe —saving your mislike of a pun—that if the truth were spread from poll to poll, we might gain a hot majority at the next election. But I'd liefer have the confirmation of my tidings in a lie than in the truth, since they are spread no nearer north nor south of either Pole than Scotland. I have it from Lord Halifax that Harley's spy, Defoe, is in Edinburgh. Prompted by St. John, Harley, who never plays a better game than when he plays for both sides, passes his report to

Godolphin; and he, I am told, takes a most serious view of the case. According to Halifax, our Lord Treasurer fears the Scots will rise against the Treaty."

"And would you blame um if they did?" roared Steele. "I'm strong as me name for the Union meself, yet were I a Scot I'd fight it tooth and nail, for the Scots—don't forget—still own a King."

"God's fish," murmured Addison, "how French wine laced with Irish emotion will pervert the reason of a thoroughgoing Whig."

"None of us forgets that the Scots *own* to a King—or a Pretender," corrected Edward, with a glance aside at Addison, who tapped away a yawn, "unless it were Godolphin——"

"Trotting in and out o' the Queen's closet with the latest tip for Newmarket?" breezily suggested Steele.

But Edward, not to be deterred from his zealous pursuit of a cause that for months had racked the Cockpit, doggedly repeated—"Unless it were Godolphin. Yet I can't think him responsible for moving up 'Bobbing John Mar' as Queen's pawn on the Union's chequerboard. He was at the Palace tonight. I never saw a fellow carry his age with less effort. He's turned thirty and he looks fifteen. But I'd sooner," Edward added wryly, "trust a rattlesnake or St. John in the nest of the Commission, than I'd trust the Earl of Mar."

"Poh, poh!" blustered Steele, flourishing the bottle, "you exaggerate their potency. I'll wager there's no venom worse than spittle in their tongues, which St. John spews in mimicry of Harley. As for Mar, even a Jacobite worm will turn to wriggle its way into favour. Their fangs have been drawn by the Treaty proposals, and before long you will see Scots and English Commissioners taking wine again together. This bottle's dead. I'll get the last, and drink to the Union of——"

"Richard!" A querulous voice on the staircase instantly silenced the rip-roaring Captain. Starting up from his seat, he strode to the door and flung it wide, exclaiming:

"Margaret! My life! Back to bed this minute! And you catching your death o'cold, with your bare feet on those boards. Away with you, me darling. Excuse me, gentlemen."

Standing as a screen between his visitors and the pale lady in her night-shift, who was heard complaining, "I cannot sleep for your noise—" Steele hustled her out. He had left the door ajar, and on the landing the recitation dolefully continued.

"You've no thought for your wife, lying sick while you tope yourself silly and come to me reeling, full as a goat. No woman in this world but I would have the patience——"

"Nay now, my love——"

"I'm not your love. I'm your banker. Will you send your guests away, or must I? You should be about your duties at Kensington tonight. How can you attend on His Highness, raddled to the hilt as you are? You'll lose your post, and much you care! There's always me, your wretched wife, to fall upon. Every guinea my poor father left me goes to your tailor or your cellarer . . . No! And I won't take back my words. You married me for money, and you'll kill me with your debts . . . Go now and wake Mr. Keen, if he's not awake already with your shouting, and ask him to give me a pilule for the bile."

"So I will, me dearest soul," Dick was heard imploring, "if you'll go back to your bed."

Addison cocked an amused eyebrow at Edward who, thoroughly embarrassed at this domestic altercation, cracked another walnut, peeled it, nibbled it, took a sip of wine and said: "It's time we went."

Tilting the dregs of the bottle into his glass Addison sighed. "See how when liberty is gone, life loses its relish. I am astonished that he proves himself so prolific a penman with four plays to his credit, a wailing wife at his heels, and the bailiffs on his doorstep."

"Kept at bay," said Edward, rising, "by the sale of his good lady's West Indian islands. Joe, I must be off. I leave London by an early coach for Huntingdon tomorrow."

"I'm ready to join you." Addison took his pipe and a jar of tobacco from the table, crossed to the cupboard where the Captain kept his wine, and deposited these articles on a shelf. "I shall know where to find them when I come here again," to Edward's lifted eyebrows he explained. "We'll leave our Benedick—Ah! that slipped out despite myself—

we'll leave our Dick to his connubial diversions. After you, sir."

With his slightly mocking, wholly charming smile, Addison made way for Edward at the door. They parted at the corner of Bennett Street, Addison strolling toward his lodgings in the Haymarket with his head in the sky and his feet in the mud; Edward to his rooms in Great Queen Street, regretting he had not retained the chaise which had brought him to the Palace. He would now have to walk home.

The sky had cleared with the greying dawn; the streets had emptied. Only the lighted windows of the taverns and the sound of drunken carousal within, denoted any sign of wakefulness. But he had not gone far upon his way when he was accosted by a girl who left her stance against a wall beneath a lanthorn to come at him with whispers.

Prudery revolted, he was about to hurry on when he discovered her to be, horrifyingly, a child. Her face, under its plastering of paint, was framed in wispy black elf-locks and pinched as if with cold, or hunger. Seen in that dim light, her eyes held a scared, haunted look, the more pitiful for the trained coquettish smile on those young, red-smeared lips.

"Good God!" he muttered, staring. "How old are you?"

Hopefully encouraged, she came at him again to answer in glib patter: "Fourteen come Michaelmas, sweet'art, and cheap at the price, tender as a duckling I can give you what you've never had and what you'd die to have if you could know. I'm well learned in all the tricks to please a gentleman o' quality."

As she paused for breath, Edward, dismayed and vaguely conscience-stricken, dug in his pocket for a coin.

"You look half-starved. Do you live on your ill-gotten gains?"

"Fine I can live—like a lady," he was told; but her dress gave the lie to that. The uncertain lamp-light revealed her in the rags of a tawdry striped petticoat and a bodice, once velvet, that had lost all trace of its texture in its dirt. A tattered scarf adorned her bony shoulders, and looking down he saw her naked toes curling up through the holes in her shoes. When in luck, he heard her say with valiant bravado, she could line her belly with pig's chitterlings or ox-tripe, though the price of a lodging took the most of what she earned. "I'm finical to that degree in my choice of a room—as you'll find—to couch as sweet with me as with Duke Morlberry's Duchess herself."

She wriggled her puppet hips at him, aping the elders of her trade in painful mimicry.

"No, no!" Outraged, yet pitying, he backed. "Take this." Gingerly, at arm's length, he offered her a crown-piece. "And," he sternly ordered her, "buy food with it."

"What!" Her claw-like hand shot out to grab the money. "Waste good silver on pig's offal? Not likely! I'll to Love Lane—" she was all gutter-urchin now—"hard by Billingsgate, and buy me Lisbon oranges."

"Oranges won't feed you," muttered Edward.

"Feed me? Yah! And more they'll feed me. Look 'ee, I can sell them in the Ring when I can buy 'em. When I can't—" she pointed the rosy tip of her tongue at him—"then I sell meself to bucks like you, or others such."

He went from her disgustedly, then turned again to find her grubby fingers on his sleeve.

"Go," he warned her, "or I'll have you in the stocks."

Cringingly she shrank away. "I only wished to say," she whined, "that if you want me service free o' charge I'm yours for the asking at the Bunch o' Grapes by Knight's Bridge. Betty Laskey, that's me name. I buried me mother last week o' the pox. She—God save her—taught me my manners. *She* was partic'lar, never to be one for the red-lamp houses. No more'm I, but who's to care? I never had a father. You'se the first as ever spoke to me as if I was a 'uman." A tear rolled down her cheek. Snuffling, she rubbed at it to leave a grimy patch amid the paint. "I shan't forget your charity," she said with elfin earnestness. "I'm as good as a witch at foretelling. The time'll come, maybe, when you'll need to call on Betty Laskey and then you'll find me waiting to serve you—and oblige."

She scampered off, darting down a side-street, swallowed in the misty dawn.

The city was astir with unseen life, the eastern sky flushed like the face of a sleeping girl. And as he stood a moment to enjoy the fresh aroma of the morning, wind-wafted from near pastureland and hayfields or Hampstead's gorse-embowered hills, that drenched in welcome sweetness the overpowering stink of the night's garbage, Edward mused upon life's shiftless contradictions and injustices. . . . That miserable waif, young enough, almost, to have been his daughter, was equally at one with him in the everlasting conflict for survival. She bartered oranges, or her child's body, for pig's chitterlings. He, and 'others such', bartered political lies and insincerities for Party honours offered, given, taken, not in the 'red-lamp houses' she despised, but in Parliament's House, high above suspicion. Is hers, or ours—theirs, he asked, the greater wrong? Was not the plight of this unfortunate a signal proof that he and 'others such', who made the laws to break the laws were wholly indifferent to the word of Christ? "For who among us all," he said aloud —to send a shocked cat, sampling a fish-head in the gutter, flying with its tail up—"who among us all is without sin?"

Resuming his walk, troubled by the memory of that poor young creature's gratitude, he determined, should he come to power with voice enough, not only to speak but to be heard, that he would strive for the betterment of these unhappy night-prowling marauders. Each case should be individually considered; those past redemption must be perforce committed to the whipping-post, or Bridewell; but the very young, the cruelly young, should be cared for, nurtured, taught the better way . . . if the better way were not irrevocably lost.

Yet, for all his generous quixotics, Edward gave that chance encounter of the streets no second thought. He was to find Betty Laskey more faithful to her word than he to his intention, when, 'good as a witch at foretelling' she, who had waited, was eventually called upon to serve.

★ 3 ★

IT CANNOT be with any truth admitted that Mary's first appearance in society created a sensation. Although admired for her beauty and flattered for her wit, she was unsought by

53

any suitor, with exception of the wealthy Mr. K.; but even his unswerving optimism was not proof against discouragement. When at the end of the season the girls returned to Thoresby, their father, who accompanied them home, expressed his disappointment that Mary had so lamentably failed in her mission.

"No man worthy of his manhood," blazed his lordship, "would wish to tie himself for life to a woman who spouts Latin at him morning noon and night. Yes, 'tis you I blame," he bawled at Mary, who stood to bear the brunt of his displeasure, "not Frances. She'll have time and plenty, at sixteen, to find a husband. Lord Mar, your aunt reports, was fairly struck. But you! When you have the chance to make a match you needs must sit before him like a mooncalf. And so he shakes his heels, and won't come back."

The Marquis paused: and as his experienced eye raked his daughter's slender body as if to strip it stark—There's a plaguy vexatious bitch it is! he resentfully reflected, noting the downcast fringe of lashes, the delicate articulation of bone structure, the tremulous ripe mouth, and all her indefinable exasperating siren-lure, enough—so ran her father's thought—to drive a man to wring her neck or tumble her! "He'll not come back," his lordship, with some violence, repeated. "He's too well placed with near on half a million to his credit—the greatest land-owner in Ireland, to go courting a rebuff. And if you think I'll waste good money on bringing you to London once a year to pick a husband when you'll not lift a finger to aid me in my search, then, my girl, you're damnably mistaken. Your aunt presents your sister Evelyn next season, and pray God He'll spare me *three* old maids upon my hands for life!"

With which pious appeal he dismissed them, and turned to refresh himself with brandy.

"So now," Mary said, "we know."

"Know what?" demanded Frances.

"Our fate. The three old maids of Thoresby."

"Speak for yourself," snapped Frances, "not for me. You heard what Papa said of Lord Mar—that he was struck?"

"Yes, so struck," agreed Mary, honey-mouthed, "that you must have laid him out in one fell blow, since Bobbing John,

54

as they call him for a turncoat Jack, has not come bobbing up to you again."

This gentle thrust was ineffectually parried with shrieks of: "Jealous! You're jealous! John Mar o' Scotland's a bigger catch than any Irish flounder—and you know it, jealous toad! You'd be glad enough to hook an earl, but you won't—so God A'mighty highty-tighty and pernickety you are. I'll wager I'll be married before you, and so will Evelyn, and then Papa'll have only you stuck on his hands for life!"

"Poor Papa!" smiled Mary, "and what a scarifying bother-some adhesion I shall be."

Whether or no she took to heart this dismal augury, it was soon after her return to Thoresby that she abandoned, for a while, her more ponderous pursuits in favour of household duties. We find her in the dairy, churning cream; or in the stillroom, brewing, under Nurse's supervision, cowslip and elderberry wines; or in the kitchen, up to the elbows in flour, making pies; but not for long. By the end of that year she was deep in a translation of Epictetus. Her father, on brief visits, gloomily observed this new absorption and wondered what the pox he was to do with her! Ink on her fingers—untidy little brat—hunched at his desk in his library, forsooth, poring over Latin. Was she crazed?

If not crazed, untidy it is certain that she was. She cared nothing for her dress nor her appearance, to the despair of Grace, her maid. She, despite old Nurse's efforts to have her out, stayed in, and vainly strove to adorn her lady in silks or satins more befitting to her rank. Mary, when not acting hostess to her father's boon companions, much preferred to go in rustic holland, a mob cap, and 'an old pair of stays, covered in Black Tabby, stitched and lined with flannel.' She disdained high heels and tramped around in clogs—'like a vagrant' her father deplored.

During the winter the almost impassable roads eliminated visits from her friends, save those who lived in the near neighbourhood. Then, as diversion from her studies and self-imposed housewifery, Mary joyed to ride in Sherwood Forest. A fearless horsewoman, she frequently rode unattended, putting her mount to five-barred gates, clearing hedges, ditches, racing over stubble field and dewy pasture on damp, sun-lost mornings, when the trees were all a-glow with autumn gold, and the air full of the bitter-sweet tang of dead wet leaves and wood-smoke. Sometimes she rode with William, who, then about fourteen and still in the care of his tutor, Mr. Franklin, was being coached for Cambridge and permitted by his master little relaxation from his books.

On one of these excursions, tempted by a falsely fair October day, Mary and her brother starting early for their ride met with an adventure of some consequence.

The sun, that had glorified the morning with almost summer heat, was suddenly obscured by leaden clouds to darken all the landscape. The brilliant tints of red and gold, the copper plumes of forest oaks swayed, tarnished and drab-coloured as seaweed, in a wind that had come from the west driving the rain before it. A flash of lightning followed by an ominous thunder-growl, brought the riders to a standstill.

"We must go back," Mary said, "or we'll be drenched." Yet even as they turned for home the storm crashed above them in one terrific thunder-clap to set their horses plunging. Mary kept her seat but William lost a stirrup, and before he could regain it his filly took the bit between her teeth and fled.

With a cut of her whip to her horse's flank, Mary gave chase, yelling, "Pull up her head! Hold her short!" Her words were drowned in the frenzy of the skies.

It was then she remembered the quarry-pit, clear in the line of the grey mare's flight; and using every atom of her strength to guide her frantic horse, she followed at the gallop. Over fallen tree-trunks and ground rotten with rabbit holes, leaning forward on her horse's neck, her hair flying from under the boyish cocked hat and a prayer in her heart that she might be in time to halt the mare, they went. Through stinging darts of rain she glimpsed her brother striving manfully to pit his weight against the terror-driven speed he was powerless to check, until, with that yawning pit a bare fifty yards ahead, she saw him fling up his arms, and fall.

In a few seconds she had reached him and dismounted. He lay huddled in the rain-soaked grass, his long hair covering his face. She smoothed back the tangled curls and saw the flush fade from those round pippin cheeks; his eyes were closed.

"William!" Her voice, high-pitched in fear, screamed above the storm-wrack. "Speak to me!"

Frenziedly she shook him, raised him, clutched him, glancing wildly around. The thunder had receded; a ribbon of silver edged the slatey sky, but the rain, released from the lowered clouds, came slanting down in torrents. William's mare had vanished—in the pit, Mary, whimpering, supposed. She wriggled out of her wet velvet riding-coat to cushion it under William's head, and went to fetch her horse, standing now subdued beneath the shelter of an oak. Looping the reins to her wrist, she coaxed him to her brother's side and knelt again. Unfastening his shirt she laid an ear to his heart and listened for its beat—slow and steady; but his pallor and that deathly stillness, living yet not living, was terrible to see. She dared not leave him lying there while she sought help. She must lift him to the saddle; lead him home.

Winding her arms about his inert body—he was tall for his age and heavily boned—she succeeded in raising him from the ground, only to find his weight too much for her slight strength to carry. He slumped forward on her breast; his pale cheek was colder. Despairingly she cried his name, " 'Tis Mary, love, who calls you! Dear God, of your pity," she implored, "send help to save him. He is dying—he is dead!"

"Neither dead nor dying; only stunned, I think."

At the preternatural promptitude of this reply sprung, as it were, from a source invisible, Mary's blood congealed. Fearing to look up lest a haloed vision should be hovering above her, she cast a shrinking glance across her shoulder and saw—with what thankfulness!—a pair of booted feet. No terrifying shape in gleaming robes was this, but one of flesh and blood, a horseman whose approach and his dismounting had been silenced on the sodden turf.

Any man, a highwayman, an oaf, the village idiot, she would have gladly welcomed at this moment, but that he of all men should have come in answer to her prayer, was surely less coincidence than wizardry—or what?

"You, sir! Mr. Wortley Montagu! How is it you are here so opportune? The mare—she bolted, 'twas the thunder—he fell—she's in the pit. We must pull him—her—must pull her out, but William first. If you can help me lift—and then find her——"

With scanty regard for this coherent speech, Mr. Wortley Montagu got upon his knees and cursorily examined, to pronounce:

"No bones broken. There may be slight contusion, but nothing serious, we hope. This should restore him."

"This" was a silver flask taken from his pocket, the contents of which he forced down William's throat. "I always carry with me a flask on a long-distance ride," said he; and then proceeded to tell how he was on his way to Thoresby with a note to Lady Mary from his sister. A riderless mare had overtaken him a furlong's length or so beyond the quarry. Guessing that there might have been an accident, he had turned back. And all the while he talked, he dosed William with the brandy. Presently, spluttering and coughing, the boy's closed eyelids lifted, faint colour returned to his cheeks, and staring up into the face above his own—"Who in the devil," William asked, "are you?"

"God be thanked!" Mary flung herself beside him. "My precious—my darling! 'Tis Mr. Wortley Montagu has saved you, sent from Heaven."

Not usually demonstrative and always chary of endearments, she smothered him in kisses, from which unwonted display of affection William disengaged, saying gruffly: "Don't throttle me." Then, sense revived, he sat up. "The mare! The quarry—is she in it? I must go fetch her out, poor beast. I'd hate to lose her."

"She is not in the quarry," was the quiet reassurance, "she passed me yonder, and is likely in her stable by this time."

"So if her neck's not broke," William said between his teeth, "I'll break it for her! There's a devil's spawn she is to get away with me. Here!" He licked his lips, eyeing his preserver with anything but gratitude, "What's this stinking stuff you've made me swallow?"

"Hush, William! For shame! You owe your life to Mr. Wortley Montagu," cried Mary, very red.

"By no means does Lord Kingston owe his life to me," contradicted Edward. "Your ladyship exaggerates. Your life, my lord, was in no danger from your fall. Nor will you suffer more ill consequence than a few bruises, I believe."

"Fall be poxed!" retorted William inexcusably. "I fell a'purpose. 'Twas the only thing to do with that damned mare o' mine streaking for the quarry like a scalded cat. 'Cod! I did fall hard!" And tenderly feeling his rump, he rose, turning a smile upon Edward to melt stones. "Sir, I regret my churlishness, but with my sister in the vapours and my mare, as I thought her, dead as mutton in the pit, I have quite forgot my manners—which I beg you to excuse."

"Does your lordship feel equal to mounting my horse?"

"Yes, sir, an it please you," William answered doubtfully. "But if I ride your horse, what'll you ride, sir?"

"I," Edward told him, "will walk."

It was not a cheerful cavalcade that ambled back to Thoresby in the aftermath of storm. William was complaining that his seat felt plaguy sore; and Mary, coatless, for her jacket that had served as William's pillow was still too wet to wear, shivered as with ague. Her habit clung damply to her legs; her soaked cambric riding-shirt stuck to her skin; her hair was in rats' tails and she had lost her hat. She had also lost her handkerchief, and, needing it, she sniffled.

Miserably conscious that she looked a sorry sight, Mary, walking her horse at funeral pace, heard Edward speak to William—not to her—of animal sagacity. That the mare, despite her terror, had swerved to avoid the quarry proved, said he, that the instinct of self-preservation was the second most powerful of nature's forces.

"And what," inquired William, "is the first?"

"The first? Ah! the first," Edward weightily reflected, "the first and most primitive instinct, which applies less to animal than to humankind, springs from the eternal cause that had its beginnings in a garden."

"Whose garden?" persisted the literal William.

"The Garden where the Lord performed the first operation in experimental chirurgery on Adam's fifth rib. Since when the sexes have been divided and must for ever seek to be joined as one again. And that," was Edward's contemplative conclusion, "is thought to be the origin—as opposed to the theory of Pythagoras or Plato—of the predominating urge which men call Love."

Mary's horse suddenly shied.

"Hi! looby, look what you're at!" shouted William. "You bumped me."

"'Twas a rabbit," mumbled Mary, "he always shies at rabbits." And bringing her horse alongside his she besought him in a whisper: "Give me a handkercher for God's sake."

"Give you a what?"

"A handkerchief," mouthed Mary.

Mr. Wortley Montagu was smiling to himself.

"I haven't got a handkerchief," said the brutish William, "Mr. Wortley Montagu, Mary wants a——"

"Handkerchief? By all means." He produced one from his sleeve; spotless, folded, silken. Handing it to William he bade him, "pass this to her ladyship."

But her ladyship, scarlet to the ears, did not take it. She had cantered on ahead.

"D'ye see that now? She don't know what she does want. She always was contrariwise," said William.

On arriving at Thoresby Edward politely refused Lady Mary's offer that he should stay for dinner while his clothes were dried. Only his jacket, he said, had caught the rain, and that was almost dry already. He had delivered the letter from his sister, requesting the loan of some books that a footman had brought and laid out on a table.

Glancing at the titles, he scathingly remarked upon Anne's choice of literature—"which lends itself to tales of lovesick princesses, love potions, enchantments and so forth. She will read this sort of trash by the hour."

"Indeed, yes," agreed Mary, "'tis my constant endeavour to cultivate in Mistress Anne more discriminating qualities. But alas, I fear her taste is flippant."

Her ladyship was scarcely to be recognized as the slubber-degullion who, half an hour earlier, had burst in upon her maid, flung off her drenched garments, and demanded of the startled Grace her new silk petticoat and her flowered taffety: the hare's foot, the curling-tongs, the powder-puff, the patch-box—and a handkerchief of finest lace. And then she ordered dinner, bade the butler open wine, "Muscadine, Madeira, Languedoc, and Burgundy—and to tell the cook to roast the ortolans—" bespoken for her father, due from London the next day. "And be sure to lay the table with the best silver plate and the linen damask lately bought from D'Oyley's."[1]

Then, after having set the household by the ears in preparations as for Royalty, the honoured guest must needs decline her invitation. Nor did it seem, for all her change of toilet, that she had made the least impression on Mr. Wortley Montagu, who was in evident haste to be gone. In order to detain him—she could smell the roasting ortolans—she dilated on Anne's illiteracy.

"These," she shrugged disparagement of 'these' which, with a superior smile, Anne's brother had collected, "these I offer Mistress Anne as a bonne bouche—a recreational reward for the pains of more serious study. For myself," she added casually, "I would never stoop to read such nonsense."

"Oh?" said Edward, turning the leaves of Monsieur Honoré D'Urfé's *Astrea*, a spicy entertainment in which Henri Quatre and his Court had delighted. And at that moment a slip of paper fell from the book to the floor. Stooping to recover it, he saw clearly written the names of the chief characters with a summary of their respective faults or virtues.

He handed her the paper. "Yours, I think."

That, she told him, blushing to her eyebrows, was a list she had compiled in her very early youth. "These volumes are too large for you to carry, sir. I'll send them."

"I will fetch them," Edward said, "another day." And casting a glance again upon the list he held, "I see you favour the beautiful Diana, the volatile Climene, the melancholy Doris, Celadin the faithful, Adamas the wise; one might well excuse Anne's interest in nonsense so delicious."

"Life no less than literature would," she said, "be dull were it not nonsensically lightened. I, like Climene, am volatile too."

[1] Thomas D'Oyley, fashionable linen-draper of Henrietta Street, Covent Garden.

"And like Diana beautiful—like Adamas as wise."

She showed a dimple. "Sir, we speak in rhythm."

"A habit quick to come by——"

"Hard to quench; and a habit that will grow from writing verse."

"Is versifying," Edward asked, "another of your ladyship's accomplishments?"

"I would not have you know it if it were." And with calculated nonchalance she added: "I'm engaged at present on an exercise in prose, a translation of Epictetus. The Enchiridion."

"Excellent," quoth Edward, very dry.

"It is by no means excellent," she answered warmly, "but when it shall be done—which will not be for years, so slow and careful am I in resort to dictionaries and grammars, but when 'tis done my father's good friend, Bishop Burnet, has offered to advise me of its faults."

He bowed.

"If any."

She glared.

"There will be many."

"My dear young lady," he spread his charming hands, "you are over modest. I believe that any study undertaken by yourself will be completed to perfection."

"You cannot tell," she objected, suspicious of his smile, "till you've seen it."

"I would hardly dare to beg so great a favour. But if your ladyship would condescend to grant an humble student of the Master the privilege of perusing your essay——"

He paused; and Mary trembled.

"You will never find the time to read it," she cautioned him, "'tis full of blots and scratches and almost quite illegible."

"I will read it were it written in Egyptian hieroglyphics," was the handsome reply to this.

And so it came about that Edward undertook to supervise the translation—through the post. She would send him pages which he returned corrected, with marginal comments. No letter from either side accompanied these efforts. Not until the summer of 1709 do we find any trace of that piquant correspondence, the most singular exchange of letters between lovers surely ever written—to be read.

*   *   *

It had been a year of political confusions. The Tories, led by Harley, were clamouring for peace, while the Whigs supported Marlborough in pursuance of the war. The Queen, prostrate with grief at the death of her amiable, gout-ridden husband in October, 1708, had retired from the wranglings of her Ministers to mourn.

The influence of the Marlboroughs was on the wane; the time fast approaching when the tyrant Viceroy Sarah was to see those chains by which she held in thrall her Royal mistress, slowly severed, and the power she had wielded mysteriously sliding from her hands. A new star, so small as to be scarcely discernible, was in the ascendant to outshine her Grace's aura; her own obscure relative, Abigail Hill, the impoverished orphan whom of her charity, as so often she recounted, she had rescued 'from a garret—from a broom', and placed about the person of the Queen, to the Duchess's bitter undoing.

According to her Grace, this lowly creature, by reptilian cunning and backstair intrigue, had wormed her way into the arms and susceptible heart of Queen Anne. But let that be the least of it. Abigail Hill, undersized and silent-footed, freckled, sandy-haired, was, for all her negligible presence, a force to be reckoned with—a Jacobite, a Tory, Harley's tool. She was also Harley's cousin, and, crowning instance of her crass ingratitude, she had got herself married, unbeknown to the Duchess, unbeknown to any save the Queen herself, who had attended the secret wedding of her handmaid to Mr. Masham, Groom of the Chamber to Prince George.

This, then, was the burning theme of Sarah's grievance, noised abroad to raise a hornet's nest and disconcert the Whigs. They, with Sarah, saw their power crumbling at the feet of Abigail Masham . . . Masham! All London was whispering her name—and what a very foolish name—when Mary came to Town again in March, 1709.

It was not the gayest season her father could have chosen

to exploit her in the matrimonial mart. The Queen, still in mourning, held no Courts, and Mary was left at Arlington Street much to her own devices. She had obtained her father's grudging consent that she take Italian lessons with a Signor Cassotti; these, and the writing of innumerable letters, occupied most of her time.

'I believe I am the only young woman in Town who am in my own house at ten o'clock tonight,' she writes to her friend Mrs. Hewet[1] of Shireoaks, Nottingham. 'This is the night of Count Turruca's Ball to which he has invited a few bare-faced and the rest en Masque,' and which Mary had not been asked to attend. 'Next to the Ball,' she goes on to say, 'what makes the most noise is the marriage of an old maid without a portion who lives in this street, to a man of £7,000 a year.' But although Mary describes him as 'filthy, frightful, odious, detestable', the bridegroom seems to have afforded her much entertainment, for 'never,' she declares, 'was man more smitten with these charms that had lain invisible for forty years; yet with all his glory, no bride had fewer enviers. . . .'

One might suspect that Mary, who, nose pressed to the window-pane, watched the bride's 'equipages and liveries that outshine anybody's in Town', and the '£3,000 worth of jewels' showered on her by the bridegroom, may have been one of those few enviers, since she, now twenty, was still unwooed, unwed. To this same Mrs. Hewet she confessed she was a 'rake at reading', and gives a thousand thanks for the letters of Madame de Noyer: nor does her rakish reading stop at that. There was the recently published *New Atlantis* by the notorious Mrs. de Rivière Manley, which created a furore for its scandal; then came *The Tatler*, edited by Richard Steele, under the pseudonym of 'Isaac Bickerstaff', which purported 'to expose the false arts of life, to pull off the disguises of vanity and affectation, and to recommend a general simplicity in our discourse.'

These principles that emphasized 'simplicity of discourse', Mary might have imbibed to her profit. Yet no question that the 'arts of life', as exposed by Mr. Bickerstaff, were talked

[1] Afterwards Lady Hewet, wife of the Surveyor General of Woods and Works.

about *ad nauseam* in coffee-house and club, in ladies' drawing-rooms, in Mary's letters, and in 'that vile paper, the *Tatler*,' as she calls it; but is not above accepting copies of the same from Anne's brother Edward, in particular the second volume of the series, handsomely dedicated to Mr. Wortley Montagu.

It was on her return home in April that Mary observed in Anne's letters from Wortley a marked improvement in style, wording, spelling. Hitherto Anne had written in her scrambling scrawl, as young ladies will, of young gentlemen, of love-tokens, valentines and such: while her most recent letter had dwelled upon her latest beau, Lord Herbert, who had begged for a lock of her hair, 'something—anything private of hers that he could value'. To which request Anne had responded by sending a thing less 'private', she said, than 'impolite to mention'.

We may therefore well believe that Mary read with some astonishment the letter that immediately followed this. So lofty and dignified was it, so carefully worded, so altogether different from its naughty predecessor, that she would have doubted Anne had written it herself had she not recognized the writing. It contained nothing here of valentines or tokens, or of Herbert; but love is hinted at—and more than hinted—in 'the thought that will include you in a labyrinth of bliss'. Then Anne makes excuse for having 'run on in a manner that might have been mistaken for flattery were it not that I know you to be too nice a judge to endeavour to please you that way, and can only tell you that *I love you dearly*. . . .'

To which sudden gush of affection, Mary, in the giggles, made imitative reply, fondly to assure her 'dear **Mrs.** Wortley':

'I will not believe that you flatter . . . I will look upon what you say as an obliging mark of your partiality. . . . How happy must I think myself when I fancy your friendship for me even great enough to overpower your judgement! Believe me, I could scribble three sheets to—(I must not name) twenty people that have not so great a share of my esteem, and whose friendship is not so absolutely necessary to my happiness. . . .

My dear, dear, adieu. I am *entirely* yours.'

Then, fearing she carries the joke just a little too far, she adds a postscript. 'I am horribly ashamed of this letter. . . . Pray heaven it will not be laughed at. That's as may be.'

It may also be she guessed the source of Anne's effusion: and with what flutters, burnings, yearnings, did she wait for another declaration while she vacillated between hope and fear. Or was it possible that simple foolish Anne had conceived a passion for her? Such emotional phenomena she knew, from her reading of the classics, used to exist on the island of Lesbos. Or, as she preferred to think, was Anne controlled by some remote and super force who, like Eros, wooed his Psyche in the dark? But all doubt as to the origin or motive of Anne's letter was dispelled when the post brought this:

'I am now in the room with an humble servant of yours who is arguing so hotly about marriage that I can scarcely go on with my writing. Everybody seeks happiness, but though everybody has a different taste, yet all pursue money, which makes people choose great wigs . . . But you have wit, joined with beauty, a thing so much out of fashion that we fly after you like birds. . . .'

How very odd of Anne! Or of the hotly argumentative 'humble servant' who claimed to be hers, with such ready access to Anne's room . . . 'Beauty', 'Birds'. 'Fly after you . . .' Who, marvelled Mary, pulsating, would want to fly after *me*? Not Anne, certainly, unless she had run mad, but the unprovoked accusation that 'all pursue money' she repudiates at once in her reply:

'I call all people who fall in love with furniture, clothes, and equipages, no less in the wrong than when they were five years old and doated on shells, pebbles, and hobby-horses!' To which in answer comes further revelation.

'Dear Lady Mary will pardon my vanity. I could not forbear reading to a Cambridge Doctor who was with me, a few of those lines that did not make me happy till this week.'

Here, for an instant, the vizard is lifted. There was only one 'Cambridge Doctor' in the neighbourhood of Wortley; and only one who would have had enough temerity, and with what significant double entendre, to suggest:

'I love you too well to envy you; but love of oneself is in all so powerful, it may be a doubt whether the most violent passion would prevail with me to forward you in the pursuit . . . to set you above me. But as I know there is so little hope of coming near you, that if I loved you not at all I should not be averse to raising you higher.'

'*I should not be averse to raising you higher.*'
There was something too self-confident in this, a hint of patronage to nettle her. Why be at such pains to keep up the pretence? Why sign herself (or *him*self) 'yours with truth and passion', and continue to stay hidden? Idiotic! Why not come into the open and declare his love, if love it were, and not a mockery? The thought nagged at her with torment. Did Anne and he conspire in a questionable trick to make of her their fool?

And still they play their subtle game of hide-and-seek, while Mary, like a fawn surprised in ambush, coyly leaps ahead to lead him on.

'I hope my dear Mrs. Wortley showing my letters is in the same strain as her compliments, all meant for raillery, and I am not to take it as a thing really so . . . For your friendship is the only happiness of my life; and whenever I lose it I have nothing to do but to take one of my garters and hang myself on the nearest beam.'

But even this dire threat failed to draw her masked lover, notwithstanding she had reason to know herself jealously watched. When in August she attended the Nottingham races she was promptly accused of flirtation, charged not only of having been 'highly diverted' by the fashionable tenor, Nicolini of Covent Garden Playhouse, but also of casting her coveted favour at another 'most happy person now in being' . . . 'When the race is over and your thoughts are free again I shall be glad,' she is informed, 'to hear you have been well entertained.'

The 'happy person' to whom this cut is pointedly directed may have been a 'Mr. D.', but he, also relegated to a mere initial, is indignantly denied as non-existent.

'After giving me imaginary wit and beauty, you give me

imaginary passions and you tell me I'm in love. If I am, 'tis
a perfect sin of ignorance, for I don't so much as know the
man's name. I passed the days of Nottingham races at
Thoresby without seeing, or wishing to see, one of the sex.'

A blatant lie that is eagerly swallowed and washed down
with abject contrition.

> 'Henceforth I will be done with all jealous tricks. I will
> not dare to speak, no, not so much as think of my dearest
> Lady Mary in a laughing way, and shall be satisfied if I have
> the same rank among your admirers that your grammars and
> dictionaries have among your books. . . .
>
> Make what you will of me, 'tis enough that you own me
> to be yours.'

She has dragged him to the brink of a confession. Would
he topple over, or retreat? Forgetful of the fib she has
unblushingly offered as excuse for her behaviour at the
races: 'You cannot sure be angry,' she pleads, 'at my resentment? To be capable of preferring the despicable wretch you
mention to *Mr. Wortley Montagu* was ridiculous, if not as
criminal as forsaking the Deity to worship a calf.'

She has shown him her hand, now let him show his. 'It
may be reasonably called presumptuous in a girl,' she says
with wistful urgency, 'to have her thoughts that way. Adieu,
my dear. The post stays. My next shall be longer.'

It was; and reproachful, too, since Anne offers no reply
to this appeal.

'I am convinced, however dear you are to me, Mrs. Anne
Wortley, I am of no concern to you. . . .'

The game was done. She would never hear again of 'Love'
from Mrs. (or Mr.) Anne Wortley, who has 'strove to kill
me of neglect.'

And although she waited all September's golden days, and
waiting, wondered, no news came.

* 4 *

It was All Hallows' E'en, a dreary day of fitful rain and a maundering wind that moaned at the heels of the hag-ridden clouds—"like a sick brat," Mary said, "at the skirts of its mother."

She was watching, as so often now she watched, for the long delayed post or a messenger from Wortley. Nurse, mending linen at the fireside, was more than usually plunged in gloom.

"There'll be witch's broth a-brewing this night, I'll warrant. I'd a pricking in my thumbs that brought a dream o' roses, red and white—that's for trouble. And this morn I laid the cards for you and saw—" she paused to bite a thread.

"And what did you see?" snapped Mary, twirling round. "A gift unexpected, a stranger to the house, or a bitter disappointment to my heart's desire? I know before you tell it how my fortune lies in your grubby bits of pasteboard."

At which Nurse fetched a sigh to burst her stays.

"No heart's desire did I see for you, my lady, but sorrow black and dolesome as the nine o' spades can give it."

"Good Lord defend us! Here's a pretty telling for an ugly day!" But despite her scoffing smile Mary shivered. "Will you be in attendance at the witches' dance tonight, flying off to nowhere on your besom? You'd be well advised to keep your mischief to yourself lest you be catched by the constables and ducked in the pond, as was old Mother Griffiths for her sins. Beware lest you follow her fate."[1]

"I've no fear of my fate. I was born with a caul," Nurse wheezily replied. "I'll never sink nor will I drown, for all I'm no witch, but the seventh child of a seventh child, and have the second sight to see what's in the wind, and the ears to hear the whisper of a fly—hey, now, lady! mind what

---

[1] Sarah Griffiths, a notorious witch, suspect of dealings with the devil, who when put to the test of her guilt by being forced under water to sink or swim, 'popp'd up again and swame like a corke.' For which incontrovertible evidence against her she was tried and committed to Bridewell. This, according to the testimony of Thos. Greenwall, July, 1704.

69

you're about." For Mary at the window had flung it wide to let a draught come whistling through the room, and was hanging head and shoulders over the sill at imminent risk of a tumble. Then she turned again, flushed and radiant, to say:

"So much you see and hear, you heard no sound of a horseman below—and no stranger to the house is he!" And running to a mirror on the wall she ordered her breeze-ruffled hair and was out of the room like a rocket. Down the stairs, helter-skelter, she went, colliding with a footman in the hall on his way to announce the arrival of Mr. Wortley Montagu, who had asked to see her ladyship alone.

He stood with his back to the fire, facing the door as she entered. To her curtsy he distantly bowed; to her greeting responded, low-voiced. His lugubrious expression and his pallor, enhanced by the unrelieved black of his clothes, prepared her for the reason of his visit. The thought came to her swiftly . . . His father! And suitably matching her hushed voice to his, "I trust," she said, "your sombre dress does not presage ill tidings?"

His silence alarmed her: there was that in his eyes, weary, heavy-lidded, to drain the light from hers.

"Why do you stare?" Her lips were dry; the whisper scarcely passed them. "Who?"

He came and stood before her to take her hand in both of his, yet did not speak. "Tell me," she cried, "who is it? Not . . ." And on that name unuttered, her throat closed.

He bent his head; his words were quiet, careful.

"'Twas cruelly sudden. A chill flew to her lungs."

"No, no!" Her voice returned to shriek at him, "not she —not Anne! I won't—I can't believe—'tis some trick of yours to plague me. You are too prone to trickery." She strove against her fear to seek the truth behind his icy cold composure; "Your letters—hah!—a brave jest, that!" And when he answered nothing, standing motionless: "Only tell me," she implored him, "that it isn't—what I cannot dare believe. O, God! It can't be so."

He gathered her close. She could feel the hurried beating of his heart. "I would give my life for hers were it not so—but so it is."

Tearlessly sobbing, shock-blinded, she clung to him for comfort, until the storm subsided and she lay in his arms, limp and lost.

"I wished," she heard him say, "to be the first to let you know." And cupping her face between his hands, he told her strangely, "I have waited, and it seems I still . . . must wait."

Then, for one timeless second, she felt her lips possessed, but even in her moment of surrender: "No," he said, "not now . . . not yet." And drew away from her and went.

She heard him go.

Later in the day she learned from those about her that Anne's death, the night before, had been caused by an acute inflammation of the lungs, already weakened, according to the doctor, by 'a creeping phthisis.'

During the weeks that followed, Mary was impelled less by the desire to forget than by a sense of outrage and resentment against life. In this annihilation of a friend more dear to her than a sister, she, with youth's inexorable egotism, saw herself the victim of some malevolent adversary who had selected her, above all others, to suffer this intolerable blow. And behind her petulant unreasoning, one thought alone stayed uppermost: their sportive game of make-believe was ended. Those letters flying back and forth, love's messengers disguised, would never come to her again. Even the recapture of that one moment when, through sorrow's incredulity, she sensed his dawning passion, was denied her. He had gone, she heard, to London; nor had he sent her word of his departure.

She too had gone to London for the winter season, and, with her sisters, participated in the social round of functions, dinners, balls. She drove in the Ring, was a regular attendant at the Opera and Playhouse. Her friend, Mrs. Hewet, received lively letters full of gossip and lampoons, and the tale of Mrs. Somebody or other who 'had pawned her diamond necklace to buy her Valentine a snuff-box . . .' 'The wars make men so violent scarce that these good ladies will put up with the shadows of them.'

Mary also, it would seem, must put up with shadows,

since the substance of him who monopolized her thoughts did not appear. From the giddy whirl of gaiety which she vows did not appeal to her, she turned to her study of Italian; but her chief source of interest during that year derived from the Duchess of Marlborough.

For this beauteous and close acquaintance of her father, Mary conceived the warmest admiration. She delighted in her Grace's vituperative criticism of the Tories and their dastardly chiefs: 'Who,' declared Duchess Sarah, had 'accused her great lord, the nation's darling, of seeking to make himself a second Cromwell—a Dictator—' and this in the face of victories unparalleled. Even the Duke's most trusted supporters in the Junto, Lords Somers and Halifax, were weakening in loyalty to turn and rend the saviour to whom Britain owed her life. 'Traitors all!' was Sarah's burden of complaint; but worse than their treachery were the wicked plots hatched against the Duchess by her lowly cousin, Abigail Hill—"Now if you please, Mrs. Masham, and on the way to be a peeress," quoth her Grace. "Ho, yes! You'll see. She has the Queen in her pocket, and eating from her hand that steals from mine."

Mrs. Masham's machinations were truly unbelievable. Mary, worshipful at Sarah's feet, heard with burning indignation how that Abigail had so far infringed upon the rights of one who 'had raised her from the gutter', that the very apartments in Kensington Palace, "*my* apartments," reiterated Sarah, smiting her bejewelled breast on which sparkled a galaxy of Royal gifts, "my private apartments have been seized and taken from me to bestow on a sandy-haired, freckle-faced Serpent! 'I am sure,' the creature had the impudence to say to me—to *me*!" screamed the Duchess into Mary's shrinking ear, " 'I am sure the Queen will always be very kind to you' . . . Ecod! *Kind!* Such condescension from a crawling maggot is prodigious comical. I've laughed myself sick!"

So comical indeed, that, flinging back her head, the Duchess laughed again until she cried.

Mary, offering consolatory murmurs, said: "But the Queen's infatuation for this person surely is no more than a passing whim?"

"Whim?" returned the Duchess, glaring, "Whim do you call it? Pah!" She spat, and Mary dodged. "So much for passing whims that this *person*, this bedroom slut, who is fit for nothing but to empty chamber-pots, will have me out and the Duke out and Godolphin out and my son-in-law Sunderland out, and her paramour Harley *in*! I have warned the Queen. Will she listen to me? No! For she's bewitched. She has Harley in her closet coddling her lapdogs, creeping up backstairs to squeeze state secrets out of Abigail Hill. Yes! She hears 'em all at keyholes, if not from the Queen's own lips, while Harley hangs on hers, waiting to step into Godolphin's shoes. Godolphin—Yah! So much Godolphin cares for his Party he has only one concern—to keep his Staff of office that he may keep his racing-stud. There's perquisites in plenty to be plucked by my Lord Treasurer from the nation's coffers. You, poor innocent," her Grace flicked Mary's chin with a finger-nail, "little do you guess what infamy surrounds us from these High flying Tories, for all you can talk Latin as if you was Herodotus."

"Herodotus, madam," ventured Mary, "was a Greek."

"Greek or Latin, what's the difference? Who's to care? I don't speak Latin nor Greek neither, and t'would be better for you than your learning of the classics if you learned how to place a patch—the *left* side of your face for a Whig, not the right. That's for Tory madams. Here—" Painfully the Duchess scraped at and tore from Mary's cheek its adornment, licked and stuck it on again the other side. Wincing, Mary timorously asked:

"Can it be truly so, your Grace, that politics are carried to the patch-box?"

"Yes, for 'tis a woman's prerogative to proclaim her husband's Party."

"But I have no husband, madam."

"There's none but yourself to blame for that. You've all to your favour—good looks, high rank—you could pick and choose from half a dozen."

"But not one in half a dozen, ma'am, has chosen me."

" 'M?" The Duchess nodded absently, her gaze fixed on the fire that burned low and would not, Mary guessed, be replenished. The price of sea-coal soared with the flight of war taxation, and the Duchess must be mindful of economy. While Mary spread her numbed hands to the languid embers, her Grace unburdened herself of more grievance.

"Did I ever tell you of my last meeting with Her Majesty?"

"No, madam," Mary lied; she had heard and was to hear the tale many times repeated during those sessions with Sarah, how that, despite her 'angel John's' endeavours to wrench 'this Pestilence—this Abigail'—from his Sovereign's side, she stuck fast. "With what result? That I—" again the Duchess smote herself—"I must wait like a beggar in Her Majesty's closet, to be summoned to Mrs. Morley's presence. I, who loved and guarded her so tenderly, I, who placed her on the Throne, was told I had maligned Mrs. Morley! How? *How?*" screamed the Duchess, clawing at the air as if it were the disembodied face of Mrs. Morley. " 'How have I maligned Your Majesty?' I asked. 'Tell me *how*—save to put the Crown on your head and keep it there! I would be no more capable of slandering Mrs. Morley,' I said, 'than of killing my own children.' And, 'answer me!' I said, standing there before her, 'ANSWER ME!' She, poor dumpling, buried in her fat like a currant in a pudding, could not answer me. She prevaricated. 'You desired no answer, you shall have none'—which I swear was a damned lie. Then pointing to the door she told me 'Go'—and sent me from her as if I were a lackey. And as God's my witness, I could see that snakish Abigail grinning at me from a window as I drove away."

At which the Duchess fell convulsively to sobbing, biting at her handkerchief to tear it into shreds.

It was all too sad and shocking. Mary could have wept for, and sorrowed with the poor distraught, so wickedly abused and injured lady.

But the Duchess was not always in such vitriolic mood. There were times when she was deistically calm, and Mary enchanted to accept the lovely Sarah's invitations to take tea with her, an honour seldom shared by one of Mary's sex though often by a gathering of gentlemen.

The Duchess had a flair for collecting round her men of wit and polish: Addison, in a tie-wig and his one decent suit of clothes turned and pressed to hide its shabbiness, delighting his audience with charming little wise-cracks; or there would come Congreve, a trifle too youthfully dressed, peering at the company from pitifully faded blue eyes that defied their threatened blindness with a smile like the flash of icicles in sunlight. And with him would come Steele, that great-hearted buffoon, always in debt and always in love; always sinning and always repenting, always full of business, launching a paper or writing a play, burying an old wife and marrying a new one; and always just a little drunk, no matter what the hour, sipping bohea with a whisper round at Mary from the corner of his mouth. "Ah! the insupportable labour of doing nothing—but drink tea!"

Lord Dorchester also would sometimes attend at these meetings; and on an afternoon in March, a month or so preceding Sarah's last and fatal quarrel with the Queen, the Marquis brought with him and presented to her Grace, Mr. Wortley Montagu. Mary was taken by surprise. Having arrived in advance of her father, she had not a notion that he would be accompanied, and least of all by him who too often, and against her will, engaged her thoughts.

Grouped around the Duchess, he and other gentlemen were emphatically informed: "I abhor young girls who have no more to say than sheep, but Lady Mary proves exception to the rule."

One would scarcely have believed it, since the Duchess led the talk from which Mary was entirely excluded. And there she sat on a chair of King Charles's time, so high that her feet were off the ground. She wore a gown of primrose satin looped above a green brocaded petticoat, and because of the Duchess's fireless grate and the chill of the Duchess's rooms, she kept her sable tippet round her shoulders and her hands in a muff of the same.

Edward, save for his speckless white steinkerk, was in deepest black from head to foot; even the buttons of his coat had been dimmed of their shine, and he wore on his finger a heavy mourning ring. Conscious that her gay attire must appear in contrast callous, Mary adjusted to her face a look of woe, with memory reviving to a blush. Who, to see him so aloof, constrained to offer her the barest recognition with his bow, would have thought she had been lying in his arms when last they met? Did he remember? One might doubt it.

The Duchess beckoned him, patted the sofa, and murmuring condolence bade him sit beside her. Could this sweet-voiced gentle lady be the same that had so often screamed to Mary and high heaven of her hate for Mrs. Masham, for the Tories, and poor flabby Mrs. Morley, her once beloved Queen? Yet what Sarah now was saying to Mr. Wortley Montagu, leaning forward till the laces on her bosom touched his chest, could—though Mary strained her ears—be heard by none. Then presently the Duchess raised her voice that others too might listen while she questioned him concerning his Bill for the Naturalization of Alien Protestants, which after much debate in the Commons had been recently passed in the Lords; and this, to Mary's vexation, the first she had known of his Bill. It might, she judged, have been more to her advantage had she sought from Bishop Burnet instruction in the moderns and had let the ancients, in particular Epictetus, go hang!

"And now I understand," crooned the dove-like Duchess, "that you are anxious to secure the freedom of Parliament by limiting the numbers of officers sitting—" (like hens, thought the miserable Mary)—"in the House. A commendable proposition."

The Duchess nestled closer till her petticoats were spread about the flattered Edward's knees. And she, Mary banefully considered, old enough to be his mother. At least fifty.

Her father was muttering behind his hand to Addison, and to another gentleman, a Dr. Garth. Pouter-chested, dapper and jovial was he, with diamond buckles to his high-heeled shoes, a diamond hilt to his sword, and in his half-closed eyes a twinkle as they rested on the Duchess. Clenching her frozen fingers in her muff, Mary slid from her seat and dared to interrupt her father's conference with Addison.

"Papa, may I remind you that Aunt Cheyne has invited me to dine with her at Chelsea?"

"The coach is at the door. Pay your respects to the Duchess, and then go." He waved her off. It had always been his custom to treat her as a child that had not learned its manners. Mortifying.

The gentlemen were on their feet, the Duchess, on her

sofa, full of smiles. "Dear child, why so sudden a departure? My lord, your pretty Mary insists on leaving us." Her Grace was often wont to use the Royal plural. "We have scarcely spoke one word to her today. You are looking peaked, my love. It is evident that London air and London's gay society does not agree with such a little"—she was playful—"country mouse. A rustic life is more to your taste and better for your health—and your complexion. You will, we trust, recover both when you return to your native Yorkshire."

"My home is in Nottinghamshire, madam, not in York-shire," answered Mary, soft. "But I was born at my father's house in Covent Garden, and I find my native air of London suits me well."

She dropped her eyes. The Duchess widened hers. "To be sure! We had forgot how your poor mother bitterly com-plained of the noise in the piazzas when she lay-in with you, and I was but a child in my teens. Yes, I dandled you upon my knee—it must be almost thirty years ago. Time flies."

And now it was Mary who smiled.

"Your Grace must be mistook. My age is twenty."

"Twenty! Thirty!" Taken with the flushes, the Duchess fanned herself. "What's your age to me? A woman's as old as she looks; a man is old when he ceases . . . to look." She flashed teeth at her circle of admirers, who received this sally with delighted approbation. Encouraged, her Grace pur-sued: "But you, my dear, should guard that fine fair skin of yours. Mark me, 'twill wither early, and you'll ruin your sight poring over your books. 'Tis certain *you* won't wear well."

"Alas, madam," sighed Mary, and she curtsied, "that's as certain as your Grace has worn *too* well."

Whereupon, before the Duchess could recover breath, Mary, very modest, took her leave.

Dr. Garth and Addison were at the door to bow her out; a footman to conduct her down the stairs.

And she was followed.

As she stepped into her father's coach, one, bare-headed, stood beside it.

"Are your heels winged?" she asked him coldly. "I left you in the Duchess's withdrawing room."

"Yes, winged with impatience to have done with our hostess's chatter. She talks, but she says mighty little and—" his eyelids flickered—"since your final quid pro quo she has been dumb."

"Sir," flashed Mary, concealing satisfaction, " 'tis no charm to me to hear that good lady disparaged. I love her."

"You were always over generous with love," he told her drily, "save where love would be most valued."

She cast a hasty glance at the wooden-visaged footman by the coach's open door, and said: "I do not understand you." Yet she rather hoped she did.

"Then with your permission I will make my meaning clearer. Will your ladyship allow me to get in?"

"In?" she asked him fatuously, "where?"

"In," said he, brushing past the rigid lackey, "here—with you."

The footman slammed the door and mounted to his stance behind the coach; and as the leaders sprang forward to the crack of the whip, Edward drew the curtains close across the windows.

In that shrouded dark his finely chiselled features were those of a stranger, and the silence between them was a veil of suspense torn aside by the grip of his hands on her shoulders, the breath of his words on her lips.

"While I've loved your mind I have been starved for this. And this!"

He took her fiercely in a tempest of desire, long frustrated, that dissolved her on a wave of exaltation. She rejoiced. She had weakened his defences and brought him to confession, confirmed in sight-blind touch, in warm sweet juice of tongue, and broken whispers. "You have me utterly . . . and I am yours."

Afterwards when, wonder-charged, she relived those moments of her triumph, she feared she may have been too eagerly responsive to the storm she had aroused. 'You have me utterly' . . . But what more than that avowal had she to prove him hers? True, he admitted he had 'loved her mind', yet it was not upon her mind he had spent his scorching kisses. Were such greedy tokens to be taken for a seal upon

78

his love, still unconfessed? He had not yet approached her father, and until he did she must believe herself less 'loved' than she was loving.

Nor were her doubts concerning the sincerity of his intentions diminished by a letter she received from him, enclosed in a parcel of *Tatlers*. In one of these she found a paragraph significantly marked and in which the editor, 'Mr. Bickerstaff', or more correctly Captain Steele, had dwelled at some length on feminine follies, especially those of a flighty young wife whose extravagant tastes had ruined her husband. In his accompanying letter Edward, careful to eliminate emotion, judiciously places before his 'L.M.', as he calls her, his doubts concerning their futures were they joined. 'Would you not be the most imprudent woman on earth to leave your present conditions, lose the prospect of richer offers, and go to one with whom you have so small a chance of being easy?'

Such cautious suggestions, and others in similar vein, may have caused her some self-flagellation for her lack of proper maidenly reserve. She should have shown resentment at his uncontrolled assault behind the curtains of her father's coach. Instead, she had returned him kiss for kiss, giving him reason enough to despise her. Why was he such a niggard with his words in ink on paper, when he had been so lavish with his words upon her mouth? . . . And then these pointed accusations in 'Mr. Bickerstaff's' disguise, that her tastes were too extravagant for a man of slender means! Surely his father, that shocking old rip—worth a fortune—would never let his son nor his son's wife want? And now she thought she could perceive his motive in dragging forth such heavy obstacles to bar the way of love. She was the daughter of a wealthy peer; he the son of a still more wealthy squire. Yet, unless their parents were disposed to offer them financial aid, they both would have to marry money. He was sounding her to see if she were willing to sacrifice the luxurious life to which she was accustomed for one of comparative poverty. But . . . sacrifice! What sacrifice lay in the exchange of social trivialities, fine gowns, a coach and six, for the shared comradeship of heart and soul and body?

Determined to deprive him of any such delusion, she sent him his answer addressed to his lodging:

79

'Over against a Tavern
In Great Queen Street
(A Looking-glass Shop)

'Perhaps you'll be surprized at this letter; I have had many debates with myself before I could resolve upon it, but I do not look upon you as on the rest of the world . . . You are brother to a woman I tenderly loved, and when I say love 'tis for ever. . . .'

Then, after expressing her dismay at 'one of the Tatlers you sent me', and her belief that 'Mr. Bickerstaff has very wrong notions of our sex', she comes directly to the point.

'I can say there are some of us that despise charms of show and all the pageantry of greatness . . . Was I to choose of two thousand pounds a year or twenty thousand, the first would be my choice. I hate the noise and hurry inseparable from great estates and titles, and look upon both as blessings that should only be given to fools. . . .'

And with a rare humility she adds, 'Give me leave to say it (I know it sounds vain), I know how to make a man happy. I have so much—' the word she had written was 'love'; she crossed it out wrote 'esteem for you' instead, yet she left its warmer substitute quite legible. 'I should be sorry to hear you was unhappy,' she continues, 'but for the world I would not be the instrument of making you so . . . You distrust me. I can neither be easy nor loved where I am distrusted. Nor do I believe your passion for me is what you pretend . . .

'I don't enjoin you to burn this letter. I know you will. 'Tis the first I ever wrote to one of your sex, and it shall be the last.'

Needless to say it was not, nor did Edward burn it; but although at least a hundred letters passed between these two, none declares on either side a fervent adoration. Never were lovers more in love and more at loggerheads, more critical, more full of doubts, complaints, abuse and squabbles; now parting for ever and meeting the next day. He, the less impulsive of the pair, was quite absurdly jealous. She could not look nor smile on any other man without bringing Edward's wrath in pen and ink upon her breakfast tray. But for all the time and paper spent in wrangling corres- pondence, they seldom had a chance to speak together or alone. Guarded always by Aunt Cheyne and watched by her sisters when they met at the houses of their mutual friends, the most formal greetings only were allowed; and even that slight opportunity was limited, since Edward, still in mourning, attended no evening occasions, no dinners, no balls, nor the play.

He haunted the Ring where the Quality drove and promenaded, to content himself with a passing glimpse of his 'L.M.', accompanied by her 'fearsome Aunt with the voice of a macaw—' so to the sympathetic 'Bickerstaff' he bitterly complained. This incurable romantic gave Edward his assurance, should he seek an assignation, that he and his 'Prue', the Captain's latest wife, would gladly place at his disposal their newly acquired house in Bury Street, St. James's.

Edward may have regretted his rash confidence. Dick Steele, in his cups, would have it all over the Town that he was courting Mary Pierrepont. He therefore heard with some relief that Lord Dorchester intended closing his house in Arlington Street when he went up to Newmarket races. Mary, with her sisters, was to be despatched to Acton where his lordship owned a villa. In that rural retreat, screened from prying eyes, the lady might be persuaded to receive him. From further inquiry he had ascertained that the 'fearsome Aunt' would not be with her there. But how to let her know of his intent? While he dallied, news came from Steele, his indefatigable scout, that his 'L.M.' was due to leave London in a day or two. He must get word to her somehow that her retirement would give them both the opportunity to meet in secluded country lanes, uninterrupted.

With this end in view, on a blue and golden April afternoon, Edward walked from his rooms in Great Queen Street to Hyde Park. Having secured a vantage post at the edge of the Ring whence he could watch the endless stream of chariots, coaches, and horsemen, he stood waiting. . . . And he waited.

The extravagance and splendour of every sort of equipage did not appeal to Edward's jaundiced eye. Some such gilded vehicle, drawn by six Flemish mares, attended by running footmen in silk jackets, lavishly gold-laced, contained her whom he doubted would ever share his life. A paltry eight hundred a year would not furnish a wife with a house in St. James's, a retinue of servants, and a coach and six. Nor, he believed, would she be content to live with him over a looking-glass shop.

He glanced at his watch—four o'clock—the hour at which she usually drove with her sisters. If accompanied by Lady Cheyne there would be no hope of exchanging more than bows, or at most a whispered word should the coach halt at the Ring-side. But if Fortune favoured the absence of the Aunt, he might induce his lady to a walk beneath the trees.

Among the gaily-coloured crowd of beaux that promenaded, side-glassing the ladies, Edward in his suit of raven black appeared as a blot on a brightly painted canvas, and the more conspicuous for that. The Duchess of Marlborough flashed him a smile from the window of her coach as it swept by, preceded by four running footmen in canary plush and conical-shaped hats. Beside her, pock-marked, stubborn-jawed and heavy-eyed, sat Lord Treasurer Godolphin. His swarthy countenance was more than ever overcast, and not, Edward judged, without reason, since Godolphin went in daily expectation that his White Staff of Office would be snatched from his hand and offered to Harley. That recent painful scene in Her Majesty's closet at Kensington, which had released 'Mrs. Morley' from 'Mrs. Freeman's' clutches, had lost nothing in embellishment when retold by her Grace to the Tories' delight and the Whigs' consternation. If the Queen's ruling goddess had fallen, how could they whom she led hope to rise? Ominous rumours were afloat of a pending reshuffle in the Junto. The agitation resultant on a sermon, delivered from the pulpit of St. Paul's, had brought to him who preached it tremendous notoriety, and repercussion unexampled in the House of Lords.

Dr. Sacheverell, a hitherto obscure High Tory parson, screaming spittle-flecked defiance at Dissenters, had won the Queen's approval. While Whiggish pamphleteers bespattered his Reverence with invective to drag him up for trial, the Tories placed a halo round his head, extolling his hatred of 'Atheism, Deism, Tritheism, Socianism (sic), and All the

Hellish Principles of Fanaticism, Regicide and Anarchy'—
that go to make a Low Church Whig.

In consequence of these alarms, and contrary to Whiggish
expectation, the lightest sentence possible had been passed
on the fiery divine, merely that he should refrain from
preaching for three years; but the result in Whig and Tory
circles was more serious. The Queen had expressed her sympathy with Sacheverell's outrageous diatribe against 'false
brethren in Church and State'.

And reviewing that tragicomic revolt as he stood among
the careless throng of Fashion in the Ring, Edward mused
upon the dangers to his Party it implied. The pendulum had
swung to its extreme in a counterblast that trumpeted the
voice of the people—and their Sovereign.

It seemed clearly obvious to Edward that the Queen had
wavered, not only in her personal but in her Ministerial
affections. There was doubtless more than a grain of truth in
the whispers that linked the name of Harley with this little
Mrs. Masham . . . Strange, how one so insignificant could
wield her furtive power to such purpose as to bring about
the divergence of two great political Parties. And, as if the
subject of his reflections had been conjured by his thought
of her, Edward recognized the approach of her carriage.

Even more ostentatious than that of the Duchess whom
she had outrivalled was Mrs. Masham's equipage, lined with
scarlet, drawn by six white horses, and attended by six
running footmen in scarlet and gold. In it sat a neat little
lady in grey; her eyes met those of Edward and she smiled, a
slow lingering smile, before the white lids drooped. Snatching off his hat Edward, nose to knees, returned that brief
acknowledgement. A rising politician, though his politics
might differ from, could not discard the favour of a
Favourite. Others too, it seemed, were of his mind. Horsemen reined in their mounts and, hats on their hearts, bowed
from the saddle to the Queen's 'Enchantress. . . .' And still
no sign of her whom Edward sought. Perhaps she would not
come today, and he was wasting time that could be spent to
better profit than gaping at the women, like St. John there
among the orange-girls whose trade served as flimsiest excuse
for more remunerative traffic.

Edward turned his back upon the sight of him he loathed, tailored to perfection, displayed in peacock vanity to a swarm of giggling sluts! The fool was buying fruit of them, arranging a rendezvous in some pox-ridden alcove of Old Drury, he disgustedly surmised, and on he walked. He would no longer stand and watch for her; his feet were cold, and the east wind had caught him in the stern to give him the pest of a rheum. He should not have left off his warm winter clothing . . . 'Button to chin till May be in, till May be out ne're cast a clout'. There was sense in these old Scots sayings.

Shadows lengthened as the sun sank lower, to brush with gold the bursting green of leaves and foamy blossom; from every tree and hawthorn-bush bird choristers proclaimed the spring; and Edward sneezed.

He was about to make his way home for a foot-bath of mustard and water, when he perceived the blue and silver liveries of the four running footmen ahead of Lord Dorchester's coach. He halted, and saw that his quest had been in vain; for the Aunt sat in charge of the niece.

Stepping forward in between the horse-posts, he bowed low; his lady inclined her head. The Aunt turned hers, looked through him, and away. The coach rolled on.

Edward's lengthy vigil was now attracting some attention. Men of his acquaintance shot quips as they passed, and repassed, to find him there still. St. John had ceased to quizz the orange-girls and was walking rapidly in his direction. To avoid more remark Edward darted down an alley, strode across the greensward and hid himself behind a weeping willow. From this concealment he could watch, unobserved, the return of Lord Dorchester's coach; yet what use that, if she were not permitted to descend from it and talk? While he meditated whether he should go or stay upon a chance, and increase the possibility of chill, he heard a footfall in the grass, felt a hand upon his sleeve. Swinging round in optimistic eagerness he saw, not her who too vividly haunted his dreams, but a trollop of St. John's selection.

He swore at her briefly and bade her be off; she stood, and refused to go.

Edward was greatly put about. To be seen skulking under trees in Hyde Park was bad enough; to engage in conversation with an orange-wench was worse. And now the creature, with a flash of white teeth in a sun-tanned face, had the insolence to ask: "Don't you know me? Days and days I've watched you hereabouts, and I've seen your lady too from time to time."

At this appalling revelation Edward blenched. Were his thoughts, his actions, his intentions, so apparent that every demirep in town, and St. John too, could guess them? He thrust aside the leaves that overhung his head and was for hurrying away when, planting herself directly in his path, "There's no cause to be scared," leeringly she grinned. "None can see us here. We're well hid from view. I'm not askin' nothing but to be of service. I've not forgot, if you have, what you done for me."

"Done for you?" repeated Edward with immense unease. "What did I do?"

"'Twas what you *didn't* do—to exercise your faculties—that I've not disremembered." And she dug him in the ribs.

A more shocking situation for a Member of Parliament to have forced upon him, thought the agitated Edward, could not have been conceived, and he said:

"I do not know you. I have no wish to know you. And if you persist in this disgraceful importunity I will have you in the stocks."

"That's what you said to me before. You an't 'riginal, are you? But, come to think of it, what *is* 'riginal, save sin? Look'ee, sweet'art," she sidled nearer, stretching her smile, breathing onions at him, "I'm Betty Laskey, who foretold you these three years agone we'd meet again—and here we are!"

He knew her then, and wished he never had.

"So you still pursue your filthy trade under cover of your fruit?"

"Ah, now, handsome, don't despise me fruit. 'Twas from fruit which may have been an orange, though they do say 'twas an apple, that sprang the first seed of me filthy trade, as you're pleased to call what you're not ill pleased to touch!"

"This," said Edward loudly, "is insufferable."

"Yet I'll warrant me you'll suffer it. 'Tis you starch-nosed Dissenters what shun the sweets o' life as they was the plague that'll guzzle with the best and the worst o' them . . . Quiet, now, quiet, let *me* speak, see? I'm not ungrateful of the silver piece you give me, big enough to buy a crate of oranges and my stand here in the Ring. I kep' it too. I don't never walk by night no more. In course there's gentlemen what calls on me—" she winked her rogue's eye at him and he averted his —"but only by me special invitation."

Edging from the stench of her and, against his will, uncomfortably conscious of her full round breasts surging up and outward from the close embrace of her tattered striped bodice, Edward brought himself lamely to tell her:

"You've grown."

"Well, and so I should! I've had a baby—a fine boy, but I lost him when I took the green sickness to sour me milk. I grieved sore for him, I did. Still, I hope to have another."

Edward looked along his nose. "Are you married?"

"Me!" Noisily she guffawed. "Who do you think I am— the Queen's latest come-kiss, Mrs. Masham?"

Was there nothing the jade did not know? And as if she took that thought from him, "I make it my business to know," she said, "what's to do in the town and the parks and the Palace. I seen you with your lady—not so long ago when you drove to Chelsea in a curtained coach and left her at the gates of Cheyne Manor."

This was awful.

"Is it part of your business," Edward questioned warily, "to prowl around the houses of your betters?"

"Better nor worse, 'tis all one to me who buys what I've to offer. Chelsea's not two miles from the Grapes at Knight's Bridge, and I happened to be visitin' "—again she dropped an eyelid—"by the river. If you knew the half of what I see and hear you'd die o' laughin'. I could tell you——"

"I would rather you did not. But wait a moment—" he sharpened his wits. "If you really wish to serve me——"

"'Arken to 'is lordship!" With diabolic mimicry she aped his frosty voice. "If you rahlleh wish to sarve meh Ahm yahs for the harsking—cheap at the per-rice, and hot as gingah! *I'll* warm you up—God's truth, you need it. St. John'll speak for me. He's one o' me reg'lars."

"You misunderstand my meaning," Edward managed to

articulate. "All I require is that you carry a message."

But even as he gave it he questioned his recklessness in trusting its delivery to so doubtful a courier. Yet if Mary indeed were leaving London he must know, send word of his intention to see her and receive assurance his advances would be welcome. Betty was instructed to intercept—"that lady's coach. I mention no names."

"You needn't." She chuckled. "I'll mention 'em for you. 'Tis the Lady Mary Peerpunt—and her father's a Lord Marquis, and their livery's blue laced with silver. I'll watch for them and get word to your pretty. Cross me heart."

"Do you know *my* name?" asked Edward, never doubting that she did; and more than he could know about himself the bitch knew, likely.

"Sure, I know your name—and I'll bring your message to her if I die! Hey! Half a minute—" She dashed forward shading her eyes with her hand to peer from under it at the dust-clouds following the coaches in the Ring. "I think the blue liveries is coming round again, and this'll be the last o' them. It's late. Past five o'clock. I'll have to run."

"Wait!" He called her back. "You must have my address. When the message is delivered, or whether it is not, I wish you to return at once to me."

"Hoo!" She poked her tongue at him. "I'm honoured."
His gorge rose.

"To my lodgings," he amended, "and tell me the result. Repeat now what you have to say."

She gabbled it off without pause. "Mr. Worl'y Montakew hopes to call on your ladyship at Acton village if you'll send him word by me Betty Laskey as to your ladyship's convenience and when. Is that correct?"

"That is correct. You will be paid," he added cautiously, "when you return with her ladyship's reply to my rooms——"

"Over a looking-glass shop in Great Queen Street," she prompted. "See? I know where you live, and if I'm not back within the hour with your lady's answer—strike me dead!"

At his lodgings where Edward, in a fever of impatience, waited for Betty's return, he may have anxiously questioned the impulse that had placed him under obligation to one of whom he knew nothing but bad. Why, he reconsidered, had he not sent his servant with the message in the proper way? Yet had he done so, and had Mary shown the letter to her father, he might have been compromised to make a formal offer for her hand. Were marriage with Mary his future intent, he must be certain that his passion lay beyond desire if not beyond regret. Though enchanted by her intellect and the charm of her propinquity, he believed he had not plumbed the depths of love . . . And what in hell, or heaven, was this 'Love'? A word, too glibly spoken, misinterpreted by poets as a mastering life force.

A log fell in the grate, and bending to replace it with the fire-tongs, so, mused he, is this vaunted 'Love' of man, haphazard, a purposeless flame-flicker, a springing up, a dying down to dust, and then—no more. But if two persons of equal rank and social status, whose tastes and interests agreed, and whose attraction for the other was reciprocal, surely this, decided Edward, was the complement of love?

A rat-tat at the street door sent him to the window, where, looking down, he could see Betty looking up—and back within the hour to the minute!

He had taken the precaution to send his man upon an errand that he might himself admit her to his parlour. There, with her basket on her arm and on her lips a garbled tale, Betty stood. All had gone well, she said, as ever he could wish. She had watched for the blue liveries and raced them to the exit of the Ring where they halted behind other traffic . . . "That was me chance. I ran forward and pushed past the footmen, crying me wares at the door of the coach right under her ladyship's nose. The young one bought an orange and the old 'un too. While they was a-peelin' of 'em I whispered to your gentle what you'd learned of me to say. She blushed up sweet and whispered me this answer while a-suckin' of the fruit—that 'the gentleman may follow me to Acton or to the ends o' the earth, for I shall live in discontent until I have his written word he loves me—', which her ladyship ordered me bring to her tonight. So help me God, and that's the gospel truth of it."

That Edward, the judicious, did not doubt the 'gospel

truth' of it but accepted without question Betty's evidence, would appear fantastic had we not a record of this incident as presented by 'Laetitia' in her narrative.[1] And it may be that the orange-girl's gift of the gab fired Edward's ardour to light a conflagration. Certain it is, as result of her purported message, he wrote Mary a letter more fervent in tone than any he had written her before.

While Edward at his desk was thus engaged, Betty, well cheered by the tissue of lies she had wrought and the reward in easy money she would gain, sat curled on a sofa concocting further profitable schemes. For the case, as she presented it, was far from the 'gospel truth'; no nearer, in fact, than her offer of oranges to Mary at the window of the coach; but the cabalistic signs and nods and mouthings that accompanied this overture caused such alarm to Edward's lady, that it failed completely its purpose.

"Pray, Aunt," Mary hurriedly had murmured, "do you see this poor creature? 'Tis a lunatic."

"What!" squawked Lady Cheyne, leaning forward as Betty, scared, stepped back. "A wild looking baggage, I declare. Escaped from Bedlam, likely. Sirrahs"—to the servants—"seize her."

She was seized; her basket fallen, her oranges scattered, her shoulders belaboured by the footment's canes.

Loudly boohooing, and softly cursing him who had brought her to this pass, Betty begged release from her captors to retrieve her basket and the remainder of her fruit that had not been crushed to pulp beneath the horses' hooves. Besides the loss of half her stock in trade, Betty had received a beating to raise weals, for which she vowed she would be recompensed in damages by him whom she silently accused of having been spewed up and not born, with additional stigmas on his mother. And the hurt she had received from 'those whoreson brothers to a pumpkin,' who had walloped her flesh raw, she judged was worth a guinea —if not two.

[1] The 'Autobiography', which apparently covers a number of years, is discontinued after the 'orange-girl' episode. But the sequel to it may be found in the letters exchanged between Lady Mary and Edward Wortley Montagu.

"Now be sure," Edward handed her a paper, folded, sealed, "that her ladyship acknowledges receipt of this. Wait for her answer. Do you know your way to Arlington Street and the Marquis of Dorchester's house?"

"May I be deflowered," Betty stated, "if I don't. Yah! I know his lordship's house as well as the palm of me hand." She held it out. "So that'll be two guineas an it please your honour."

"Two!" protested Edward. "Half a guinea should suffice you, and half a guinea is all that you will get."

"Come, sir, I've lost three hours' honest work and my good fruit in your behalf, to say nothing of what I'll lose on my night trade—that's to say," she supplemented as a sop to the gentleman's raised eyebrows, "there's more selling of oranges to townsfolk in the evening than ever was sold to the Quality by day. Two guineas is me price, sir. Would you grudge it— all considered?"

All considered he did grudge it; but thought it wiser in the circumstance to pay the sum demanded, with a warning. Should it come to his ears she had gossiped of this matter to her low acquaintances, or any living soul, he would have her brought to Bridewell for a bawd.

"Cross me heart!" She crossed it, appealing to her Maker to have her head green and rotting on a pike at Temple Bar if she breathed one word of this most sacred trust to man or beast.

Unrelieved by any earnest of fidelity, Edward, from his window, watched her scuttle down the street, hard put to it not to recall her. What if she should fail him, show his letter to a horde of her associates, and those others—St. John for example—who called on her by 'special invitation'? They would never have done grinning. Although he had been careful not to sign his name to his declaration, the jade knew it, and the consequence of his foolhardiness, he fussed, defied conjecture. . . . Which in view of subsequent events was just as well.

Lord Dorchester, returning from a session at the tables, found upon his doorstep a commotion. Two footmen were holding by the arms a dishevelled screeching object, whose

sex was recognizable only by its breasts shamelessly protruding from its bodice.

On inquiring the cause of the disturbance, his lordship
was told that this year disrepibable Person ad been seen in
the Ring that Harfternoon pullin Faces at er Ladyship in a
manner most Obstrepherous for which she ad received a
Beatin, and now she ad the Himpudence to come to the
Front Door aringing of the Bell and insistin on a Hinterview
with Er Ladyship. When told to go she Aggled and was
Saucy. His lordship took snuff and took stock of the
struggling Betty, to find her not unpleasing: young, well-
formed, well-featured, but—"God's Wounds!" said the
Marquis, cramming perfumed Orinoko up each nostril,
"how she smells!"

Perceiving that his lordship's eye was not unmindful of
her too obtrusive charms, Betty served her heels to the shins
of her custodians, wriggled from under their hands, and fell
upon her knees, imploring, "Me lord, of your goodness, only
hear me! I am bound on a mission to her ladyship from
the lady's mantua-maker with samples of lutestring—most
urgent. May I die here at your lordship's feet if I speak
aught but gospel truth, seein' as me father of blessed memory
was a parson and me left orphaned without a groat to earn
a honest wage, me lord, as seamstress."

"My lord, the Woman lies," averred he whose silken shins,
now oozing red, had borne the brunt of Betty's kicks. "She's
no better than Town Trash, my Lord. An Orange-Wench.
A Wanton."

"Me Lord!" yelled Betty, " 'eed him not! I'm 'armless as
an infant, well-born, well-nurtured, brought up in the 'Igh
Church."

"Damme!" quoth his lordship, "were you so? A Tory I
take it?"

"Yes, me lord, a Tory of the 'Ighest."

"The more reason then," said he, "that you be flogged."

"Oh, me lord! No, me lord! Pity me, pray!" blubbered
Betty, covering her face and peeping up through her fingers,
encouraged by his lordship's loosened lips and slanting
smile. "Yet I dare swear 'twould be my privilege and honour
if—" she whispered it—"you'd flog me."

91

"Od's my life!" The Marquis recoiled, outraged. "What have we here?"

Realizing her mistake, Betty grovelled, calling upon heaven to witness that her innocence was slandered, and she, an honest maiden, wrongfully accused.

"Search her," commanded his lordship.

And Betty, now in greatest fright, was searched, the letter discovered, tucked inside her sagging stays, and handed to his lordship.

"Hah!" He broke the seal, began to read, and roared with laughter; then read it through again and laughed no more.

"Let the strumpet go. She is not to blame for this. Bid Lady Mary come to me at once."

She came in wonder, which increased to stupefaction when her father flourished before her startled eyes a paper penned in the angular crabbed writing that, unmistakably, was Edward's.

"So this is how you trick me under guise of your book learning! You're no better than the harlot you employ to bring this blather! Who is he that writes of love—and love —and lovesick dribble? S'death!" The Marquis tore the pages into strips and flung them down. "I'll call him out for this. I'll slit him up!"

"But Papa," she was all innocence, "I do not understand. I beg you to believe I can think of no man who would write to me so freely. 'Tis a hoax."

"And you're a liar!" Her father stooped to gather the fragments littering the floor, searched among them for a signature; found none. Whereupon his wrath exploded in an avalanche of rage till he looked, Mary feared, to have a fit. When at last, pop-eyed and red of face, he ceased from sheer exhaustion to hurl abuse at her, Lord Dorchester pronounced his breathless verdict.

"Tomorrow you go—to Acton—that has been arranged— but now you go there—guarded. Your sisters will keep watch upon your movements. The servants will have orders to admit—no person to the house unless—careful inquiry—has been made into their business. Henceforth your correspondence—will be—intercepted."

Yet though he sent her from him weeping, her heart sang.

She had not read the letter, but the scorn her father pointed at those words he briefly scanned had told her all she longed to know: that she was loved!

Determined when at Acton to overcome captivity, defy parental orders and conduct her own affairs, Mary went to bed, but not to sleep. Before her throbbing eyelids the face of him whose 'blather' had brought this trouble to her swam in vacancy, enlarged and growing larger, till it seemed, absurdly, like a monstrous pink-mouthed moon. Then it floated iridescent, sprouted wings and vanished; reappeared and slobbered . . . Most confusing! Her head, too, felt peculiar, as if bound with iron straps. She burned and was cold, shivered and was hot, and from a weary doze at dawn she woke and dressed. She must send word at once to Edward; and in a hasty scrawl she told him that her father had 'surprized her letter, was in the utmost rage against her for receiving it'—(she hadn't, but her father had. Best not go into that)—'and as he had occasioned the mischief, she left it to his conduct *to justify her.*'

So! Nothing could be clearer than this decided hint. Would he take it and approach her father with an offer, or would he shilly-shally to leave her in a torment? "Decidedly," said Mary, "I'll run mad."

She rang for Grace, and with the bribe of half a guinea pledged her to hold her tongue, hire a chair, and deliver this at once. No answer was required.

Grace, who, from chat among the gentlemen below-stairs, had gleaned enough to flavour her suspicion of intrigue, swore herself to secrecy and the promise to return at eight o' the clock to bring her ladyship her chocolate.

But Mary drank no chocolate. It hurt her throat to swallow. Remarking she was flushed, Grace hazarded a purely sentimental reason for her lady's heightened colour.

Grace was wrong.

When Mary came to Acton in the evening, she found a scarlet rash upon her chest and arms, and—bitter anti-climax to romance—she had the measles!

*　　　*　　　*

It is highly improbable Betty recounted, with any degree

93

of the truth, the result of her visit to Arlington Street. Having given Edward the assurance that his letter was safely delivered, she proceeded to embroider semi-fictional fact in the colour of her own imagination.

She had presented herself as a seamstress in 'neat-like' clothes borrowed from a chambermaid at the 'Bunch of Grapes'. She had a bandbox on her arm to carry out her part —"even to the samples, sir, of lutestring, for knowing how cruelly slandered is my calling, as if the very fruit I sell was poisoned if not poxed, I deemed it best to give them Blue Ones at the door no cause to doubt me——"

"Yes, get on with it!" interjected Edward; and on with it she went, to say that the letter was hid in the bandbox with the samples and taken to her ladyship. She was told by the Blue One to wait on the step; then seeing the Marquis arrive in his coach she had stood a way off till 'the lord' had gone into the house.

"Presently," continued Betty, warming to invention, "a female comes to the door, looking up and down the street as if for me. I took me chance and approaching her with careful signs made it known I was a trusty servant of a gentleman— no names—what had brought a letter for the Lady Mary. She said she was the lady's maid and that his lordship had come upon her ladyship a-kissin' of your letter, at which the lord had grabbed it from her, read it through and 'owled with rage." Then the lady's maid—thus ran the story—bid Betty tell the gentleman how her ladyship was placed, and that she would write to him in secret if he could recommend some worthy person to fetch and carry letters to and from his lordship's house at Acton. When Betty volunteered to undertake this mission, the maid had expressed herself 'obleeged'. "And that the wedding-bells ring out right joyous for you and for your lady, sir," said Betty in conclusion, "is my prayer."

But was it Edward's?

The note brought by Grace the next morning, while it confirmed Betty's statement that his letter had been duly delivered and 'surprized', did not induce the response that Mary had wishfully hoped for. In a previous letter she had told him he 'distrusted her'.

He did; and his reply to her appeal that he amend the

94

'mischief' he had made, was analytical, evasive, and written, he declared, 'out of Punctilio and not with the vanity of hoping for success.' He had 'believed the compleatest form of felicity was to enjoy one woman friend, one man, and to think it of little moment whether those that were made use of to fill up some idle hours were princes or peasants, wise or foolish'.

This, said Mary, blazing, is unmitigated insolence. *Fill up some idle hours*—be damned to him! What next?

'But had I you,' was next, 'I should have all the charms of either sex.'

Indeed!

And then, for one instant, revealingly, he thaws. 'Could you really love me we should both be happy beyond all example. Should you *seem* to love me and after cease to do it, we should, I fear, be wretched.'

Was ever woman in such humour wooed? Yet never in such humour to be won.

★ 5 ★

THROUGHOUT the month of April, back and forth along the Queen's Highway to Acton, went Betty bearing letters inscribed 'With Care and Speed by Private Messenger'. She had kept her ears wide, her wits sharp, when on her first sortie from London she had lingered for refreshment at the village inn. There she had met and made free with a footman employed at Lord Dorchester's villa. From him she had learned of her ladyship's illness; and to him, with a bonus, she gave two letters to be handed to the lady without fail and in secret. What the footman—not a 'Blue One' and certainly not green—gave Betty in return is of the least importance.

When later, in the moonlight, she trudged back to Town, Betty determined that to make her mission pay she must have a guarantee it would continue. The gentleman had told her he would soon be leaving London for the North. It suited not her pleasure nor her purse to dance attendance on a lean-carcassed slug-a-bed Jew, thus she anathematized her reticent employer, from whom it was as hard, she said, to pluck a guinea's worth as to pluck a fair profit from a pimp. Born to wear the horns was he, decided Betty, and his lady would do well enough to clamp 'em on his head, good luck to her, poor pretty, were he caught! She judged the lady jiltish, but thought it might be welcome if the gentleman could know that her ladyship, though sick, could still be kind.

That Betty could not read nor write was no deterrent to her purpose; she had acquaintances in plenty only willing to oblige, at her dictation, to the following effect.

'Dr Sir, I ask pardon for my presumption but the occasion that happened makes me take this liberty. My Lady Mary gave orders to let you know she received your two letters this day . . . and is very ill of the measles; but as soon as she comes to London she does design to see you. Betty took a great deal of trouble, going often to Acton to see for a letter but Lady Mary could get no conveniency to write. She gives her love and respects to you, but if it is not expressed as is proper you will excuse it as from whence it comes instead of my lady. Lady Mary desires you to direct your letters for Betty Laskey at the Bunch of Grapes and Queen's Head in Knightsbridge. She had not time when Betty gave her the letters to read them. She signs her name to this, for I showed it her.'

The letter is initialled 'M.P.'.

Edward was on a visit to his Uncle John, the Dean of Durham, when he received this information forwarded by Steele, who had undertaken to collect his correspondence and despatch it to his temporary abode. Guessing the nature of the missive he enclosed, Steele endorsed it briefly . . . 'I send you no news for this will employ you better.'

It could scarcely have employed him worse.

'Tho last night I was perfectly well till I got the letter signed by you, I am this morning downright sick . . .' Anxiety on her account, magnified by distance, induced him to believe her at death's door. He fretted himself to a frenzy with the doubt of 'a thousand to one she would recover, for

96

even the worst can happen from the least dangerous of dis-
tempers' . . . Yet he would be 'overjoyed to hear her Beauty
was impaired, since it would lessen the number of Admirers.'

Poor comfort this to Mary, whose Beauty in the peeling
stage was very much impaired; so too her temper and her
patience. She had suffered enough. She would suffer no more
from his ungallant, unpredictable behaviour. 'Downright
sick!'. . . . Yes, and so was she, sick to the marrow of his
moodish vacillations, his reluctance to commit himself in
more than written words which he instantly retracted. Fired
to a pitch of molten indignation, she poured upon him hot
denial of the letter never written, never signed, nor seen
by her.

'Your conduct is more surprizing every day. How could
you think of employing that Creature? . . . . She has imposed
upon you in a thousand ways. I suppose she writ the letter
you speak of. I know nothing of it. You have heard, I dare
swear, fifty lies from her own mouth. She has made everything public to every servant in the house! . . . A pretty
pickle,' laments Mary, 'I am in.'

Edward's response to this shows less concern for the
'pickle' his 'L.M.' is in than for those 'fifty lies' that are let
out. Betty, it would seem, had extended to some purpose her
acquaintance with Lord Dorcheter's domestics; and, by way
of defence for employing 'that Creature', Edward somewhat
inaccurately states: 'Before I left Town you know that I
never sent Betty but with answers to what she brought from
you . . . The letter you now disown expressly orders me to
direct all my letters to her. I am sorry you know nothing of
it, because it is more favourable than any of the rest . . .'

Yet in order to extract her from her 'pickled' situation
he is willing to go to her father and represent his fortune as
even less than it is worth, 'that I may be secure of a repulse.'
Or, if she wished, he could circulate among her friends
that he had proposed for her and had been rejected. He
would, in short, do anything but marry her because—'the
probability of happiness together is remote.'

But this kindly effort to make her see reason served only
to make her see red.

'Betty has prattled all she knows and all she *supposed,*

which goes a great deal farther. 'Tis not her custom to make secrets of names. I am mighty happy at Mr. Steele and his wife knowing this affair. He over a bottle, she over a tea-table has (I don't question) said many witty things.' She bids him break with and forget her. 'Either think of me no more, or,' she adds significantly, '*in the way you ought.*'

She was done with him, well rid of him, provoked beyond endurance. Between each line he wrote she read his disapproval of her character, 'one part of which is not so good nor t'other so bad as you fancy it. . . . You think if you married me I should be passionately fond of you one moment and of somebody else the next. Neither would happen. I can esteem, I can be a friend, but I don't know whether I can love.'

Nor did he, who, on receipt of this, spent sleepless nights reviewing a future that with or without her would not bear contemplation. He wanted her, despaired of her, he wished he could be quit of her, but to see her the wife of another would drive him distracted. Nor can he be persuaded to 'think of her no more', nor will he 'break with her—at present'. He will wait till she sends him back a letter unopened.

She is, moderately, melted.

'If you wait till I send you back a letter unopened, you will wait very long,' she allows; then, inconsistently, begs him not to write, 'for any letters coming to my maid will be suspected. Even one attempt of that kind would ruin me . . .' But if he will not break with her, ' 'tis only to my Family that you must speak'.

She has hurled at him a challenge. Would he take it or refuse? A score of times she asked herself if any girl on earth, since Salmacis first pursued Hermaphroditus, had been so great a fool as Mary Pierrepont? What *was* this man, this half a man, this pompous prig, this chanticleer, whose vanity excelled her own, who calculated every step before he moved an inch? Who was churlish, argumentative and critical, and yet—on him her heart was squandered. Why? Because he represented all that she would wish to be were she her father's son and not his daughter.

And now, having written him her, presumably, last letter,

she went down to Wiltshire, cured of her measles, to stay with her cousins at West Dean.

More nights of misery for Edward, the unwilling. His 'Punctilio' revolted against his passionate obsession for this impossible, incalculable child who proclaimed herself the wooer not the wooed. The Greeks had an answer to the conflict of emotion into which her caprice plunged him. They married their wives, but they loved those others, the *hetaerae*, the intellectual courtesans who combined the esoteric and erotic. Were she his mistress . . . He murdered the thought. Were she his wife, with his body he might worship her and tire of her pedantry—God help him!—in a week. If he could find the strength to put her from him and forget her, he would choose that bitter way to kill his craving. Yet, while every sense struggled against her seduction, he knew that surfeit only could satisfy desire.

At length, in desperation and a welter of uncertainty, he braced himself to call upon her 'Family': the Marquis.

He was given a cordial reception. Lord Dorchester's difficult Mary, whom he feared would have never been sought, was now suited. Nothing, declared his beaming lordship, could afford him greater joy than to see his daughter wedded to the son of his life-long friend, 'your dear father' . . . So far, so good; but the case demanded better. A bottle or two to mellow the subject of settlements, tactfully broached.

Mr. Wortley Montagu would be interested to hear—in strictest confidence, it was understood, that: "My son, Kingston," his lordship dropped his voice and raised his glass, "is to marry a Fortune, the daughter of another old friend, Thomas Baynton. Under the terms of the settlement agreed by this most happy union, Mary, on her marriage, will receive the capital sum of ten thousand pounds. Paid down."

There was a pause.

Edward thought, but did not say, that Mr. Thomas Baynton, whoever he might be, had paid down handsomely to secure a budding Marquis for his daughter.

"Which being so," his lordship winningly pursued, "what would you consider as appropriate return for Mary's jointure, which will equally be yours?"

"Return, my lord?" Edward's eyebrows lifted.

Retaining his smile, his lordship suggested that since the least allowed by law to a wife was the third of her husband's estate, a proportionate provision should also be assured to the life of an eldest son. Did not Mr. Wortley Montagu agree?

Mr. Wortley Montagu did not at all agree. "My present means, my lord, are insufficient to provide for the future of a son unborn."

"Exactly so." Lord Dorchester gave him a goggling glance. "But your father might be persuaded to offer substantial security for you or for your heir——" if, he added silently, the fellow can beget one. There was little favour in the Marquis's survey of Mary's suitor where he sat with his scarcely sipped glass in his hand, one black-stockinged knee primly crossed over the other. The nut-brown curls of his periwig framed a pale dome-like forehead, and a face faultlessly modelled, girlishly fair; but the womanish mouth and the firm compressed lips looked to have been grafted upon steel . . . A spiritual cormorant, was his lordship's summary, and: "How is your father?" he genially inquired. "When I saw him last he was complaining of the stone."

"He has dispersed it. My father," said Edward morosely, "has not suffered, to my knowledge, a day's illness in his life."

Masking discouragement, Dorchester undauntedly returned to the attack. They argued for an hour, and finished at a deadlock. Edward insisted he would not dispose of any part of his heritage on issue hypothetical. Moreover, he would have his lordship realize that although his future prospects undeniably were great, he could offer Lady Mary no immediate security.

"God damme, sir!" The Marquis lost his smile, showed his fist in a thump upon the table. "My daughter can't marry on prospects. Your father may outlive you, he's hearty enough—can drink me down four bottles deep. And what of my grandsons? I'll not see them beggared."

Edward on his feet, and pale, said: "There's no beggary, my lord, in the prospects I can offer to my wife or to the children she may bear me. But I refuse to be committed to any settlement on her or on my issue. That is final."

"And this too is final!" His vinous cheeks mottled with fury, Lord Dorchester heaved himself up from his chair. "I forbid you to meet or correspond with her again. Your offer is an insult to me and to my daughter. The treaty is closed."

Edward bowed. "Your lordship's servant." And, nose pointed to the door, out he went.

If Dorchester believed that by his curt rejection the 'treaty' had indeed been closed, he was mistaken. Unremarkable for sensibility, he had not foreseen Edward's immediate reaction to dismissal. His blood was up, to face and overcome the bluster of one whom he considered to be a fitting 'life-long friend' of his 'dear father': a fornicating, loud-mouthed libertine, a lecherous habitué of stews. Edward held no brief for the mode of life beloved of the parent he heartily despised; and it may be that his boyhood's revulsion to concupiscence had inhibited his manhood, to make him as he was.

Thus, when Mary returned from West Dean, she received a declaration from her laggard lover that proclaimed him predisposed to take her in defiance of her 'Family'. 'But'— there was always a 'but' in Edward's calculations—'if I am to engage at all it must either be upon a Bargain, or to have you without any . . . Some men have parted with their Fortunes to gain a woman, others have died of despair for the loss of her. All I am worth,' he assures her, 'would be yours, and far short of your merits.' He was ill, on her account entirely. White nights and loss of appetite had brought him to the verge of a breakdown. His doctor advised a continental change of air and scene, a sojourn at the 'Spaw' to drink the waters . . . 'I will write,' he promised her, 'at least once a day', and hopes she will write to him as often, 'for when you write you shine out in all your Beauty'.

Surprising change of front, to put Mary in a state.

He sailed from Harwich in August, pursued by her letters sent under cover of Steele. None of them was answered. His silence persisted—to scare her. What if he took her at her word and took his congé? Or was he still dwelling on tiresome terms? 'You know,' she reminds him, 'I have no hand in the making of settlements; my present duty is to obey my Father. I shall so far obey blindly as not to accept where he refuses, tho' perhaps I might refuse where he accepts . . . It is not from severity that I write no more, but you know it is forbidden.'

And she wrote in all six more, each harping on one theme.

'If you expect Passion, I am unacquainted with any . . .' Not for the world must he believe her panting to fall at his feet. 'People talk of being in love, just as widows do of affliction.' Or if he would have her say that she was 'violently in love', she was not 'humble enough', she informs him, 'for that!'

She waited, uncertainly hoping. Surely now he would answer . . . And when he did not, she was frantic. Had his voluntary exile afforded him the opportunity to review the situation and discard her? Or had he met with one more beautiful, more witty, more in every way to be desired than herself? Finally, fearing Steele had misdirected her letters, she superscribes the sixth of them, *Pray send this to Mr. Edward Wortley Montagu wherever he may be.*

'Have you forgot me entirely? . . . I conjure you to write, I beg it of you, and promise to tease you no longer.'

If he had not 'forgot her entirely' he had forgotten his promise to write every day, or regretted it. Steele had been told to retain his letters until his return in October, when he found a voluminous packet from Mary, which took him a month to digest. He had decided while abroad, to 'call a truce to Business, Politicks, and Love.' All of equal status in his regard, apparently, with a bias in favour of the first two items . . . He is at a loss to know why she is 'at such pains to assure him he must never expect anything of Passion from her', for he is aware that she is perfectly 'incapable' of any such emotion. But if he 'could see into her heart and find there a Partiality to him, he might be persuaded to break through all difficulties and run the hazard, no small hazard she would own, of losing her'.

Here follows a *gaffe* past all redemption. 'You can't wonder if so long an absence, variety of other acquaintances, and your unkindness, shall make me less forward than I have been.'

If he had called a truce to love it was an armed one, to be met with fierce reprisal.

'Indeed I do not at all wonder that absence and variety of new faces should make you forget me; but I am a little surprized at your curiosity to know what passes in my heart, (a thing wholly insignificant to you) . . . I begin to be tired of my humility. I have carried my complaisances farther than I ought. . . . Our aunts and grandmothers always tell us that men are a sort of animals, and if ever they are constant 'tis only when they are ill-used. 'Twas a kind of paradox I could never believe; experience has taught me the truth of it. You are the first I ever had a correspondnce with, and I thank God I have done with it for all my life . . . Adieu for ever.'

Then she sealed and sent this last of any letter she would write to him. Her mind at rest, she could face the dreary years ahead with equanimity. If doomed to spinsterhood, as her Papa had prophesied, she would retire to the country, make cheese-cakes and milk cows; or she would go into a madhouse or a nunnery, or kill herself; or, at the worst, would marry 'Mr. K.'

It was the end.

* 6 *

SLEET, rain, snow, a month of biting cold, heralded March daffodils in the dawn of the New Year, 1711.[1]

Captain Steele, seeking copy for the successor to *The Tatler*, which was now in sad decline, strolled through Queen Anne's London alert to note the comings and the goings of his busy fellow citizens. What though he owed his butcher, his tailor, his wig-maker, his poulterer, and all his friends a total of a thousand pounds or more, he would pay it, and with interest, when he should produce in co-operation with Joe Addison, that non-political daily review, *The Spectator*, about to be launched.

Not without regret did 'Mr. Bickerstaff' renounce his spicy

[1] Old Style Calendar

tattle in *The Tatler*, but since he and his Prue and their children must live, *The Tatler* would have to die. He had tattled too much and too often. *The Spectator*, designed to be more circumspect and less audacious, was sponsored by one 'Sir Roger de Coverley, Bart.' of the County of Worcestershire. Sired by Steele, Sir Roger was conceived to be the leader of a Club, a convivial bachelor gentleman who would drink brandy, crack jokes with the best and worst of the bloods of St. James's, and give gratuitous advice on every kind of subject to his fellow bons viveurs. The lusty emergence of this gargantuan infant had caused Steele to suffer a long protracted labour, narcotized at the Smyrna in Pall Mall. So, on a breezy spring morning, we find him on his way to the Exchange to pick up 'copy'.

An endless variety of sound and sight was offered by the flotsam of the streets, that Steele, the philosopher-humorist, likened to a river whose swirling cross-currents teemed with the flood-tide of life.

A gilded coach, splashing through recent rain puddles, cast up a fountain of mud, disgustingly to spatter Steele's new velvet coat for which he had paid, or owed, two dozen guineas. Halting to survey his stained front and soaked ruffles, "Out, damned spots!" he swore, to bring a band of loiterers about with him with offers of stinking rags to rub his honour down; and a lank-haired 'prentice from a shop across the road, who had watched his opportunity to dash beneath the horses' heads with persuasive cries of 'Tweezers, sir? A tooth-picker—a walking-cane to ease ye?"

"Will tweezers or a tooth-picker ease me of this filth?" roared Steele. "And what would I with a walking-cane when I've a blade"—clapping a hand to his sword, he unsheathed and flourished it—"to slit your gizzard? Let me pass."

"A groat—of your mercy!" whined a half naked noseless hag, cringing on all fours around his ankles. "Blessings on ye, gentleman, I starve."

"By God, and so will I," Steele slid back his sword and fumbled in his pocket, "if I'm bled o' me last penny from the goodness of me heart." He flung a handful of copper coins among the noxious crowd, and: "D'ye see that now?" he queried, eyes to heaven. "Would these be souls immortal or

Satan's sons, that buzz about to settle on their findings like blow-flies on a dung-heap? Dung, begar! and so 'tis—this lucre they feed on, even as do I, come to that—though none gives it me gratis."

And elbowing a passage through the rabble, on he walked, dodging pedestrians for right of way. There were keen-faced business men in tie-wigs and sad-coloured broadcloth, hurrying cityward; and dainty fops with muffs to warm their precious hands, who, descending from their chariots, flapped perfumed handkerchiefs before their up-turned noses to keep off the smell of common folk; and at the kerbless pavement's edge, a blind old fiddler scraping away at 'Lillibulero'; and here a scarred and ancient Cavalier, jauntily hobbling in the rusty tattered uniform of sixty years ago, with a suppurating ulcer on his cheek, every curl of his scanty grey shoulder-length hair precisely gummed, his white moustache waxed—and all but dead, God bless him, thought Steele, but I'll warrant he'll go roistering to hell, or heaven may be!

There were shop signs, gaily carved and painted, creaking in the wind and so low hanging that a tall man might have had his hat knocked off, and many did. There were magistrates and aldermen, and gallowsmen and all sorts; a blackamoor, a showman shouting through his trumpet, "Vivat Regina! At Hyde Park Corner near the sheep pens will be seen the wonder of the world—a male child born with a live bear a-growing on its back!"

And, mightily diverted, as always when he strolled through London's streets, Steele came to the Exchange, half deafened by the babel of voices and jostled by insinuating 'preternatural b——erantos', was his disdainful thought of the highly rouged young gentlemen who clustered round the stalls. Not for them was the roving eye of Steele, but for those 'pretty merchants', as in the best of his plays[1] he describes 'some little lisping rogue', who baited his ears with enticements of 'ribbandths, gloveths, and tippeths', and another, in a mob and a striped pouched petticoat: "Does your lady want a hood, a scarf, or a pair of green silk stockings?"

"I'll stake me life she does, and she may want," was Steele's reply to that. "I've no money to buy baubles."

[1] *The Lying Lover.*

"Come, sir, you're a grand gentleman, and so finely dressed. Pray tell me your pleasure—I'll supply it."

"Faith, will ye an' all? And had I but the shirt on me paid for I'd take ye at your word, I would, me darlin'!"

Dimples, titters, rosy pursed lips pouting, invited encouragement to this remark. Steeles flashing smiles, lingered, just a second, long enough to whisper: "Never tempt me, darlin', lest I fall!" And on again he swaggered, looking back at her to see if she were looking back at him.

The pillars of the walks where stood the booths were plastered with advertisements for 'Soap-Balls and Aromaticks by Charles Lillie, the Perfumer of Beaufort Buildings', and 'Essence of Jasmine, Aqua Mellis, Eau sans Pareil, Cordials and Elixirs', all boldly lettered, alongside the famous 'Bohea of Mr. Garey, Druggist, sold only at The Bell in Gracechurch Street at Sixteen shillings the Pound.' Hawkers, shoving barrows, outvied stallholders in a cacophony of: 'Maids! Any coney skins?' 'Crab, crab, buy a fine crab', 'A fork, a fire-shovel', 'Bed-mat, a door mat', 'Long thread laces', 'New river-water', 'Old satin, old taffety, velvet and cere-cloths', 'Puff pies', or 'The London Gazette!' There were monkeys for sale, canaries, white pheasants, 'Fresh vipers alive-o and sold by the dozen'; love-charms, aphrodisiacs, 'guaranteed never to fail!'

"'Od's Beard! Do ye think that I need um?" asked Steele, all a-grin, of the damsel who cajoled. "I could prove ye how little I need um—in less time than it takes me to tell."

When he left the Exchange, having emptied his pockets of all but a crown piece, and that he had promised his Prue to lay out in oysters for dinner and patties of calves' brains, his steps took him into the Strand.

Passing Colman's toy-shop, he paused to gaze in at the window. His child and Prue's, which she was expecting, would soon be enjoying a toy, were it not tempting Providence to be premature, wondered Steele. Then, even as his eye alighted on a rattle hung with silver bells, he heard a voice behind him, soft, "Wait for me here, Grace, and if I'm not out in half an hour, come and call me."

Reflected in the bow-window's green bottle-panes Dick saw a vision, blurred, but fair enough to set his heartbeats racing.

Although cloaked and hooded, she was dressed in sweetest fashion, as could be seen in her petticoat of peach quilted satin, from which a tiny foot peeped out; as he turned for closer view, she raised her velvet vizard tantalizingly to hide her face, but not her ripe red mouth.

Small she was, and childish of figure, slight as a reed and swaying as she walked; and every step she took, as if on air, an invitation.

Into Mr. Colman's shop she vanished; and after her, as deep in love as ever he could dare to be, with Prue waiting for her patties and her oysters, went Dick Steele.

He saw her at a counter, turning over toys. "Show me some babies[1]," she ordered Mr. Colman, who came washing his hands at her with fawning bows. Babies were readily produced. Now what in the devil, asked Steele of himself, would she want with a baby, unless she should have one at home? She had not the look of a wife nor a matron, but was a virgin pure, he guessed her, as a young birch tree. Edging to the counter, piled high with babies, Steele touched a china cup and saucer, a fairy thing of Sèvres, and called to Mr. Colman, "This I'll have—and this—" He took a china tea-pot, and heard her dainty voice beside him say:

"I care for none of these. Have you nothing better? Not a baby."

"Will madam see some models in porcelain of cats or birds? Or I have a mouse, exquisite of design."

"No, not a mouse. Mice nauseate me. Show me birds."

Mr. Colman brought birds, enough to fill an aviary. She fancied a parakeet in green with crimson tail—for a moment; but behind the velvet vizard Steele could see her eyes were roaming to the door, and suddenly he saw her in a tremble, with a tooth pressed down on that red underlip. The para-keet dropped from her fingers to the floor, and broke into a hundred pieces.

"Oh!" she cried. "What have I done?"

Steele knelt at her feet.

"Madam, pray allow——"

Mr. Colman was all smiles. "Do not discommode yourself, dear madam, I can supply you with a duplicate."

[1] A doll was called 'a baby' in Queen Anne's reign.

"But I must pay the price of this—so careless—Ah! Good day, sir. What a curious coincidence. I came to buy a toy for Mrs. Hewet's little daughter."

Steele straightened up, and seeing him to whom she spoke, swiftly turned his back upon the pair. He bought and paid Mr. Colman for his purchases, and with a shilling's change, not half enough for oysters nor for patties, nor a rattle—went away.

So this, then, was a tryst. Disappointment warred with envy of Mr. Wortley Montagu. He should have known those eyes, shining through the velvet, blue as bluest water under rain. . . . "Love! Love!" sighed the sentimental Captain, " 'How great, how exquisite a pleasure there is in being really beloved!' "

"I think I hate you more every time we meet," hissed Mary from the cover of her mask. "You have kept me waiting twenty minutes."

"I could defend myself on good excuse if you would hear me."

"There can be no excuse, sir, for such scurvy conduct."

His smile was acidulous.

"Today you hate me. T'other day you told me I was 'silly'. Am I to take these compliments as literally true?"

"You can take them how you will. I exceedingly regret I succumbed to your suggestion—and what a ridiculous suggestion!—to meet you in this place for all the world and Mr. Steele to see. He followed me in—thank God my face was hid—doubtless thinking me to be what I am not."

"That is," he eyed her lengthily, "impossible."

"All things are possible save that you can harbour any interest in me or my concerns."

"If you believe me indifferent, why," with gentle irony he asked, "do you pursue me?"

"O, but this is barbarous!" She lowered her mask to glare at him like a basilisk. "How can you be so bold, so utterly devoid of taste as to suggest that I—have you forgot the last letter I wrote?"

"You wrote me so many I lose count, but I have one here——"

In his breast pocket he buried a hand and drew out a bundle tied with pink ribbon.

"For heaven's sake—" she swept an arm across the toys collected on the counter as if to grab the packet. Another gimcrack fell; a china mouse. She gave a little scream. "I *told* him not to bring me mice! Now see what you have done."

"I?" Up shot his eyebrows. "Don't be childish."

At which she gasped again and, with a glance at Colman who was polishing his silver, she furiously murmured: "I forbid you to carry my letters around. Suppose you should meet with your death in the streets and they were found on your person?"

"In which case I would die happy." Then taking from the packet the pages he sought, he re-tied the remainder and replaced them. "This is what you tell me——"

"I do not wish to hear it."

"'Let me beg you,'" he read softly, "'only to consider yourself in this affair and let me entreat you if I have committed any follies to forgive them . . .' What," he inquired, "am I to infer, when in one breath you acknowledge your faults, and in the next you denounce me as contemptible, despicable——"

"As so you are!" Then, seeing an involuntary spasm cross his face, she masked her own, relentingly to add: "Sometimes . . . And sometimes you're agreeable, but always you distort my words to mistake my meaning. Have you not insisted again and again that our letters can only cause confusion? They do. But how otherwise can we solve our uncertainties? You say we must meet to discuss them. Where," she demanded, "can we meet? In India-houses[1] as you most improperly suggest, and where no girl who values her reputation would be seen? Or in the salons of those ladies you named in your last, where even a word, a look— you have said it yourself—would be marked."

"No, I said—may I remind you—that 'though one look of grace, one whisper from you would be worth ten thousand letters, should my eyes once glance in your direction, they would betray me.' I am not," he said unsteadily, "master of

[1] Tea-houses.

109

myself enough to gaze at you unmoved. Only let me say—"
but what he had to say was surely not "Damnation! Who
comes here?"

Her maid came there. "My lady——"

Mary turned to bid her "Wait," and watched till she
retired . . . "And now, sir, what have you to say?"

He hesitated, fidgeted, and lifting from the counter a tiny
wooden horse, examined it unseeingly. She gloried in his
discomposure to find him more than ever to her liking. He
had long since discarded his black, and was wearing a suit of
saffron silk. It would have cost him something too, decided
Mary, laced with gold and broidered. He must be possessed
of means enough to keep a wife, so why should he persistently
refuse her father's terms? . . . Hardening her heart against his
indescribable attraction, she imperiously called him to
account.

"Well? I am waiting."

He tossed aside the wooden horse. "I have this to say—
that I positively must see you in private. Your letters deceive
me to think you single-minded. You are not. You're hypo-
critical——"

"And you," she flashed, "are *hyper*critical!—heaping
insult and injury upon me. Let me go!"

"I will never let you go." His equability deserted him.
Sliding a hand to hers he turned it upward, crushing his lips
into her palm. "All the service of my life," his tone was
urgent, "would be yours if you would show me one atom of
kindness, but you won't. I am slighted at the dance, at the
opera, even at the chapel of St. James's where—may I be
forgiven—I go to worship you and not my God. Whenever or
wherever we meet you disdain me and—encourage him!"

"Good Lord, sir!" With an effort she recovered from the
sweet surprise of touch to ask, "encourage whom?"

"That bowing, scraping coxcomb," quoth he, with a stare,
"that mangel-wurzel from the bogs."

"Mangel-wurzel? Bogs?"

Nothing but simple amaze was in her face, for an instant
unscreened.

"Your ignorance," he sneered, "confirms suspicion. Do you
love him?"

110

"Are you raving?"

"Very likely. If I arrange a meeting-place where we may be together undisturbed, will you—" his look was savage—"condescend to honour me?"

"I condescend to nothing. We only meet to quarrel. You accuse me of flirtation——"

"'Tis you," he loudly interposed, "who rave. I used no such word."

"Hush, pray! Must you shout? This Colman is all ears. You implied it. Who save a goose-girl would flirt with Mr. K.?"

"Ah!" Triumphantly he pounced. "Kay! So that's his name."

"It is not," said she suavely, "his name. 'Tis but the first letter of a fantastical long, unpronounceable name. Kilmacree—Kilmulloch—Kil—something of that sort."

"And kill him," he glowered, "I would for a pigeon."

She pealed with silent laughter.

"Lud! What's in a name?"

"Too much. His name or any other would stink as foul when it signifies wealth untold."

"Which signifies nothing to me. I would take you—no!" She backed from his eager advance, extending her ivory-handled mask between them at arm's length. "Hear me out, sir. I was saying I would take you were you poor as this poor broken toy of a mouse," she tipped the splintered china with her toe, "if you were rich in heart, but you are not. Your heart is a bankrupt, impoverished of all that makes life bearable."

"You break me to pieces," he muttered.

"Not you! That which I break is less inviolate than your enshrined solidity, or should I say *stol*idity? A mouse, a parakeet—this pretty thing—I would have bought it. Now you may buy it for me. Gather the fragments. Keep them as a symbol of our gimcracked love, or as you choose to term it, our—" she paused to snap the word at him—"'Esteem'."

He stayed silent, enfolded for a moment in detachment, and avoiding her smile: "Beyond forgetting," he breathed out, "I will cherish this smashed toy . . . Sirrah, you!" He beckoned the listening Colman. "I wish to pay for the damage to your wares. Wrap the bird. I'll have what's left of it."

With indulgence for the vagaries of Quality, Mr. Colman hurried forward naming the cost of the 'damage', far in excess of its worth. A heated argument ensued with the result of two groats substracted from the total. The gentleman dived for his purse. The lady's eyes mocked the transaction.

"I am much in your debt, sir. Some day, maybe," her white even teeth became visible, "I will repay you."

"My duty, madam, and my pleasure to oblige." And taking his cocked hat from under his arm, he swept the ground with its brim as she passed.

Dick Steele and his Prue were at table that same evening when Warren, their maid, announced that Mr. Wortley Montagu had called and desired a word with the Captain alone.

The word with the Captain alone took more than an hour to say, while Mrs. Steele, who before her marriage had been Molly Scurlock from Wales, sat by the fireside gnawing at her thumb.

She was lovely, with a temper as hot as her red flaming hair, at that moment dressed in curl-papers. She had been —not a child—when Dick led her to the altar of St. Margaret's Westminster, for all she had given her age as twenty-four, some five years short of the truth; but what of that? Dick would have died for love of her and very nearly did on the consummation of the marriage, which his capricious bride had postponed in her tantrums for a month. Never let it be admitted in the faithful heart of Dick that his adored Prue was a scold were she so minded. And on this winter's evening, huddled on a stool in a slightly soiled gown of yellow taffety, Prue was very much so minded. What a wickedness of Mr. Wortley Montagu to snatch her husband from his supper—and a mean enough supper, withal, of stewed carp hashed up from yesterday's dinner—because he had forgot to buy the two dozen oysters as promised, and patties of calves' brains. A woman in delicate health must be pampered, and who in his senses would feed her and her child unborn on stewed carp?

The watchman was calling the hour, 'Nine o' the clock and a fine frosty night', when Prue heard the sound of chairs scraping the floor below, followed by the tramp of feet and voices on the stairway.

Leaving the solace of her thumb, Mistress Prue, who had a score to settle with Mr. Wortley Montagu for deliberately excluding her from his 'word' with the Captain, scrambled up from her seat, clapped a hand to her head, and uttered in a taking, "My curl-papers!" Then she hurried to a looking-glass to tear off the twisted scraps that bore remarkable resemblance to a holocaust of last year's *Tatlers*. These she bundled in a heap beneath the sofa, thrust ineffectual fingers through her hair, and turned to the door as it opened.

"Here, Prue, me darlin'!" Dick was in the room, his visitor behind him, "is Mr. Wortley Montagu to beg a favour of your sweetness."

Prue's smile as she bobbed was anything but sweetness.

" 'Tis not in me, look you, a poor neglected wife," she cast a knife-edged scowl at her husband, "to grant favours, whatever, being as I am but part and parcel of the goods and chattels in this house. Mr. Wortley Montagu, be seated, will you not? Dick, fetch the Languedoc. And what, sir, may be the favour with which I can oblige?"

"Why, madam," Edward hemmed, fingering his steinkerk, following his host's endeavours with a cork, " 'tis a—'tis on your hospitality I would—humha!—encroach."

"Poor hospitality is it, I can offer," retorted Mrs. Steele, tossing back her uncombed curls that clung close as Medusa's serpents round her face. "Yet you are welcome to our board and bread, though it be our last crust and the bailiffs dressed as footmen to wait on us at table—may I perish if I lie—as they were when my good man entertained his company to dine last week and no secret, since every soul in town knows the tale of the bailiffs."

"Now, heart's delight," cajoled Dick, "wait, will ye, till you hear. 'Tis not, as you imagine, Mr. Wortley Montagu himself who would beg your condescension, but a lady."

"Ho! A lady!" Prue swung round upon her husband. "One of yours, by damn, Lord help us! I will not——"

"Yes, you will." Dick slid an arm about her waist, held

113

a crystal goblet to her lips, and crooned in a wheedling baritone, " 'But leave a kiss with-i-i-n the cu-hup, and I-I'll not ah-ask for——' "

"May the devil fly off with you, dizzard!" cried Prue, dashing the glass from his hand to spill the contents on his white buckskin breeches. Dick caught it smartly as it fell.

"And me tailor dunning me," he moaned, "these two years for them." Dismally he surveyed his red-stained breeks. "Here's a shrew, rhymes with Prue—Ah! be easy now, will ye, my angel, and say that you'll receive the lady."

"And a fine lady, is it," flared Prue, "who cannot speak for herself but must come backhanded to adulterize my husband!"

"Never in this world!" was Dick's stout disclaimer. "See how me very legs blush for that word ye used, syntactically unknown, but most venomous incriminating. Listen now, while I tell you that she who so desires your acquaintance is none other than the Lady Mary Pierrepont."

"What!" shrieked Prue, her eyes and lips in circles. "Not the Lady Mary?"

"Herself it is, the beauty," Steele closed with her to whisper, "but not so great a beauty as me jewel."

"And why should Lady Mary," Prue, unpacified, persisted, "wish to visit me?"

"Because she's a woman of wit and discernment," was Dick's wily answer, "and she knows you to be her match in quality and parts. Her ladyship possesses unexampled connoisseurship."

"Dear to goodness!" ejaculated Prue, "I'd never dare to set myself in equal parts with Lady Mary. Mr. Wortley Montagu, is this a pack of lies invented by my husband? His imagination is riotous, indeed. I will not be tricked. Now then."

Edward, looking down into his glass, mumbled to effect that it was her ladyship's desire to meet her at Mrs. Steele's convenience.

"My convenience," Prue submitted, mollified, "is hers. I will be joyed to receive her ladyship at any time, whatever. Go, Dick, and change those breeks. I will soak them in salt."

"In the salt o' the earth, which is Prue, and as true as 'those

114

thousand torments',", Dick kissed her hands, self-quoting, " 'that do dwell about thee, yet who could live . . . and live without thee?' "

And so it happened that Mary received a peremptory message from her lover commanding her to call on Mrs. Steele. 'He would be in the house, reading.'

Mrs. Steele had never been more flattered than on the day that Lady Mary came to visit with a surly, long-faced sister in attendance. Prue's curtsy was a thing to wonder at. "My ladyships!" The only ladyships she had ever entertained in all her life. "Am I honoured indeed!"

Chairs were offered. The ladies sat, silk and satins enviably rustling. Conscious that her kincob was anything but modish, Prue, behind the tea-urn, splashed bohea into cups, pressed cakes upon her visitors, while Frances, crinkling her nose as if a smell were underneath it, gazed about her.

Mary, very gracious, praised Prue's 'chaney', brightly skimming small-talk, from the weather, "bitter cold, ma'am. I think there will be snow—" to the Mohawks. "A truly shocking problem. The streets at night are never safe from the ravages of these undisciplined young gentlemen. I am told Bishop Burnet's son is among them."

"Mohawks well neemed, indeed." Prue was making brave attempt to speak in English fashion, slurring her consonants and drawing out her vowels, "called after those bloodthirstily Red Indians, so may hahsband tells may."

"Your husband, madam, would be well advised," suggested Mary, "not to venture out alone after dark."

"My man has been a soldier, look you!" returned Prue, abandoning her effort in a burst of wifely pride. "He will slit up the noses of those devils should they set on him. It is not the stronger that they mischief, see, it is the weaker, there's the cowards that they are. I have heard tell how they rolled a poor woman in a tub down Snow Hill on her way to market. And another time they hooked an old man as nimble as a fisher hooks a trout, to play him from Charing Cross to Temple Bar. They did so!"

Prue was in her element and Frances out of hers. What on earth, she wondered, could have induced Mary to patronize this dreadful Welsh-tongued person with the hair?

She was not left long in doubt. Steele, magnificent in crimson plush, made his entrance grandly, and proceeded to enlarge on the arm of coincidence that had lengthened past belief, for: "Mr. Wortley Montagu, a neighbour of yours from the North, mesdames, is downstairs in my library, studying at my request a column I have written for the new *Spectator* in defence of me own face. Sooth to say, ladies, I am unhappy in its mould which, for example, is not near so long as it is broad, and which so often puts me out of countenance, that I've been at pains to conceal it—" he pointed to the pyramid of curls that crowned him—"by the wearing of a high fore-top!"

His exuberance fell flat. Mary's smile was a trifle screwed as if she had the toothache; Prue bit her thumb; and Frances, tucking in her lips, prepared a tale to carry to her father . . . A pretty plot, no mistaking! And Mary was in it along with this loud-voiced preposterous Steele and his wife—what a gowk!—in a dress of the year before last.

"So now," blundered Dick, "will your ladyship honour my library?" This was braggadocio; he possessed no library more than a couple of shelves to hold those of his most treasured books not in the care of his Hebraic acquaintances. "I have some rare first editions which will interest you, for sure, Lady Mary."

Nothing could have been less diplomatic than the wink that accompanied this offer, intercepted by the lynx-eyed Frances and accepted by Mary with false enthusiasm. What possessed the man, she asked herself, to mop and mow there like a gaby, giving Frances and his wife profound ideas? She rose; so did her sister, who was told in swift aside: "You cannot leave our hostess . . . Madam, I beg you will excuse me. I doat on rare editions."

She was doubtfully excused and conducted down the stairs by Captain Steele.

Into the parlour—nothing of a library—where Edward waited, she was ushered. Dick closed the door upon them, and stood sentinel outside it.

If Mr. Wortley Montagu had hoped to find his lady more conciliatory than when he last had seen her, he was shocked. A hot-eyed virago quenched the declaration burning on his lips and nearer to his heart and hers than any he had uttered, and which certainly would not be uttered now. As he bowed to her hand she snatched it from him; as he stammered, his practised words flying: "That you come to me here proves that my—hum—my esteem is not discarded——"

She interposed harshly, "Discarded it is! I am sick of your 'esteem'! Not a letter you write, not a phrase you address to me but does not repeat it. Your vocabulary is as limited as your good taste. How could you dare to drag me to this house on so flimsy a pretext? That woman will worry my name to chase it through London. Don't contradict!" She stamped her foot. "I say she will. When you wrote for me to come you gave me no hint that Steele and his wife would be parties to our meeting."

"Untrue!" he cried, warmly. "Did you expect me to smuggle you in like a thief in the dark and confer with you in cupboards? You pick quarrels where none should exist. Ah, yes! I see a motive in your purpose of abuse. You wish to be released from my attentions—and you have succeeded. Go then," he threateningly neared her, "go! Untrammelled, open-armed—to your Irish buffoon."

"Dear Lord," she breathed, aghast, "grant me patience!"

"'Tis I," he said, close-lipped, "who should pray for patience. Yet I'm generous enough to own him the more proper match, if no such proper man. His estate is prodigious. One of his compatriots has named the value of it. You see how just I am that I willingly renounce you in favour of my rival."

"I strive," she panted, "to be calm." But there was no calm in the face she raised to his. "Your incivilities, your incessant, unendurable fault-finding have brought me to such abhorrence of you and of your attitude that I can only repeat I will have done with you—for ever!"

"Good!" He nodded. "Very good. We now know where we are. You have so often in writing done with me for ever, but not until this moment in the spoken word. I'll take you at your word." And saying so he gripped her hands with force enough to drive her rings into her flesh. Ignoring her squeal of protest, "I have stumbled," he continued, "on the truth at last, if truth is in you, which I doubt. I am unloved.

And this other poor devil—to be pitied—wins the prize, and what a prize, ecod! A she-imp with a flail in its tongue would be more douce."

"O, infamous!" She struggled, sobbing in her rage, "Tormentor! Beast of cruelty!" But the more she fought to free herself the more closely did he clutch. "I hate you, I detest you! Let go my hands—you hurt."

"Not so much as I am hurt."

Half maddened by her nearness, the perfume of her hair, and the hurry of her breasts beneath the 'tucker', he released her with such violence that she almost over-balanced, then recovered to come at him with her nails.

"Ha!" Shoving his fist beneath her nose he showed her the imprint of three scarlet crescents. "See how I am branded. A sweet signature, in sooth."

Unabashed she stormed at him: "'Tis no less than you deserve. How *can* you use me so!"

Between a second and a second they stood facing each other; both showed some signs of affliction. Two bright spots of colour scalded Mary's cheeks; his were white.

"I'd use you worse," he said, "before I'd use you better." And then he lost himself. His arms engulfed her, his mouth hovered above her parted lips; her eyes were closed.

"Good God!" he muttered huskily, "Tantalus could not have been more tempted! Can there be no end to this misery between us? I think that if I ever have you——"

"Never," she whispered, vanquishing her weakness, "will you have me." She laid her hand against his chest to push him from her, and composed her voice to tell him, clear: "Mr. Steele is at the keyhole. This diverting comedy will be cheerfully retailed in every tavern in the town. I'll bid you farewell, sir, and hope you *do* fare well when you take to wife another, something sweeter to your taste than I!"

Darting to the door, she flung it open to surprise Dick in so arched a posture on the mat outside that he all but tumbled in.

"Gently, sir," she smiled, "I trust you've been agreeably entertained. Have the goodness to inform my sister I am leaving. Gentlemen," she curtsied to them both, "I'll be with you in spirit when you split a bottle—and your sides—at my expense tonight. My adieux, Captain Steele, to your good lady."

And all the way home to Arlington Street in the rattling coach Frances railed. Mary, she said, had made cat's-meat of herself, had put to shame her Family by stooping to a clandestine appointment in the house of 'that vulgarian'. "If our father chooses to acknowledge in his club or at an ordinary, a man so far beneath him in rank 'tis his affair, but never would Papa present to us, his daughters, this low-life gazetteer."

"Our father has already presented this low-life gazetteer to one of his daughters—me!" retorted Mary. "And at the house of the Duchess of Marlborough. She's proud enough to receive him."

"The Duchess," sniggered Frances, "would be proud to receive the garbage man, now that she's dropped in the dust."

"The Duchess received Captain Steele," pursued Mary with murderous chill, "when she stood high as second lady in the land. And the name of Richard Steele, I'll have you know, will live immortal when your name and my name and *all* our names are dead."

"What! That peddling playwright, that rhyming buccaneer, whose only claim to immortality is in the debts he'll leave behind him? I wonder Wortley Montagu can sink himself to favour one with jail-bird writ large as print upon him, to say nothing of his standing sponsor to Steele's daughter by that Welsh woman. Did you know that?"

Yes. Mary did know that. "Which only goes to prove how greatly Wortley Montagu values Richard Steele."

"As greatly," scoffed Frances, "as he values you, which is somewhat less than I value my pet squirrel. But at least I keep her comfortable and gladsome in a cage, and that's more than he is prepared to do for his pet, truly! Were he so fond as you believe him, he'd move earth and heaven to win you. But he won't. He'll sit on his father's money-bags till the old man is in his grave before he'll move himself to marry you. Will you wait till you're forty to wed? I tell you," fumed Frances, "you're wickedly perverse. Here's a prodigious match down on his knees for you, and you won't have him. Yet until you—the eldest—are settled, Papa has said he's not prepared to treat for me and Evelyn. Mary first, he says. It always *has* been Mary first. Why should *I* be made to suffer for your selfishness, you pig! Am I to lose my chance in life because you won't take yours?"

The coach, bumping on the cobbles, jolted the silent Mary against her sister's shoulder. Frances jerked her off.

"You make me sick! Of all obstinate, plaguy sly bitches you're the worst. *I'll* tell Papa!"

"O, go tell him then!" cried Mary, hot, "and let him turn me out into the streets where God knows I would be happier!"

"And where 'tis evident, God knows, that you belong."

Frances had the last word, for even as she spoke the coach clattered to a halt at the entrance to the house. Mary ran in and up to her room, and wrote to him on whose account 'my sister read me a long lecture . . . I wish there had not been so much reason in what she said.'

For what Frances said had dug deep. Only too clear was the ultimate end of this association with a man who had proved himself so disregardful of her reputation. How unavailing had been their countless letters, their eternal farewells, their bitter reunions, yet:

'While I foolishly fancied you loved me (which I confess I never had any great reason for, more than that I wished it), there is no condition of life I could not have been happy in with you, so very much I liked you—I may say loved— since it is the last thing I'll ever say to you. This is telling you sincerely, my greatest weakness; and now I will oblige you with a new proof of generosity. I'll never see you more.'

There could be no redress. She was defeated. She would have to go away and lie fallow in the country to forget him; and, more urgently, to dodge her father's wrath. That Frances would 'tell Papa' of the meeting at Steele's house she did not doubt; any moment now the blow would fall.

At Thoresby or West Dean, she cared nothing where she went, she would be safe from interference. But at the last minute, with her baggage packed, and permission granted from her father that she depart for Thoresby the next day, having heard old Nurse was ill—Mary's own invention—came an abject apology from Edward, admitting his 'Passion which I endeavoured to conceal, but I could not. How,' he pleads, 'could any woman break off so suddenly with one she lately valued?' He too would leave Town—in a fortnight. Would she not meet him once again at Mrs. Steele's?

Very well then, once again for the positively last time. Her letter, penned in haste, interlarded with dashes, indicates confusion. 'I am very silly—what has become of my anger? I tremble at what I am doing. My sister reproaches me with fondness for a man that does not care for me.' She was afraid of 'finding company at Mrs. Steele's.' She did not wish to be shown 'as a *sight* to Mr. and Mrs. Steele's friends . . . I will come tomorrow to Mrs. Steele's early.'

She came, unattended, in her father's coach, not very early and not at her best, with a streaming cold, her head in a scarf, and so high in the air that she did not perceive she was watched.

That genial busybody, Dr. Garth, visiting a case in Bury Street, St. James's, alighted from his chair in the dusk of the evening at the same instant that Mary arrived at Steele's house. The coat of arms on the Dorchester equipage, to say nothing of the blue and silver liveries, were striking enough to have attracted attention even had they not been stationed in that very narrow street.

It was unfortunate that the Doctor who saw Lady Mary go in did not wait to see her come out. Whom he did see, however, after the briefest of calls on his patient, was Mr. Wortley Montagu, whose approach to Steele's doorway appeared to be, to say the least, conspiratorial. Peering between his chair-curtains Dr. Garth watched the gentleman furtively admitted. Much intrigued, and even more amused, the jolly little Doctor was hoisted up and carried away, chuckling. He might have chuckled less had he known that Edward had come to find his lady gone and Mrs. Steele in bed. She had been kept awake all the night before attending on her husband with the gout. But the doctor knew nothing of this and readily accepted the circumstantial evidence, in due course to be related to the Marquis.

At first incredulous, he, on the assurance of his good friend

Dr. Garth, was persuaded to believe that not only had his daughter violated his command, but the utmost limits of propriety.

The thunderbolt had fallen.

Throughout that same night, bumping over bad roads, heavy-eyed from loss of sleep, Lord Dorchester sped northward in his post-chaise. With every turn of the wheels his temper heightened. The posting-inns were dirty, the food uneatable, not fit to fling at Newgate felons; and the wine with which he had washed down the worst of it had sourly fermented in his stomach. And here was Mary whose wanton misbehaviour had given Garth, and the deuce alone knew who, to think her raped.

Never had been heard in Thoresby such a racket as that of his lordship's arrival. Into the hall he flung, shoving aside the white-haired butler, shouting at a footman, "Her ladyship—where is she?" Throwing off his purple cloak, casting down his cocked hat, tramping the oaken floor and cursing to high heaven. Footmen scattered; chambermaids were pale-faced. The housekeeper came curtsying, was swept aside.

Upstairs in her parlour, Mary, at her writing-desk that overlooked the park, listened to the shindy with a sinking of her heart. She glanced at the unfinished page before her ... *'I have trusted my reputation in your hands. Perhaps I have been indiscreet. . . .'*

And now her father was descended without warning to punish her—for what she dared not think.

Snatching her letter she thrust it in the bosom of her gown and went to meet him.

There in the hall, warming his rump at the blazing logs he stood, his hands beneath the tails of his corbeau velvet coat. A three days' growth of stubble decked his heavily-creased chins, sunk in the lace of his steinkerk. As she dipped to the bob his bloodshot eyes protruded; as she rose to kiss his hand he thrust her back.

"So! For all your cunning, you've been catched!" roared her father. "Creeping like a trollop up backstairs to go a-courting! What! My daughter to disgrace my name in the house of a Grub Street hack—I say you did! You were seen. You borrowed my coach. I took you for a girl o' sense —as much sense as'll sit on a farthing! My liveries are known in all London, you fool. Why didn't you hire a chair?"

Who, she wondered, could have told him? She heard herself accused of sending letters 'under cover of a mopsy, picked from the gutter to act as go-between . . .' But Betty's doubtful assistance had been dispensed with these six months. What more did he know? He was at pains to tell her, for the maidservants peeping over banisters to hear. The rafters rang. It was horrific.

"Not only are you guilty of arrant disobedience, but have cast away your last hope of marriage—not with Wortley Montagu—that unconscionable scrimp! I'd sooner see you dead in a ditch than wed to one who cares so little for you and for your future that he can hum and ha upon a settlement. A fine husband he, who finding me obdurate gratifies his lust in holes and corners, to serve you like a seaman's drab from Wapping."

"Father!" Convulsively she pressed her hands together, her face contorted with a passion uncontrollable as his. "To deny your filthy accusations would drag me as low as you who speak them. Take back your words, sir—they stink in your mouth! I will have an apology, or else——"

And she doubled her fists.

If a horned demon had come hurtling down the chimney to replace that trembling figure there before him, his lordship could scarcely have been more confounded. She, whom all his life he had cowed, dared now to turn on him with eyes that darted fire and voice commanding, to rob him of his faith in himself and his absolutism. This undersized chit, with the face of a seraph, but no seraph now, Hecuba more likely, demanded a withdrawal of his words—'they stink in your mouth'. Holy Heaven!

In his knotted forehead a vein stood out like whipcord; but, though shaken to the depths of his ponderous foundations, Lord Dorchester struggled to regain his lost preeminence by ignoring Mary's outburst.

"One hope for your redemption I'll allow you, and you'll

take it, or—" his encrimsoned visage greenly faded—"or I'll turn you out—I'll lock you up, I'll—" He swayed, and looked as if to fall. Putrid wine, lack of sleep, and the shock of mutiny had wrought their bane upon him. He flapped an aimless hand and belched, called chokingly for brandy, and staggered to a settle.

Mary fled.

Later, cleaned and rehabilitated, he sent for her again. She would return to Town, he told her, within the coming week. The evil she had brought upon herself and her family, "*my* Family," his lordship vociferated, "can be put to rights only by submission to my will. Your sisters are proposed for by eligible suitors. Lord Gower has approached me for Evelyn, and Frances is already pledged to Mar, to which I've no objection beyond that he's a Jacobite and firebrand, but money enough and amenable to treat with me according to my wishes, which your mimsy high-nosed gentleman is not."

She flushed. Impious hate was in her heart and a sob, not of sorrow—of fury—in her throat.

"But until," her father emphasized, "you show some tractability, your sisters, like yourself, will go unwed. Would you stand in their light while you smother your own? 'Sdeath, how I'm cursed in you! Proud I was once—" self-pity swelled in his blotched handsome face. She saw him near to tears. "Proud I would be still if you'd see eye to eye with me. There's a match in a thousand waiting if you'll take him."

"And who," she asked with delicate irony, "is he?"

"You know as well as I. He has danced to your tune these four years and more, and has made me an offer. Will you treat?"

He turned his charm upon her, summoning a smile, extending sausage fingers to be kissed. Dutifully she knelt. His hand caressed her hair; he pinched her cheek, and with wheedling persuasion: "So that's my girl," he said. "You always was my best-beloved, but wilful. I have cause enough for grievance, yet so deep is my affection—" and so deep his sigh, producing abdominal growls—"that I'll forgive your sauciness today."

Sauciness! It was the best he could do, thus to dismiss as a mere bagatelle her recent cyclonic explosion. Mary's veiled eyes acknowledged his diplomacy. A corner of her upper lip slid sideways.

"My arms," said her father, spreading them, "receive you." He clasped her. She could smell the perfumed snuff that clung to his wide hairy nostrils. His mouth slobbered on her brow. "My poor, sinful, motherless child! Had that dear saint who bore you been spared to me she would have guided you aright. For her beloved sake I adjure you, purge your heart."

Mary forbore to remind him that it was not her heart but his stomach, she judged, from its grumbles, that should require purging; nor, though she itched to say it, did she suggest that the 'dear saint', her mother, may have suffered a saint's martyrdom in her brief married life.

"Sir," cramped with kneeling, she temporized in whispers, for if she did not stop him he would maunder on all night. "Sir, I crave your pardon for my wickedness and folly. Deal with me as you wish. My will is yours."

* 7 *

While the battle of resistance between Mary and her father had been fought, by the Marquis, to its successful end, that other battle of resistance in universal quarters was turning toward the long desired peace.

The Marlburian faction had crumbled, with bitter accusations directed at the great Duke of assigning, to his own use, certain bread contracts commissioned for the Army.

Such small accounting, whether or no it were accurately prompted, might have been disregarded by a grateful Queen if not by an ungrateful people. Yet, he who had served her with a life's devotion was now dismissed, disgraced. One, high in royal favour, had supplanted the nation's hero; honour after honour was heaped on Robert Harley, 'man of

125

mystery' so-called, created Earl of Oxford and Mortimer, Knight of the Garter, Lord High Treasurer of England. The Whigs and their idol were out.

A dozen newly elevated peers sat in the House of Lords, among them Mr. Masham, husband of Abigail, Her Majesty's adored; and in October, 1711, the Tory Ministers came to terms with France. A year later St. John, taking to himself full credit for the Treaty of Utrecht, was duly rewarded with the viscountcy of Bolingbroke. He had aspired to an earldom and was offered this 'skim o' the Lords in return for twisting the tail of that old buzzard, Louis', so to Lady Masham he bitterly complained. The Whigs of the Kit-Cat at 'Upper Flask', their summer haunt on the fringe of Hampstead Heath, heard with aching sides of St. John's discontent. Steele and Addison, the latter out of politics and more than ever out of pocket, fired squibs at the Tories through the omniscient mouth of 'Sir Roger de Coverley'.

Jonathan Swift, shivering against the cold in the following winter of 1712, sat up in bed with a shawl round his shoulders, no fire in his grate and wormwood in his pen, bitterly reporting to his Stella: 'They are always mauling Lord Treasurer, Bolingbroke and me . . .' Moreover he was plagued with bad authors, verse and prose, 'the vilest,' he said, 'I ever saw'.

Not among the 'vilest', surely, who submitted his verse to the virulent Dean, was a dwarfish little monkey of a boy with a crook in his spine and a hump on his back, but despite his lowly stature, destined to rank above all poets of his time; destined also to cross the path of Mary, and to leave his mark on her palimpsest, unerased.

That for the future; for the present she, with Frances, exquisitely suffered to see their sister Evelyn married to Lord Gower. Virtually a stranger to them both, Evelyn, from the all-embracing shelter of Aunt Cheyne, had emerged courted, unopposed, to be wed by the man of her choice—and her father's; an initiate in knowledge denied her elder sisters, the equal of matrons, wife of a peer, their superior in precedence. Was this to be borne? Yet with every sign of outward joy they bore it.

As Evelyn, a creamy-skinned golden girl, sailed to the altar on her father's arm, none to see her sisters in attendance would have judged them cheerless, crabbed to the core. Frances, hankering for her John Mar—who in his fanatic devotion to the Cause appeared to be as slippery a suitor as Mary's Wortley Montagu—hid despairing envy under giggles. Mary, red-eyed with weeping at the loss of a loved sister, onlookers supposed, shed smiles, strewed the bride's path with roses, and danced as light-heartedly as the gayest of the guests at the Ball held in honour of the bridal pair.

Yes, she had wept, for nights on end, pounding at her pillow in puny impotence against the inflexible decree of her father, to which she had so meekly acquiesced; meek to all intent and to his lordship's purpose, but not hers.

During the months that had elapsed since her startling revolt she had turned from a termagant into a turtle. The Marquis rejoiced; he had quelled her, and now had nothing more to seek but her good riddance. Little did he guess that her dulcet passivity screened determination to defy. Cunningly she plotted and, her goal in sight, her mind resolved, infected Edward with her courage and her folly. Letters flew between them every day; meetings were forbidden, but they met; once again at Colman's, twice again at Steele's.

That his 'L.M.' was pursued by the favoured 'Mr. K.', and likely to be snatched from him, sent Edward to the Marquis with a last appeal, which, when again relentlessly refused, brought matters to a head and decided Mary's future.

"All is concluded with this other," was her lament to Edward, "nor will he be put off. . . ."

And at her sister's wedding 'this other', amid congratulatory addresses, was proclaimed Lady Mary's betrothed.

After the banquet held in the evening for members of the Family, Mary found herself inveigled to an ante-room and, for the first time, alone with 'Mr. K.' Nor could she tell how she came to be there. Wine and emotion had rendered her dizzy. A mirror reflected a ghost in white satin with a face no less white than the roses in her hair.

As they entered, or to be precise, as 'Mr. K.' entered with Mary tucked under his arm, he closed the door carefully, standing with his back to it.

Splendidly attired in hyacinth blue and a periwig of chestnut curls that fell to his sword-sash, he exposed his gums and lyrically addressed her.

"Ah, Lady Mary! The eyes of you, like violets peering under hedges, delight me dreams."

"And you," she said softly, "haunt mine."

"Do I now?" Eagerly he grabbed her hand. "Imagine!"

"Let me finish, sir," she disengaged, "haunt mine as in a nightmare."

"Ye destroy me!" A gentle dew beaded the powder on his forehead. He took a silken handkerchief and mopped. "Am I spurned?"

"May I pass?"

She made a dash for the door. He spread his arms against it in an attitude of crucifixion, eyes rolled up, long upper lip pulled down.

"Pass ye may, over my corpse, where 'tis nailed to the cross of your unkindliness. Me heart is at your feet."

"Then you had best retrieve it, sir, for I will not. Moreover, I don't relish your sacrilegious notion of a jest."

"No jest, dear life, at all. Nor is it sacrilegious. My pain is torture. A dying Christian in the Colosseum could not have suffered worse than I in your contempt. You've never been to Rome, I think? I have. I'll take you there, an ye'll give me the sublime privilege of showing you the wonders of the ancient world. You'd take to them as joyful as a filly to a stallion."

"The wonders of the modern world, sir, will suffice me."

"Then—" the whites of his eyes were lemon-tinted like his teeth—"come to my country," he coaxed, "where the hills are purple and the grass is green, and the women are fairies, but none so fair as you. And where there's no hunting in any land to compare with the chase o' the fox in the grey o' the morning. Sure, I'll give ye a mare bred from pure Arab strain. Ladies go hunting in Ireland. D'ye care to hunt, Lady Mary?"

"Not the fox," she smiled. "Greater game."

His gaze feasted on the colourless small face before him; and, a prey to doubt of her, his head moved plaintively.

"Ah, my winsome! Why is it you're so sharp with me and

sour, when the very sight of you bedazzles to think you honey-sweet? I'm blunt—faix, I am—but not uncultured. I speak French. I spent two years in Paris and have danced at the Court of Lewis, may he rot! Yet I've lived a bachelor till I'm five and forty, finding none but yourself to stir me guts. And you do that an' all. What's your objection to me, Lady Mary? I can give ye the earth."

He seized her hand again. She dragged it away and furtively rubbed her palm in the folds of her gown. A slight in-drawing of his eyebrows acknowledged her repulse; the up-turned tip of his undistinguished nose quivered as if it had been struck. Nervously he flicked his scented handkerchief at imaginary snuff upon his sleeve, while, desperate, he blurted:

" 'Pon me soul, I'm in that degree of adoration I would gladly die for you if I am not to live for you. Your father demands and will have fifty thousand for your jointure. What more would ye be wanting? I'll teach you how to love."

Her level-glancing eyes looked through him as though he were a window. Covertly he watched her; and watching, saw her face transformed. Her lips parted, and it seemed her body trembled toward him like an opening flower. Misinterpreting this change in her to think himself encouraged, he attempted to assert his rights as her affianced. Clumsily he captured her, enveloped her, sought and found her mouth ... Had he wished to verify suspicion that she spurned him, he could have asked no further evidence than in her horrified recoil, and her cry as of a wild creature trapped.

He dropped his arms; she raised one of hers, covering her face to obliterate the sight of his.

"No, no," she murmured, "no! Can you not see—" every breath she drew was deep and fast as if she had been running, —"that you disgust and sicken me? I am not to be sold by my father to you as he would sell a blood mare."

Light fell on her where she stood, so that to him, dazed and shocked by her words, she seemed to be ethereal, almost transparent. His native superstition usurped the little reason that remained to him. He crossed his thumbs and brooded, sunk in misery. A witch or a she-devil, this one! Then his drooping shoulders squared. He would break her yet, reclaim her, defeat her, and win her with his wealth, if not with his desire. No woman, he reasoned, could remain unconquered by so strong a bait . . . Yet, even as that thought darted through him, and as if she read his mind, he heard:

"What life have you to offer me? A stable—or the Grand Tour with you alongside in the Colosseum—would be equally obnoxious. Not all your scented trappings can disguise your smell. Yes, you smell—of money. You exude it like the sweat of those that toil for you in your fields, on your lands, these vast acres with which you and my father would tempt me. I don't want your money, and I don't want you! 'Twould be a wickedness to marry you since you will never know—" her voice cracked on a note of hysteria—"how much —how much I *loathe* you!"

Laughter bubbled in her throat and escaped, shrill, equivocal, to shatter him. Blindly he bowed; and groping behind him for the door-handle, turned from her, dumb as a dog.

* * *

When a shrunken, pale 'Mr. K.' recounted to Lord Dorchester the gist, with reservations, of this interview, a deceptive heartiness assured him that Mary's animosity indicated the reverse. Courtship, his lordship gave the doleful gentleman to understand, was a trying ordeal for both parties; but whereas between men—a knowing wink—there were ways and means to pacify the male urge, allowance should be made for humoursome virginity. "Zooks! You'll find her up and ready when you—" gaily the Marquis prodded his ribs and drank a bottle to the strength of 'Mr. K.'

Somewhat cheered, yet doubting still his lady's caprice, he departed with a deposition in his pocket on which, for added surety, Lord Dorchester insisted. This would necessitate certain alterations in the draft of the settlement deeds, and a journey back to Ireland to consult with his legal advisers.

By the removal from Mary's immediate vicinity of her unwelcome betrothed, the Marquis had contrived not only to double her jointure, but to span the awkward interim before her wedding day. On no account must he risk a recurrence of mutiny, at the instigation, he suspected, of another, not so willing to endow her with the fifty thousand pounds or more agreed by 'Mr. K.' And in order to ensure that his awful daughter should not evade her fortune and her fate, the Marquis packed her off to Acton, where William, with Rachel, his foolish little wife, was then in residence; and there throughout the summer, Mary stayed.

William, married and a father before he was out of his teens, had taken the easiest way of non-resistance. Too young to discover that the heiress chosen for him had no more to recommend her than her face and half a million, William, within a month of his honeymoon, wretchedly regretted it. But although sympathetic to his sister's tangled love-affairs, he could offer little more than his advice for their unwinding. It was his suggestion she should write to her father stating her case.

"Let him know," William said, "that he can't force you to marry against your inclination. You are not a minor. Your will is your own—or should be your own—unless you will have him ruin your life as he has ruined mine."

Never till that moment had William given her an inkling of the truth. "My dear!" Her heart turned over. "Are you so unhappy?"

"Not now." His shoulders moved in a shrug. "I am resigned."

Anxiously her gaze, love-sharpened, searched his face, discerning there a subtle change in the fine coin-like markings stamped around his eyes, in the nervous twitch of the blunt-cornered mouth, an unyouthful restraint in his bearing, wholly foreign to himself and his former gay insouciance. It was as if the tender shoots of boyhood had been prematurely sown, to wither in the frosts of disillusion-ment before his years proclaimed him man. And watching him she saw a smile, cynically repressed, wander up and die upon his lips. Following his glance she looked out of the window that opened on the lawn. In a hammock, swung between two trees, Rachel lolled on silken cushions. A pampered only child, egocentric, feather-brained, she relinquished her baby son to the care of servants, dressed him in tinsel finery and alternately petted or beat him. She had an ungovernable temper, would scream were she thwarted, and though her clothes were of the finest, she very seldom washed. Her incessant chatter and her brainstorms racked William's nerves till they were raw, his youth destroyed.

"Was it worth it?" Mary asked him.

Evasively he answered: "Money, they say, is the root of all evil. They are wrong. 'Tis not money but the want of it that's evil. I have my compensations."

"O, William! This is not you." She wound her arms about his neck, her tears wet against his cheek, downbent to hers. "You have never wished for money, nor have I."

"Maybe, but 'tis our father's god. He has educated me in his religion."

"His idolatry you mean—the Golden Calf! Why did you do it, William? Had you desired wealth so much, you would have had all and more than you could wish for in the future. Our father is rich enough, God knows, and so will you be rich, beyond measure."

"Exactly. But the rich, having learned the power money gives them, must strive always to increase it. Whole empires are builded upon money."

"And wars fought and lives broken in its cause! I won't believe you think this way."

"I think no way, but for my son. If it were not for him I would—" A shamefaced grin replaced that cold, old smile of his—"I would have bolted long ago. But I am tethered. Not to her. She has no hold on me. 'Tis the boy—he's all I have." And what was he, at not yet twenty, shouldering the burden of his parenthood with a gravity that defied the chicken-down upon his chin?

Mary swallowed a rock in her throat and mechanically said:

"You haven't shaved this morning," as she had used to say, 'Go brush your hair and clean yourself.' And: "He is not all you have!" she cried, "you still have me. If we could go away together—you, I, and the boy. If we could!"

"Yes. I can't." He was silent a moment. "You can." He spoke hurriedly, urgently. "Put up a fight for your freedom—stake your all, and play to win. Though wedlock, we know, is as risky a game as the throw of a dice, your luck may be in, as mine is out. Write that letter to our father. Call his bluff . . . No more of this now. Here is Rachel."

She ran into the room, pettishly complaining: "I've seen you through the window! You've been talking about me. What have you said? Mary's making mischief as usual, I'll be bound."

"I've been admiring your new decorations," Mary told her. "This panelling, I vow, is in the sweetest taste."

"William wanted green," said Rachel sulkily, "but green is unlucky, they say. You hear that, Will? Mary thinks my taste is sweet. I don't believe her. Oh, lud! I've left my fan in the hammock. Go fetch it, William."

He went out quietly, as if it were his custom to be ordered, 'Do this, do that' and fetch and carry. Mary's blood mounted, and only with an effort did she restrain her hand from Rachel's ear.

"Mary, will you drive with me to Ealing?" she heard. "There's a Fair this week at Ealing and a new droll called 'The Distressed Virgin' which—hee-hee!—might have been writ for you. And my woman tells me there's a troupe of rope-dancers and an elephant and castle and a three-headed cat. Will you come?"

"No. I have letters to write."

"You are always writing letters. Let them wait and come with me. I won't be crossed. Unkind you are, and hateful!" Those shallow clouded eyes and pouting lips betokened storm. Fearing a scene should she persist in her refusal, Mary went to the Fair and came back with a flea, and a tertian fever that kept her in bed for two days. No sooner was she up again than William went down with it, but:

'Sick as my B. is,' she wrote to Edward, 'I have spoke to him concerning my affairs. He agrees with me that there is nothing to be treated with my F. . . .' For the letter she had sent her 'F.', imploring him to reconsider his decision and free her from her promise to the absent 'Mr. K.', had brought the Marquis post-haste to Acton with his sister, Lady Cheyne, to support him.

Between his lordship's thunder and her aunt's abusive croaks, Mary stood her ground and felt it slipping.

She was "a stubborn, stiff-necked, romantic little fool to throw away a fortune," chid Aunt Cheyne.

"And more than that she throws away," broke in her father, "my goodwill and her inheritance. All she'll have from me hereafter will be a beggarly four hundred a year."

"I can live prosperous on that, my lord, I'll warrant you," said Mary.

"Goddamme, girl! You'll starve on that. It won't keep you in petticoats."

"I'll need no petticoats," she quavered, "in a convent. A hair-shirt beneath my robe of mercy is the most I'll wear."

"Hair-shirt! Convent!" yelped Aunt Cheyne. "The girl's mad."

His lordship's eyes were bolting, his swollen lips parted to shout: "Yes! So mad that she has let me spend a fortune on her wedding-clothes—the slut!"

"Believe me, sir, I did not know my wedding-clothes were ordered," bleated Mary.

"Well, and now you do."

"Aunt, for pity's sake," she clasped her hands beseeching, "won't you intervene with my lord to save me? I cannot marry him my father chooses. I hate him, I tell you I *hate* him! 'Twould be a grievous sin to give myself to one I——"

"Tush, child. Give yourself!" cried the scandalized Aunt Cheyne. "Such wanton talk. For shame! 'Tis he who gives and you who take—all he has to offer. What a match."

"But," Mary sobbed, "I cannot love him.'

"Love!" her father bellowed, "Holy saints! See here, bedlamite, I've had enough of your nonsense and——"

"Fiddlededee," his sister contemptuously chorused. "Look around the Town and ask yourself how many women are in love—as you call it—with their husbands."

"Maybe," Mary said, greatly daring, "they are in love with some other woman's husband. But none the less, they love."

"Hearken to her bawdy!" cried her ladyship. "So much for her book-learning, and what has it taught her? Sinfulness past praying for. Take this to heart, wretched girl. I know the world. You don't. Love lasts a year at most, and money lasts a lifetime——"

"——when it's tied to you, as yours will be, so it can't be

squandered." His lordship was perspiring. He loosened his cravat. "If she's got, as I suspect, some other fancy, then— God's Beard!—I'll grind it out of her. Now go to your room—" he raised a hand as if to strike her down—"and stay there till you come to your senses."

She was left with no alternative but to stay there, since her father had carried out his oft-repeated threat to lock her up, confined and strictly guarded, so he thought. But he had reckoned without William. He, recovered from his fever, saw that her letters to Edward were delivered and collected from the house of Cassotti, who taught her Italian.

Events were moving rapidly through those early August days. Having determined that some 'other fancy' was the head and front of her offending, Lord Dorchester decided it were better to remove this renegade of his from the danger of accessibility. He therefore arranged that she be despatched to West Dean within the coming week.

Much may happen in a week, or even in a day . . . What did happen was apocalyptic, to humiliate the Marquis, and to set all London talking, clubland grinning; yet, dreadful though it was, the inevitable consequence of seigniory dominant, that might have wounded less were it foreseen.

*   *   *

On a sultry night in mid-August, Lord Dorchester's villa at Acton appeared as a house of the dead. No light shone above the doorway nor at the curtained windows; not a breath of wind stirred the dust-laden air, heavy with the day's expired heat that lay in clammy mist on field and meadow. No human footfall disturbed the muffled silence, nor any shape its shadows; not a sound, save that of predatory night-flying things, the winged savage pursuit of the slayer, the agonized shriek of the captured, the comforting homely bark of a dog; and somewhere in the distance a church clock solemnly chiming ten strokes. Then, even as the last of them quivered through the stillness, could be heard the stealthy approach of hooves along the bordering grass of the lane.

A rider, cloaked and muffled to the chin, dismounted, tethered his horse to the gatepost, and slunk into the deeper shade of the garden wall. There, in a ditch, he crouched.

Slowly the minutes passed, marked by the ticking of the watch in his waistcoat pocket. Turning his eyes skyward, he searched for a glimmer to lighten the dream-solidity of that brooding dark. Suddenly a silver ray pierced the parting clouds, and a young moon rode out on a gossamer drift . . . Again that far-off steeple chimed: the half-hour. A host of misgivings besieged him. Why was the house so closed, so black and still? Had all its inmates departed—with her? Or had he mistaken the date?

He felt in his wallet for her latest letter. Not a word of the writing could he read. Taking his tinder-box, he struck a flare, and holding the paper close to his eyes scanned, for the fiftieth time, her directions, implicitly followed. This was the garden wall, there the summer-house looming above it where she had told him to wait. Here he was; but she was not, nor any sign of the coach and six she had bidden him order, and which he thought to be needless expense and a cumbersome conveyance for swift travel. Yet all had been done as she had wished; the coach commanded to stand at the appointed place, a furlong off, in the road beyond the curve of this wall at ten o'clock. It was now half past and no rumble of wheels had been heard. Could she have repented of her resolution—changed her mind at the last minute? Which he guessed would be a deal more likely than that she should follow her original intent.

Her hasty scrawl confirmed his doubt. She 'trembled' at what she was doing. 'Are you sure you will love me for ever? Shall we never repent? . . . I come to you with nothing but a nightgown and petticoat.'

His frenzy deepened. In the few weeks preceding this climacteric adventure, all his caution had left him. 'His Hart,' he wrote, 'was laid quite open with the joy of being so near this greatest happiness.' But now, at the eleventh hour, which was on the point of striking, he seemed to be no nearer 'greatest happiness' than the misery that ended any decision taken by his lady. Had she failed him again, to entice him here on a fool's errand? Where was that damned coach? Could it have missed its way? He must reconnoitre.

Still crouching in the shadows he crept along tiptoe till

he came to the cross-roads. From there, on all fours, his knees dew-soaked, he could see in all directions, and saw nothing. The roads were empty.

Back again he went, gritting his teeth at the stamp of his horse and its whinny. Rashly he left his concealment in the ditch, and rushed toward the upraised head to stifle with his cloak a startled neigh. . . . What now! A gentle step upon the garden path, a figure hooded, wrapped; a hand that beckoned, and a whisper floating.

She came to the gate, lifted the latch and slipped out. Breathing thankfulness, he caught her up, swung her off her feet, and crushed his lips to hers. . . . "Beloved!"

A squeal; a panting voice, "Oh, sir! No, sir, pray! You are mistook—her ladyship, sir, bids me——"

"Hell's devilment! What's this?"

Dismay and panic seized him. He had clasped and passionately kissed, not his lady but his lady's maid.

Astounded and mortally vexed—the jade would certain sure to go yapping to all her fellow servants—he learned from Grace that his lordship had arrived unexpectedly that evening. "I was to tell you, sir, my lady is distraught. Her sister, Lady Frances, has been put to spy on her these three days, and though my lady's brother, my Lord Kingston, is heart and soul in league with Lady Mary, as am I, sir, believe me——" here an interval for sobbing.

"Yes. Go on."

Grace, tearfully, went on to tell how that neither she nor William could evade the watchfulness of Frances, "who," wailed Grace, "my lady suspects of having carried your letters, sir, to my Lord Marquis, for he, heaven save us, has laid hands——" Grace wrung her own——"on what you've writ, and all's revealed!"

"A pox!" uttered Edward—and something worse than that. "So now what's to do?"

Grace told him what to do. "My lady leaves here at my lord's command at seven o' the clock tomorrow morning. Her ladyship begs you will ride ahead along the road to West Dean."

"But where's the coach I ordered?"

Grace said she had been sent to intercept it on its way

from Town and turn it back. "And as you will have a good start, sir, my lady requests you set off directly and await the chaise at the first posting-stage."

"I will!"

Then as he went to untether his horse, Grace breathlessly continued: "One thing more, sir—I'm in such a pother—I've disremembered that my lady says she will contrive to leave notes for you along the way. She travels with her brother. I am forbidden to attend her—my Lord Marquis suspects me of aiding and abetting her ladyship, and oh, sir," she was in tears again, "what will my lady do without me? She can't untie her corset-strings unaided."

"God send that I'll untie them for her," Edward said. "Goodnight!"

He swung into the saddle, clapped spurs to his horse and was gone, a flying shadow in the shadows of the dark.

*　　　*　　　*

On the morning of August 18, a post-chaise containing a lady, a gentleman, and a female attendant, drove into the courtyard of the village inn at Stockbridge.

The landlord, much impressed with the arms emblazoned on the chariot, no less than with its occupants whose speech and appearance betokened the nobility—and a bridal pair, he hazarded—hastened to offer them the best his house and table could afford. Would his honour and her ladyship wish accommodation for the night? If so, the south guest chamber that once had harboured Royalty and the very bed in which her Gracious Majesty Queen Bess of olden time had slept, would be at their disposal, and also——

He was curtly interrupted.

"We do not lie here the night. Breakfast only is required, a private room, and a meal for the maid and the postilions. Make what haste you can, sirrah," the young gentleman commanded. "We must be off with the least possible delay."

Into the house they went, preceded by a bowing, backing host; and through the empty inn parlour with its great open fireplace and oaken counter, ribbed with age, deep-stained from drink-droppings of centuries, where stood a good enough array of glasses and tankards, clean-washed and sparkling, to serve a battalion. Above it were shelves containing every kind of home-brewed cordial and liquor, that winked colourfully from their dusty bottles; and so up a twisting staircase and into a lattice-paned low-roofed chamber, the air of which could not have been renewed by ventilation for a year.

Reciting his menu of mutton collops, broiled ham, venison pasty, goose or chicken-pie, the landlord bowed them into this apartment and stood awaiting orders.

"Bring anything," the lady told him. "Hurry."

"Bring all you have," said the gentleman, "I'll eat it."

"At your service, madam—your honour—as you say, m'lord. There's cold salmon and cowcumber besides—" The host vanished in a fantasy of food.

"I would have preferred," said Mary at the window, "to have breakfasted below. This room smells of cats."

William sniffed. "It does. But no worse than half a dozen such encountered on the way." He came and stood beside her. "Why this sudden urge to eat in public—ah! I see."

And looking down into the courtyard, then at her, he twinkled.

She wheeled round, her cheeks flaming, to intercept herself between him and the casement. "What, may I ask, do you see?"

"That same stranger who aroused our curiosity at Basingstoke."

"Silly!" She was dodging this way and that to block her brother's view. "You must be suffering from hallucinations. You see strangers and conspirators at every post."

"As so do you." William's grin widened. "Have you forgot how mine host at the last stage warned us of a mysterious gentleman and his distinctly odd behaviour, glowering in corners of the tap-room, writing notes on sheets of paper, darting in and out of doors to hide behind them as we passed?"

Mary bit her lip.

" 'Tis not the same man here. T'other wore a russet cloak and this one's wearing blue."

"Foh! My dear, you're colour-blind—though I'll allow," said William, peering through the leaded panes, "that he seems to change his wig every ten miles. Last night 'twas flaxen, and when first I noticed him he wore a tie-wig, brown —and now, begad, 'tis black as his boots."

"So it is, to be sure!" Mary gave him a push. "Move out of the way." William moved. "Was there ever such a fool as to make such a show of himself! This Griffin, that Aunt Cheyne sends to guard me, swears he's a highwayman. I gave him credit for more wit. How can he hope to evade remark when he goes to such lengths to attract it? And what can he be doing with his horse down there—why don't he come in or go on? William—" she turned her laughing face to his— "won't you invite him to breakfast with us?"

"No fear! I can shut my eyes but won't open my mouth to the fellow. You are in my custody, and I'm in duty bounden to our father to deliver you at West Dean."

"As if I were a parcel," Mary murmured. "Well, if you won't oblige me by offering this black-headed needy gentleman a breakfast, maybe you'll inquire what can have happened to mine. I am famished."

She was not; excitement had fed her, and no sooner was William out of the room than, unlatching the casement, she drew from her pocket a paper screwed round a peg, and let forth from her pursed lips a whistle, clear as a blackbird's or a boy's.

He to whom the signal was addressed, looked sharply up, saw her looking down, and, lifting a warning finger, turned his back and was once more busy with his horse. Taking careful aim, Mary shied her missile at the stranger's head. Grazing its mark, it fell on his shoulder. He caught it, unfolded and read the note, glancing up again to nod assent.

"My lady—" A voice like a crow's; the Griffin, sour-visaged, elderly, moustached, was at the door. Her small beady eyes, or, to be precise, one eye, surveyed her charge; the other was directed to the ceiling in a formidable squint. She had a face like an over-ripe cheese.

Mary shut the window.

"Well? And what is it you want?"

The Griffin bobbed.

"If your ladyship requires a convenience it is the first door on the right."

Mary sat, pulled off her gloves, and minutely examined her nails.

"My lady." And now the other eye was roving. "I have taken the liberty to advise his lordship to be on guard against a hold-up on the road. This ugly customer who follows us, my lady, is the leader of a gang of thieves, I am informed."

"Who so informs you?"

"The hostlers here, your ladyship. And the women of the house. We may be robbed or murdered."

"Bring me towels, a basin of warm water and a soap-ball. I will wash. And if you're afeared of this ugly customer, you had best go back. The public coach will take you."

Then, as the Griffin, disgruntled, went out, William, followed by breakfast, came in.

"That ill-favoured fiend," Mary told him in whispers, "is vilely suspicious. Do pray go down and tell him not to loiter. His disguise would not deceive a cow."

"No." William took her firmly by the shoulders. "See here, my girl, you're in my charge. I'm no party to your plotting. What's to eat?"

While William, with keen appetite, sampled every dish, Mary left hers untouched, and every few minutes was to and fro the window, until: "At last! Thank God," she breathed, "they've brought him a fresh horse. He's going . . . Now he's off."

"And let us hope," William drained a bumper of strong ale, "we don't have this performance at the next stage. For if so, I shall feel compelled to call him out. You've eaten nothing."

"I can't eat."

"Then let's get on."

Jingling, jolting, with a clatter and a dash, passing sign-posts, overtaking wagons, slow-going coaches, and smocked farmers driving shaggy mares as were never seen in any other land; a halt for a herdsman marshalling his steers through a farmyard gate; beggars by the roadside, a line of gypsy caravans, journeymen, a showman leading a jaded dancing bear—and on through village, town, and hamlet, westward-bound they went; a hard climb for the horses up a heavy hill and a view from its summit of cornfields, patterned red with poppies against the spinach-dark trees of waning summer; the careful, creaking, brake-guarded descent to a cluster of lichen-covered roofs and stone-walled cottages, mellow as ripe peaches in the sun. The scent of meadow-sweet and pasture swept through the open windows to mingle with the smell of saddle-cloth and leather, of steaming dung, of William's snuff, and the vinegar with which the Griffin, who travelled ill, refreshed herself.

They had covered the next fifteen miles before sundown when, from another hilltop, could be seen a fairy sight: frail spires quivering pellucid in the hazy air; a city, topaz-pointed, where the last gold sun-shafts fell. Salisbury . . . So near now, and all this, her England, soon to be left, could she dare to leave it, for Italy, for Naples! There, he had written, would he take her. No question now, her doubts and 'fears' and 'trembles' notwithstanding, that he loved her, madly. There were pages of it. He would 'sooner chuse to see his Hart torn from his breast than be from her divided'. His 'Passion' (no longer his 'Esteem') appears in almost every line. 'He was hers till she turned him away.'

She had not the least intention of turning him away, who was riding full gallop ahead with a licence in his pocket, and, since she was leader of this outrageous enterprise, the instructions that she left for him at every posting-inn.

The Griffin was their chief impediment, her vigilance untiring; limpet-like she stuck, and contrived to sleep, if not in her lady's room, on the mat outside the door. And now they were at Salisbury, the final stage of their journey, with something less than ten miles more to go. Her last chance of escape must be this night—or never!

Luck favoured her arrival at the inn, for the Griffin, overcome with travel-sickness, was hurriedly compelled to retire or disgrace herself. In the brief interval afforded by her maid's indisposition, Mary received from the landlord and behind her brother's back, a sealed packet. This she tucked between her breasts.

Pleading fatigue, she bade William goodnight so soon as she had supped and, followed by a green-faced Griffin, went to bed.

142

"You poor soul," said Mary kindly, "you're the colour of a pea. Pull the bell. You shall have a glass of wine."

Wine was brought; Mary filled the glasses, surreptitiously tincturing one with the contents of a phial she had secreted on her person, and gave it to the skew-eyed Griffin.

Drearily she drank, undressed and couched her lady, but herself did not undress. Nodding, yawning, she sank in a heap, fully clothed, on her pallet of straw beside her lady's bed; and there she lay.

Peeping through the curtains of the massive four-poster, Mary fearfully watched the collapse of the Griffin, heard her heavy breathing, slow and stertorous. Pray heaven the dose has not killed her, she thought wildly, for if so I shall be hanged! . . . No time to dwell on horrors. She must dress herself as best she could. Her fingers were all thumbs, her bodice gaping open, and she had lost her garters, or the fool had hid them somewhere. She must go without garters then, and have her stockings dangling round her feet. She would come to him, in truth, as she had promised, with nothing but a petticoat and nightgown. This she stuffed into her reticule and, with a last terrified look at her sprawling victim, crept past her and fled from the room.

Down the unlit staircase, clinging to the banister, step by step she felt her way to the entrance door where someone waited.

Across the silent courtyard, under the archway, and along the empty street, her hand in his, they sped. The night was void of moon and stars, the sleeping houses shuttered, and only they in all that quiet seemed to live. No word passed between them, till, when they came to the bend of the road where stood the dim outline of a chaise and four, "Thank God!" he said, "I have you now, for always."

In the shrouding dark and the shadow of her hood, her face was like a flower and her words were like a prayer.

"Love me," she whispered, "for I am all yours. Love me . . . and use me well."

8

Queen Anne was dead and in three weeks forgotten. On the Throne of the last reigning Stuart sat a King in whose Teutonic veins ran one distant streak of Stuart blood, handed to him by Elizabeth, his grandmother, 'Winter Queen' of Bohemia, daughter of James I.

Attended by a retinue from Herrenhausen of pot-bellied equerries, pages, cooks, and his two ugly middle-aged mistresses, he landed at Greenwich in September, 1714.

Bouncing along in his great golden goach, with flags flying, bells pealing, and every throat yelling its jubilant glee, he drove into London and over its Bridge. Grinning, bowing, white-wigged and cocked-hatted, his uniform plated with Orders, his podgy hands phlegmatically acknowledging the loyal acclamation of his subjects, this little fat marionette of a man, Britain's Heaven-blessed and soon to be Anointed George the First, came; and he conquered.

Happy England, happy Marlboroughs, recalled, restored, and on their knees to the Hanoverian, God bless him! The day of the Whigs had dawned. They were in and were up with the sun and the King, and the Tories were out—and down. They had fallen with their vacillating, drunken leader, Oxford, who had received his dismissal before Anne received her death blow. Bolingbroke was fled to France in the wake of his exiled Prince, whose unswerving adherence to his Faith and his Church had lost him his Kingdom and Crown. Who cared? Not the Whigs, and but few of the Tories, save those that wore the White Rose of his Clan and drank their secret toasts to him—their King over the Water.

The Parliamentary reshuffle that attended the Accession brought with it a harvest of plums to all who denied the 'Pretender's' claim and declared for England's chosen, German George.

Here is Mr. Addison, in a fine new suit, with money in his pocket, but not so much as lies in Lady Warwick's coffers; yet a tidy income is now in store for him, since he has been appointed a Commissioner for Trade and the Colonies as stepping-stone to Secretary of State.

Nor is Steele forgotten. While his stricken Queen lay dying he had used his pen as a sword to strike a blow for the cause of the Elector and, 'for the common good,' he wrote, 'without regard to fame or fortune'. Both were his reward when, in a smart new coach, he lined up outside the House to take his seat inside it. There among his fellow Whigs he sat, with Addison sardonically smiling on his left, and stout Robert Walpole on his right. He, who two years before had been expelled from the Commons on 'breach of Trust and notorious corruption', had been reinstated, soon to rise higher as First Lord of the Treasury, Prime Minister of England. No man that had served the Elector in deed, word, or song to the tune of old 'Lillibulero', but was not handsomely remembered. And half a year after King George the First had come into another King's own, Steele was summoned to St. James's Palace.

A dumpy, beery, leery little man with bags beneath his eyes and not one word of English in his mouth, save those few he had laboriously learned for the occasion, stood to receive Captain Steele where he knelt . . . How his heart must have drummed in his ribs! How his thought must have pridefully flown to his Prue as he heard young Lord Clare read the loyal address he had written in praise of his Monarch. 'Our joy is the joy of men whose past fears heighten their present satisfaction.'

In all his life Steele had never known the equal of this 'present satisfaction', as the Sovereign repeated his carefully tutored guttural thanks, took from one of his gentlemen a sword, touched the kneeling Captain on each shoulder, and bid him: "Rice Sirrichardt!"

Swaggering forth from the Palace in a glow of glory, 'a Knight Bachelor,' Sir Richard reflected, 'must be valiant, honest, faithful, discreet, and, above all, well dressed!' And before he returned to his Lady-wife he paid a visit to his tailor and told him to send in his bill before he sent home his new suit. He could pay for it now. He was done with debts and bailiffs and horrid dreams of prison walls around this honoured trusty knight and servant of the King.

Others too were honoured: peerages and baronetcies handed out to commoners, the promise of a Countess's coronet to his large-sized, overpowering, good-natured Kilmansegge, nicknamed by tittering English Court ladies 'The Elephant'. And then there was Ermengarde, the Schulenberg, who, with the Kilmansegge, amicably shared the Royal alcove. She, dubbed 'The Maypole' by scornful British peeresses, was painfully bony, inelegantly tall, and King George's best beloved, destined to wear the strawberry leaves: Duchess of Kendal.

Another on whom this high insignia would shortly be bestowed was the Marquis of Dorchester, created Duke of Kingston: nobody quite knew why. But no coronet nor knighthood, nor any rise to statesmanship did the new Accession bring to Edward Wortley Montagu; nor did he secure so much as a seat in the re-elected Parliament until the First George had been King for eight months, and Edward a husband three years.

What of those years? . . . In the first flush of their crack-brained adventure neither Edward, the cautious, nor Mary, the rash, had cared a fig for the future. It was as if that long courtship had been a dead orchard, frost-blighted of its blossom, until, from the warmth of fulfilment, had sprung a second blooming. She loved, as she had never dreamed that it was in her stars to love, surrendering in wifely sweet submission to her husband, lord and master—so her letters in the early months of marriage assured him, and herself. If they somewhat failed their intention to convince it was not for lack of protest on her part, unless it were she did protest too much.

When, after travelling all through that August night, the runaways found in the morning a parson to marry them, melted by Mary's entreaties that shame worse than death would be hers if he didn't—he did.

Out of a village wayside church she had walked on the arm of her lover, a wife! Her path lay before her, cleared of its thorns. That she had no roof and only one petticoat and nightgown to cover her, rather enhanced than diminished her feckless delight and his satisfaction . . . And as for a roof, there were roofs in plenty to be offered at other people's houses till they should find one of their own. For lack of funds they had abandoned their romantic notion of a honeymoon in Italy, and their ecstatic little visionary deaths in sight of Naples. Hostelries and posting-inns on their leisurely way North provided blissful alternative enough; and this beatific condition sustained them to their journey's end.

If the bridegroom ever questioned his temerity in taking to himself a wife without a penny, he gave no hint to his unblushing bride that his happiness was marred by banal consideration. Guided, or more correctly pushed into taking the plunge, he floated with her on a sea of content in those first few weeks of their folly. He, too, had suffered from that lengthy wooing. An inherent Puritan, his early past experiments in Paris had resulted in an ascetic restraint; this, now released by holy wedlock, gave his eager young wife no reason to doubt that his love was as hot as his ardour for her was excessive.

A somewhat exhausted, pallid pair of lovers arrived at Wharncliffe Lodge to be greeted by Edward's old reprobate father with a more generous welcome than they had expected, or deserved. Their mad escapade appealed to his boisterous humour as much as his son's pretty wife to his taste. His board and a bed, he promised, were theirs for as long as they wished to stay; which was all very well, and very kindly, but old Sidney and his entourage that, besides his sottish cronies, comprised ladies of easiest virtue, were not the most agreeable company Mary would have sought. Thus, for the first two years of marriage, we find her flitting from this friend's house to that, the guest of charity.

If such mode of life may have suited Edward's pocket, it did not suit Mary's pride. Yet in the very first letter she writes as a wife to her husband, there is no indication of the arrogant take-me-or-leave-me aggressive 'L.M.' in her pretty little message: 'I lament your absence as if you was still my lover . . .' He had been called to Durham on some business to do with his father's estate, and her letter is addressed from Walling Wells, the house of a Mr. White, whose daughters were friends of her girlhood . . . 'How much reason have I to rejoice in the hope of passing my whole life with you!' She is afraid to tell him she returns thanks to

Heaven every day for her good fortune, 'because you will charge me with hypocrisy'. And in a fold of the note she sweetly inserts, 'Pray, my dear, begin at the top and read till you come to the bottom.'

But though marriage had made Edward more of a man it had not made of him a better correspondent. This letter from his bride of two months went unanswered. Her fond imagination seized upon disaster. He had fallen from his horse, lay dead and rotting on that lonely road to Durham; he had been taken ill, or worse, had found some other more engrossing interest to steal his heart and thoughts from her . . . 'I am peevish with you by fits,' she declares, 'and divide my time between sorrow and anger.' A spark of the Mary unwed and untamed is here rekindled in the sharp reminder, ' 'Tis the most cruel thing in the world to think one has reason to complain of what one loves . . . Mr. White drinks your health twice a day, which you don't deserve if you can be so entirely forgetful. Pray, my dear, write to me, or I'll be very mad.'

No reply to this rap from her pen is recorded, but that she suffered 'an uneasiness of mind and a swelled face', attributed by her to his persistent silence, is stressed in a further complaint, more acid than sweet but none the less wifely. 'I don't hear of any money, and am in the utmost necessity for it.'

She had only herself to blame for that.

Of her own volition she had forfeited her father's goodwill and her dower. Nor did his wrath show any sign of abatement. Unlike his 'dear old friend' the Honourable Sidney, Lord Dorchester held no brief for the foibles of lovers. Withdrawn into a fortress of accumulative injury, the Marquis—not yet Duke—had forsworn her, disowned her, and nurtured a festering grievance that no plea for his pardon could soothe. He had been monstrously maltreated. Four hundred pounds had he spent on her trousseau, had boasted far and wide of his daughter's impending magnificent marriage, and of fabulous settlements agreed. Invitations for the wedding had been issued and accepted, and there was he with cupboards full of clothes and fal-lals on his hands, all clubland a-snigger in its sleeves at the débâcle, and a mortally offended 'Mr. K.' to be consoled. And he was inconsolable. Not to be appeased by the supporting indignation of the Marquis, he took himself to Ireland and out of Mary's life.

She, untroubled by conscience pricks concerning 'Mr. K.', strove to placate her implacable father. If he would only realize that her marriage by elopement—which admittedly was shocking—had proved an unqualified success, he surely would be melted. She badgered Edward to bestir himself and plead her father's clemency. 'Down on your knees to him. Beg his forgiveness. Say,' she urged, 'that without it I am desolate and never can enjoy one moment's peace.'

Edward, whose previous interviews with Lord Dorchester still rankled, had no wish to go 'down on his knees'; but after much persuasion he was unwillingly induced to go, armed with the olive-branch, to London.

His first approach, made to Aunt Cheyne. resulted in her showing him the door. 'Which does not surprise me,' Mary writes, 'since people are seldom grieved (and never ought to be) at misfortunes they expect. When I gave myself to you I gave up the desire of pleasing the rest of the world and am pretty indifferent about it. . . .'

At this time she was visiting at Hinchinbroke, the seat of Lord Sandwich, Edward's uncle, and, save for the servants. was alone in the house; also she was five months pregnant. Her solitude and her condition disproportionately magnified her husband's lack of interest in her welfare. She may have had reason to think herself neglected. Here was she, as far removed from the outer world as if she were in the Desert of Sahara, and there was he, for whom she had given up a fortune, engaged on ambiguous 'Business' in London. What 'Business' other than his own, having dealt so unsuccessfully with hers, could detain him for so long? The house at Hinchinbroke had become a tomb and she its ghost. Roaming around in search of books she came upon a closet stacked with volumes. Eagerly she scanned the titles, only to find they were dry-as-dust treatises on law and mathematics. The blank discovery of these and a walk on the terrace for two hours were 'the most considerable events', she plaintively informs her errant spouse, 'that have happened to me in your absence, except that a good-natured robin redbreast kept me company almost all the afternoon . . .' Until sundown, when the wintry dusk drove her indoors.

With a kitten in her lap for comfort, she sat by the hearth in the great empty hall staring at the crackling logs.

Unbidden tears rushed to her eyes. She lifted the little creature in her arms to cuddle it against her cheek. Unused to caresses, it spat at her wickedly, shot out its claws and scratched her face.

"Be damned to you!" cried Mary, vainly striving to detach it from her shoulder, where it clung like a burr. "I'll wring your neck for twopence. Get away!" It got away, hissing, and fled.

Not a living thing in this great house and only a redbreast outside of it that cared for her. She was forsaken. And he whose seed was fructifying in her womb had left her for 'Business' in London! What a thrice-cursed fool had she been to renounce the sparkle and glitter of life she had known for a prison; discarded, unloved.

Some such mood of melancholy is reflected in a dirge she composed and entitled 'The Bride in the Country' or 'Melinda's Complaint'.[1]

> 'By the side of a glimmering fire,
> Melinda sat pensively down,
> Impatient of rural esquire,
> And vex'd to be absent from Town.
> The cricket, from under the grate,
> With a chirp to her sighs did reply;
> And the kitten, as grave as a cat,
> Sat mournfully purring hard by.

> *　　　*　　　*

> What though I have skill to ensnare
> Where Smarts in bright circles abound;
> What though in St. James's at prayer,
> Beaux ogle devoutly around;
> Fond virgin . . . .

She hesitated at that word. Not even poet's licence could

[1] A revised version of the former, by Lady Mary Wortley Montagu, founded on a popular ballad of the time.

concede her virginity now; but 'Fond Wife' would not scan, and 'Fond Matron' was clumsy, so:

'Fond virgin, thy power is lost
On a race of rude Hottentot brutes;
What glory in being the Toast
Of noisy dull 'squires in boots?
Whilst here we are left in the lurch,
Forgot and secluded from view,
Unless when some bumpkin at church
Stares wistfully over the pew.

* * *

The last humble solace I wait,
Would heaven indulge me the boon,
Some dream less unkind than my fate
In a vision transport me to Town.'

It was, however, no vision that, nine months from the day of her marriage, transported her to Town where she could receive better medical attention than that afforded by the village midwife. And in the month of May, 1713, Mary was delivered of a boy.

No more dirges now, and no more solitude, with nothing to enliven it but robin redbreasts, kittens, or boozing booted squires . . . Incredible that from her tortured terror, from those convulsive rendings and tearings apart of her agonized body should have emerged this exquisite being, this crocus-limbed infant Apollo, heaven-sent, heaven-born of the gods!

So to his besotted slave did he appear, and to all other eyes but hers, no more nor less revolting than every repetition of his kind; red, crumpled, hideous, bald, greedily demanding, and patiently supplied with endless nourishment.

The birth of her child made her the more determined to subdue her father's rancour. "Surely to God," she complained to Edward, "he cannot be so cruel as to refuse to see his grandson? My Angel. Sweetest Life."

From his brief experience of parenthood Edward had learned not to take these, nor any similar endearments, to himself. He was resigned. He knew his status, lowly as an earthworm, and that henceforth he must be regarded as a cipher, a nonentity, beside this preponderant atom who for

151

nine months had monopolized the body of his wife, and now dominated her soul.

"Why," Edward asked, "is he making these frightful grimaces?" And, with shocking nonchalance, he added, "I hope he's not born with a tic?"

"A tic!" shrieked Mary, gazing feverishly down at the crimson writhing face at her breast. "What monstrous fears do you put on me? Oh, my dear God! Yes! he foams at the mouth. He's in a fit. Nurse! *Nurse!* Where are you?"

She, who had been brought from Thoresby to relieve the midwife, was behind a screen and in a doze induced by a suspicious looking bottle at her elbow. White-capped, white-haired, and, of late, white-bearded, she waddled from out her enclosure to inquire:

"Did you call?"

"Look!" cried Mary, distractedly pointing. "Look at him. *Look!*"

Nurse, almost as red as Mary's Prince of Loveliness, looked and, unconcernedly, nodded. "Ay, 'tis ready for its feed. Don't clutch it so, my lady. You're squeezing of its innards."

"Heavenly Grace," gibbered Mary, "can't you see? He has a tic. He gasps, he's suffocating! There, there, my precious. Quiet. Mother has you safe . . . Send at once for Dr. Garth." Her voice soared to the ceiling. *"Send!* My boy is in the convulsions."

"Convulsions! For gracious sake, child, how you talk!" Nurse peered closer. " 'Tis naught but the wind, and don't you go screaming, my lady, to curdle your milk. Sir," to Edward, "must I tell you twice not to come worriting here of her ladyship? You've outstayed your time. Ten minutes is all you're allowed." She rescued the young Wortley Montagu from his mother's enveloping arms, and remarking, "No wonder he's fractious. He's wet," Nurse bore him away to her hide-out.

Edward took a handkerchief and wiped his forehead which also appeared to be wet.

"All the same," he muttered, "it might be as well to have Dr. Garth's opinion."

"Listen to this senseless ass!" Her tension relieved, his

wife turned on him unfairly. "You're full of these silly alarms. All babies make faces. And pray don't stand over me glaring like a ghoul. You give me the fidgets. Go out—or sit down." Edward sat down. "And tell me," she said, "of my father."

He had nothing to tell of her father, more than that Mary's uncle, Lord Pierrepont, and her old friend, Dr. Burnet, Bishop of Salisbury, had each attempted to ease the situation and conciliate the Marquis, with niggardly result.

"How cruel of him! How hellish!" Mary smote the bed-clothes. "There's a monster of vengeance he is—with me lying here! I might have died for all he cares. And fancy not wanting to see my heart's treasure!"

"My love," reproved Edward with a glance in the direction of the screen, whence issued a yowling as of tortured cats, "pray do not discompose yourself. You heard the nurse warn you—your milk——"

"And if my milk be sour 'tis you who have curdled it. Why can't you come to peace terms with my father? I'm served by a couple of old women—you and Nurse. Who would wonder if my angel, God forbid, develops tics?"

"Sir," Nurse poked her head round the screen to say above the ululation hymned by Wortley Montague, the younger, "must I bid you twice have a care of my lady? And I beg you, sir, remember your duty to your son. His bile's running over, thanks to you."

"Thanks to me be damned!" quoth Edward, incensed. "Is it I who give him suck, old fool? Very well then, go I will, and not come back."

He strode to the door, hurt and angry, an intruder on that intimacy where, until a week before, he had reigned as monarch, unchallenged and supreme. Let it not be confessed that he resented the arrival of the squalling disturber of his peace. No. His resentment, if any, was restricted to an apprehensive doubt that he never would regain complete possession of that room and bed, whence he had been ejected to make way for a usurper. Not now on him did his love's long-fringed eyes rest in adoration; the very tone of her voice was changed, and harsh in contrast to the infinite cadences of tenderness she showered on this animalized morsel of humanity, whose every yell she would have walked through flood or fire to obey.

He was at the door, when:

"My darling," he heard, softly spoken.

He turned, and with something of the magnetized suspicion of a rabbit beguiled by a cobra, gazed down at her whose arms stretched up to him. It was as if he had been drawn into a bed of roses . . . "And the next thing," she whispered with her lips against his ear, "that we must make together is . . . a home."

She was up and about again, preparing to leave London, when news came that William had taken the smallpox. To Edward, whom she had despatched to Hinchinbroke in search of a house, she wrote: 'Dr. Garth says it is the worst sort and fears it will be very full, which I should think foreboding if I did not know all doctors (and particularly Garth) love to have their patients thought in danger."

But Dr. Garth in this case proved to be no false alarmist. William, not yet of age and the father of two children, died the first day of July. . . .

House-hunting and her baby filled her time, but did not fill the gap in Mary's life caused by the death of her brother. The shock of it had lowered her vitality to give her fearful thoughts. What if her baby, the Light of her Eyes, or Edward, a secondary consideration, should take the smallpox? 'I cannot bear that *if*,' she confessed, 'but since the loss of my poor unhappy brother I dread every evil.'

She was glad enough now to leave Town for the North, with old Nurse and Grace, who had lately returned to her service.

All through that summer and well into the autumn the search for a house went on. The selection of furnished establishments offered were either too small or too large, too low-lying, too high, or too bleak or too damp. One owner would not include linen in the rental; another refused the loan of pewter plates under two and sixpence the dozen; but while Mary complained that the country around this particular house was 'disagreeable', it had the advantage of a garden and was situated within a few miles of Rotherham, where

Edward could, if he wished, indulge in the 'Sports'.

In what 'Sports' he might wish to indulge is not stated; and although Mary declared she would not enter into any transaction without his advice, he had no voice in the final arrangements that secured them the lease of a house at Middlethorpe in Yorkshire. Since his wife had taken to herself all responsibility of the removal, Edward returned again to London, leaving her to deal with it. She seems to have had more hindrance than help from those about her. There is mention of a certain officious 'Mrs. Smith', a housekeeper presumably, who, her lady reported, had laid in, unknown to her, sundry provisions of coal and beer . . . 'I hope not in too large a quantity. Your child, I thank God, is very well, which I can't omit speaking of though you never ask after him. Mrs. Smith says the Queen is very ill. . . .'

*   *   *

That summer of death to the Stuarts was for Mary a glad resurrection. From her interment in the Ridings of Yorkshire she saw a return to the lost London life she had known, and which Edward, still on 'Business' bent, pursued. All her letters to him during the past year had harped on his neglect, and in those stirring August days of 1714, she may have had some reason for 'taking it unkindly that you do not write to me when you may be assured I am in a great fright and know not certainly what to expect of this change. . . .'

The whole country was in a 'great fright' at the change that followed the passing of Anne and the coming of her Hanoverian successor. Mary, who at Middlethorpe was within easy distance of York, saw the King proclaimed in that city when an effigy of the 'Pretender' was dragged through the streets and burned amid much insobriety and general rejoicing.

'I hear that Parliament sits but six months,' Mary is careful to remind her husband, 'and you know best whether 'tis worth any expense or bustle to be in for so short a time.'

If he did not, she certainly did think it worth his 'bustle' and money to be in, since he had been out of Parliament a year. It was evident his 'Business' had not yet resulted in material success. Mary had hoped to see him secure a firm place with the newly elected. Not at all! He hung back and let others push him aside. She had no patience with such laissez-faire, easy-come, easy-go methods.

'No modest man ever did or ever will make his fortune. Your friend, Lord H.[1], R.W.[2], and all other remarkable instances of quick advancement have been remarkably impudent. The Ministry is like a play at Court; there is a little door to get in and a great crowd without, shoving and thrusting who shall be foremost. People who knock others with their elbows and disregard a little kick on the shins are sure of a good place. Your modest man stands behind in the crowd, is shoved about by everybody, his cloathes tore, almost squeezed to death, and sees a thousand get in before him. . . .'

Not a thousand, but some hundreds did get in before him. He was still without a place in the new Parliament, having given up his certain seat of Huntingdon to—of all 'others'— his father.

Not his *father*! Her letters scream dismay and disapproval of his 'unnatural conduct' . . . 'Your father is very surprizing if he persists in standing at Huntingdon, but there is nothing surprizing in such a world as this!' . . . And why could he not have made sure of some borough: Aldeburgh, York, for example? In either of these he might have stood a fair chance of election. 'Delay is a sure way to lose, as you have done.'

Then, having lectured him as if she were a governess, she changes and writes like a child: 'You made me cry for two hours last night. I can't imagine why you use me so ill or for what reason you continue silent. . . .'

But not all her troubles were to do with Edward's failure. Her father had married again, a girl as young as or even younger than herself; Lady Belle Bentinck, known as the 'Fair Isabella,'—'a gibbering silly-faced fool', Mary told her confidante, the still devoted and unwedded Mrs. Banks. Heaven be thanked that her beloved William had left a son to carry on his name. She would not care to think that the future Duke of Kingston would be born of a half-wit. Pretty, yes, no doubt, large-eyed and babyish, but what sort of a

[1] Halifax.   [2] Robert Walpole.

156

wife would she make for a man almost three times her age?

Even more vexatious than her father's marriage was that of Frances to the Earl of Mar, manoeuvred and blessed by Aunt Cheyne. She, with an eye to advantages that outweighed 'Bobbing John's' fanatical adherence to the 'Pretender's' losing cause, had persuaded her brother to accept him as his son-in-law, which in view of his own matrimonial intentions, Lord Dorchester had been nothing loth to do.

Since both her sisters were now the wives of peers, Mary was more than ever concerned with her husband's advancement. Persistently she nagged at him who, while history was made and a dynasty born, stood lurking at Parliament's doors with no right of entry there. Why, when all his intimate acquaintances had secured governmental appointments, should he have been ignored? . . . 'Being chose of your country is more honourable than holding *any* place from *any* King' . . . A stinging reminder of Steele's knighthood. Yes, even he, 'that Grub Street hack', had achieved high honour, doubtfully deserved. 'And why,' she acidly suggested, 'can you not learn from Steele how to write to your wife?'

It was October; the new King on his Throne, the new Parliament assembled, and Edward nowhere in it. Recriminations poured from her pen and may have been, for all she knew, flung in the fire unread, since less and less frequent were his answers. He did, however, hint that he had been offered a post, but this was not yet certain, in the Treasury.

Not certain? But it *must*, she insisted, be certain. If he only would bestir himself and had so much ambition as a fly, he might, with Lord Halifax behind him, rise to be Speaker of the House! Yet his lack of initiative, for all it exhausted her patience, she could have better excused than his lack of attention. Could it be possible he had ceased to love her?

'I know very well that nobody was ever teized (*sic*) into a liking, and 'tis perhaps harder to revive a past one than to overcome an aversion, but I cannot forbear telling you !

157

think you use me very unkindly . . . You write seldom and with so much indifference as shews you hardly think of me at all. Multiplicity of Business—or *diversions*—may have engaged you, but all people find time to do what they have a mind to do. . . . This is my last complaint.'

A stronger complaint than any written since her marriage, and with it an underlying threat. He was startled. True, she had threatened him often enough in their courtship, and had always retracted. Those days were gone. She now had a child to console her beside whom he knew he took a very second place. Her letter, with a hint between the lines of an intended break, caused him to review the situation. Perhaps he was at fault to have stayed away so long, although what else could he have done while she constantly insisted he had neither ambition nor initiative? How could mortal man deal with such a woman who for ever would be urging him to 'shove' himself forward, and when he remained in London seeking the first opportunity to force his way in with 'the crowd', heaped reproaches on him for his absence? 'She would not have him believe she was impatient to be in Town, but only impatient to be with him.' Very well, he would comply with her demand, as it seemed he always must, and, looking back upon his wooing, as it seemed he always had. He would take a house for her in St. James's, which he could ill afford. Let her make all haste to join him and bring their child with her.

A house was found in Duke Street, and Edward's endurance stretched to breaking point when Mary, instead of being overjoyed at his decision, raised every kind of obstacle against it. All those houses in Duke Street were known to be damp. Such a locality would be fatal for the boy. Also, she had heard the roof of one of those same houses owned by George Montagu, had collapsed on his head. If *that* were the house he had chosen for her she would never live in it. Moreover, Mrs. Montagu and her child had both died there of the smallpox.

No death, nor case of smallpox, nor any collapsible roof in that vicinity had been reported, Edward long-sufferingly replied; nor had any George Montagu lived in that house.

It belonged to Lord Seafield, who had agreed to move out when she was prepared to move in.

This, then, was excellent. Yes, she would move in on one condition: all bedding and blankets must be disinfected, for despite his assurance she did not believe him. She was positive there had been a case of smallpox in the house; such rumours had always some foundation, which being so she had decided *not* to take her 'dear little one' with her. In any case it was too long a journey for him to undergo in the winter. He should join them in the spring. He had grown 'very *pritty* . . . And if you had twenty children you may never have another one like him.'

For his mother's peace of mind and for his father's too, it was as well they could not know how, in the years to come, they were to thank their God they never had another one like him.

★ 9 ★

A very different London from the London she had left as Mary Pierrepont awaited the return of Mary Wortley Montagu. The curtain that had fallen on a darkened room in Kensington rose again upon a Transformation Scene.

Taking their cue from their little stout Chief Player, a throng of second-rate supers postured on the stage where poor dropsical Anne, last symbol of a dying House, had passed. But with her unremembered passing, the echo of those unforgotten victories that had glorified her reign rang out to reassert the claims of her United Kingdom, personified in a strutting, not ill-natured, not ill-mannered—though his manners were not ours—'Honest Blockhead'. Thus Mary describes him, and thus to his smirking courtiers he appeared. Fans were raised to hide the smiles, chins stroked to hide the grins of those who knelt before their Queenless King.

Whispers floated round the almost legendary figure of her who, once his wife, endured a living death, imprisoned in a German castle for her sins with a Swedish adventurer. Never a word must be spoken or breathed of that blot on the Royal escutcheon. She, who had been the daughter of the reigning Duke of Zell, was as dead to her husband and son as Queen Anne . . . Long live the King! Long live the Prince of Wales!

He also had a wife, the beautiful accomplished Wilhelmina Caroline of Anspach, whom, in his fashion, he loved.

At these two rival Courts, where the son vied with the father in the chase for popularity, Mary was royally favoured, and much enjoyed her rôle of leading lady. What mattered now that Edward sat unnoticed in the audience, a supercilious critic of her gay performance? As a 'Bride in the Country' she had been defrauded of his love and his attention, as a wife in the Town she could well dispense with either. She would 'warm her hands,' she declared, 'at the fire of life!' Nor did she fear to burn her fingers.

That she might have under-estimated Edward's slow endeavours to 'shove' himself 'foremost' she would not admit. He had failed, and she had no use for failure, particularly in a husband whose neglect of her during her sojourn in the wilderness she might have excused, had he, by frequent absences, established his position. But to gain no recognition whatsoever at the cost of her lonely forbearance was inexcusable. She was therefore much astonished, perhaps a little piqued, when his tortoise-sure methods won him the race for Westminster.

This long deferred achievement she credited to her advice, by which her dilatory Edward had profited at last. Incredible good fortune! Better far be a member of Parliament at no remuneration at all than a salaried Junior Treasury official, with which argument Edward refused to ag. ee. However, his appointment on the Treasury Board, which he had eventually secured, he did not retain for more than eight weeks. With the death of his kinsman, Lord Halifax, through whose influence he had gained this minor promotion, he was again out of office when Walpole, as head of the Treasury, re-set the Board with four of his chosen men.

Edward's brief triumph was ended. That of his wife had begun.

She flashed upon London Society like some brightly plumaged small exotic bird, as fastidious in her choice of fruit to peck as in her choice of the variegated company that flocked together at her feet. Women loathed her, men adored her, and the King sent his Kilmansegge to call on and command her to his Court, of which in after years Mary wrote her impressions with her tongue in her wrinkled old cheek.

Within a few months she had become the toast and the talk of the Town. The beaux and 'pretty fellows' of St. James's who had avoided Mary Pierrepont like the plague, clamoured for the favour of Mary Wortley Montagu. As another man's wife she delighted, no longer dismayed them. A greater fool had dared rush in where once they feared to tread.

She held a salon graced by every noted politician, dilettante, literary light; and among them one whose meteoric brilliance swept across that sparkling constellation, to leave a fiery trail in his track.

Steele had talked of him; Addison heaped praise on him, and Mary had read his works. Magnificent! Superb! What a satirist, what wit, what mastery of the heroic couplet! Her enthusiasm was unbounded; her hosanna inexhaustible, and when Edward casually let fall that he had met him . . .

"*Met* him!" screamed Mary. "Where did you meet him? And having met him, why did you not bring him to meet me? You surely must have known how I would rejoice to entertain the greatest poet of our age. However," she flounced to her writing-desk, "since you will not invite him here, I will."

She did, that very day.

She had been prepared for an outstanding personality, but never such a one as he, who, accompanied by Addison and the Abbé Conti, a recent acquisition to her circle, minced into her cream-panelled parlour at the Abbé's high red heels.

Hiding wonder in her greeting as he tiptoed to her hand:

"It is my pleasure and my privilege," said Mary, very gracious, "to meet you at last, Mr. Pope."

Indeed, the greater privilege was his, thus the assurance of the misshapen little creature who, bewigged, over-dressed and bedizened, must have looked as he hopped to and climbed on a chair, like something from a raree-show.

Nothing more gratifying could have been conceived by Mr. Pope than Lady Mary's condescension. Drawing her attention and her lovely eyes to his, he outrivalled Addison in epigram and quip, and interrupted the Abbé's elegant address, interspersed with improvisations in execrable verse, by reciting his own. The Abbé, in dudgeon, retired; Addison presently followed. Mr. Pope had the room to himself, with his hand on his heart and words on his lips that defied his pitiful deformity and lifted him, in Mary's flattered sight, to Mount Olympus. In the course of half an hour little Pope had full possession of that field where the Abbé, by virtue of his melting Latin eyes and other assets, had hitherto held the monopoly.

The Abbé Conti, born in Padua, was swarthy, stout, asthmatic, scientific, and had come to England in search of the celebrated Newton. The Abbé could exert his charm to discourse on the higher mathematics or *La vita conjugali di miladi Montagu,* with equal partiality and fervour. In his fatherly capacity as counsellor, confessor, friend, or what you will, he had Mary in his pocket and Edward in a state.

"I forbid a Popish priest—this dabbler in the High Mass or the Black Mass or the higher mathematics—and more, a Popish poet—this Pope," spluttered Edward, "to my house!"

"Faith, love!" laughed Mary, "your fierce alliteration sprays its bubbles in the air. Why so tetchy? Do you believe the Abbé gives me aught but ghostly counsel, or that he will convert me to his ways? We never speak upon religion."

" 'Twould be better," snorted Edward, as he banged out of the room, "if you did!"

But not even the persuasions of the cultured polished Conti could compete with the illuminated genius of Pope.

If his body were crooked, his mind was arrow-straight, and swift to dart on his detractors, those of his acolytes who struggled at the doors of the 'Temple of Fame' which he, the dwarf in the stride of a giant, bestrode: a hunchbacked Pan with wild strange beautiful eyes, set in the face of a sickly boy. He was so tiny that when he sat at table his chair had to be placed on a wooden box to raise his head on a level with others. That his twisted little carcass housed so mordant a humour, a spirit so rare, Mary but dimly perceived, yet sensed, as a blind man feels the warmth of the sun he cannot see. His presence in her salon she encouraged; to his letters she sedately replied, little guessing that those same raptures had been previously penned to his first love, Mary Blount. His exaggerated advances added flavour to her new exciting life. In contrast to his unveiled adoration, the Abbé's heavy compliments, his offerings of books and flowers, trinkets, insignificantly faded. Mr. Pope handed no trivial gifts to mellow their ripening friendship; no flowers, save those that fell from his lips; no jewels but the gems of his verse.

It was in the early months of their acquaintance that Mary felt herself inspired to write her *Town Eclogues,* that series of diabolically clever little side-lights on Society. How much of these may be attributed to Pope's revision, with, as has been suggested, additional verses by Gay, is not known; but that they were ascribed to and ultimately published in the name of Lady Mary, is accepted; so let them pass for hers, since neither Pope nor Gay has wished to claim them.

Seated at her bureau in the privacy of her chintz-curtained bower, she joyed to read aloud to the attentive Mr. Pope of 'Roxana', 'Coquetilla', in waiting on the Princess of Wales: 'At the Drawing Room'. The originals of both these ladies were, if not her friends, acquaintances of Mary; 'Roxana' is the Duchess of Roxburgh, and 'Coquetilla' the Duchess of Shrewsbury, neither of whom was allowed to escape a painfully sly scratch of Mary's pen.

She opens her attack on 'Roxana', who:

> *'... From the Court retiring late,*
> *Sighed her soft sorrows at St. James's gate ...*
> *"Thinking I never could attend too soon,*
> *I've missed my prayers to get me dress'd by noon.*
> *For thee, oh! what for thee did I resign?*
> *My pleasures, passions, all that e'er was mine,*

> *I sacrificed both modesty and ease,*
> *Left Operas and went to filthy plays,*
> *Double entendres shock my tender ear,*
> *Yet even this for thee I choose to bear.*
> *Ah, cruel Princess, for thy sake I've lost*
> *That reputation which so dear had cost"*.

But nothing so great a loss of reputation as that of 'Coquetilla', the lively, attractively plain Adehilda, Italian-born Duchess of Shrewsbury.

> *'Yet Coquetilla's artifice prevails*
> *When all my merit and my duty fails;*
> *That Coquetilla whose deluding airs*
> *Corrupt our virgins, still our youth ensnares.'*

"Sublime! Sublime!" We may fancy Pope shrilly applauding, waving little bony hands to cap this laboured effort with a neatly turned impromptu.

> *'Ah! Worthy choice! Not one of all your train*
> *Whom censure blasts not, and dishonours stain!*
> *Let the nice hind now suckle dirty pigs,*
> *And the proud pea-hen hatch the cuckoo's eggs!'*

"Pope!" cried Mary, "you're outrageous. If I could dare to plagiarize or thieve from you! May I?"

"Madam," he protested, "would you ask of me 'may you' —to set your diamonds beside my paltry paste? Take what you will of my poor versifying, which in comparison to the wealth of yours is odious."

She could never have enough of this. Little did she guess, self-inflated by his praise and condescension, that he had probed her secret envy of 'Roxana', 'Coquetilla', who were placed about the person of the Princess of Wales, while she had been honoured with not so much as backstair-entry to the Bedchamber. And why? Because, forsooth, the Prince had glanced more than once in her direction, had been heard to remark on the length of her lashes, and to say for all to hear: "Lady Mary's taste in dress is faultless." Which Her Royal Highness's was not. So never would Mary be called upon to sigh 'soft sorrows' at St. James's gate.

"Lud, Pope!" She smiled tenderly upon him, "I would I might believe you—but I can't."

"Believe this." He crossed diminutive knees; his feet swung a clear twelve inches from the floor. "I solemnly adjure you to publish your Eclogues." His smile, incredibly sweet, answered hers. "Leave that to me. I'll take them to Tonson."[1]

Bereft of his customary flamboyance, his words and the earnest little face with its broad pale forehead and sensitive lips, gave her to think or hope him sincere.

"If," said she modestly, "my verse meets with your approval, I am content to remain a humble student at your shrine. Praise from Pope I would value more than any publication."

Compliments were flying like shuttlecocks between them.

"I'll confess you have surprised me. I detect a rare audacity in this delicious trifle, which Gay—" he pursed his lips— "who is cursed with uncommon timidity, might well imitate to his advantage."

"Gay?" Thoughtfully Mary nibbled the point of her quill, leaving a sooty stain upon her underlip. "I have heard tell of Gay and," she shrugged, "I'm not enamoured."

"Praise God for that!" cried Pope, "yet I'll swear he'll live long after me."

"Gay may likely live long after you, as our life's span is reckoned," her eyes moistened as they rested on that hunched, crippled figure, strengthless and small as a child's. "But you, Pope, will live in immortality. You come among us as a conqueror and you will stay, unconquered."

His heart leapt; his young beautiful face, half-devil's, half-angel's, was flushed with emotion and pride.

"Madam does me too much honour." A pulsing moment passed; then, in lighter vein, he continued, "Your wit enchants me, yet will you strike only at the ladies? What of the men?"

"I can strike at them too." She searched among her papers. "Here 'tis—a first draft and unfinished—of the 'Coffee-house'. You must understand that Patch and Silliander—"

"And they represent," Pope silkily insinuated, "whom?"

[1] Pope's publisher.

165

She experienced a qualm. What if this wicked little Pope should too closely identify her victims, to create a *scandalum magnatum*? "Patch and Silliander, as I name my pair of braggarts," she hastily assured him, "represent no particular persons. They typify merely my contempt for the inanity of fops, who boasting of their amours, say:

> *'I could say something—see this billet doux*
> *And as for presents—look upon my shoe;*
> *These buckles were not forc'd, nor half a theft,*
> *But a young Countess fondly made the gift.'*

"And not to be outdone by Silliander's conquest," pursued Mary, "Patch replies:

> *'My Countess is more nice, more artful too,*
> *Affects to fly that I may fierce pursue:*
> *This snuff-box which I begg'd she still deny'd*
> *And when I strove to snatch it, seem'd to hide;*
> *She laugh'd and fled, and as I sought to seize,*
> *With affectation cramm'd it down her stays;*
> *Yet hop'd she did not place it there unseen,*
> *I press'd her breasts and pull'd it—from between!'*"

"In the grand manner—as I live, a poet born!" Pope bounded from his seat. "Dear lady, why have you so long concealed from me, from all of us, this treasure trove? 'Poets lose half the praise they should have got, could it be known what they discreetly blot' . . . Give me more and more of this!"

She would willingly have given more and more of that had Edward not stalked in, and with his entrance her muse fled, her papers scattered.

He was, she could see, in a most damnable temper, demanding—of all things—a meal! Her finely pencilled brows met as if in anguish. "I have ordered you a meal. Is it not prepared?"

"No. I expressly asked you that my dinner should be early served because tonight the House sits late."

"How careless of the cook," said Mary vaguely. "Mr. Pope considers my 'Town Eclogues' should be published."

"To set the Town aflame." Pope got himself out of his

chair and bowed. "Her ladyship, sir, is remarkably gifted."

"With the gift," muttered Edward, "of the gab."

Pope was at the lady's feet; her hand upon his down-bent head. Edward, feeling slightly sick, standing like a ramrod, repeated his remark about his dinner.

His wife rose.

"Pope, will you dine with us? Pray do."

"I thank you, madam, but I've already feasted—at the banquet of your mind. Your ladyship's servant." And rolling his eyes at his host, Pope fastened a sting in his smile and said, as he made for the door: "I eat to live. Food is for fools, starvation feeds the brain. If I must eat, I'll eat with you . . . again. My duty, sir."

*   *   *

Thereafter, on several occasions, Pope dined at Duke Street with the Wortley Montagus, not at Edward's invitation. A silent host at the foot of his wife's table, he maintained an attitude of iciest neutrality toward his unwelcomed guest. Keenly did he realize his position as a complaisant third in the duel of wits that flashed around his board; yet, were he to forbid the freedom of his house to the most prominent literary master of the day, he would have brought upon him not his lady's wrath alone, but the ridicule of the social world she led. He could fancy how malice-tinged insinuation would speculate upon the cause of Pope's dismissal from his ménage and her boudoir. No, never that. Impossible! . . . Yet was it so impossible? While the youthful poet's crooked body placed him at a disadvantage among his stalwart fellows, might not that same physical deformity enhance his attraction for women, when allied to genius?

Bitterly did Edward brood upon his wife's infatuation for this little grotesque whose scintillating impudence had welded *The Rape of the Lock*, that exquisite combination of filigree and foppery, and whose mercurial dexterity of speech was imaged in his verse, addressed to her.

Dizzily she hung on every word he uttered for Edward's ill-concealed contempt. It was not he, however, but Addison who thought fit to warn Mary of danger in her friendship with Pope. 'Leave him as soon as you can. He's certain to play you some devilish trick . . .'

She laughed, and said she would not, *could* not leave him, for he never would leave her!

All clubland was agog to know the worst. Did Lady Mary's interest in this little punchinello place him in the running as a rival to—the King?

For it had come to that.

She shared the honours of His Majesty's own table with his two dreadful old mistresses, German-tongued courtiers, and the King's gentleman, Baron von Bernsdorff. A suave-mouthed, narrow-eyed, crafty individual was Bernsdorff, who having taken the 'von' to his name by facile sleight of hand, dealt with His Majesty's private affairs and knew more, it was said, than any man alive of that tragic love story to do with the King's imprisoned wife and her dead lover, the unscrupulous fascinator, Königsmark.

It was after one of these dreary dinners in the King's private apartments, where every kind of sickly food and sauerkraut and sausages, and little conversation—they were all too busy eating—circulated round the table, that Mary found herself the focus of attention; but not as she had hoped or wished to be.

On that particular evening she had arranged for an intimate session at home with Pope, Addison, Steele, and Edward, of course, could he be lured from the House, to hear a reading of Pope's *Iliad*. The King's command at shortest notice must, however, be obeyed; yet with the gracious intervention of Ermengarde, the Schulenberg, Mary had been granted His Majesty's permission to retire early. She was feeling indisposed, she explained to Ermengarde, an excuse not entirely inaccurate. Sauerkraut and sausages and lumps of frightful bread speckled with caraway seeds, as a prelude to goose-livers and a ghastly something called 'Wiener Schnitzel', His Majesty's favourite mess, which he guzzled between gulps of pale beer brought from Hanover, had caused her a prodigious discomfort.

The King, swollen with Lager, was loath to let her go.

"*Was ist das?* You leaf us, Lady Mary? We are désolé—" and slightly drunk. A beefy hand shot out to raise her. "Na!

De night yet junge ist, and I have moch to say mit you . . ." A nod, a wink, and a murmur breathing mystery and garlic in her face. "I haf some grafe newss of your brother heardt."

"Sire, my brother is dead."

"Ach, so?" The bulging gooseberry eyes blinked in a startled relief. "De Earl of Mar is den deadt? Gott be tankful!"

"Lord Mar, sir," Mary patiently corrected, "is married to my sister and is certainly not dead."

"Your sister? Andt Lord Mar ist not deadt?" Disappointment protruded the moist underlip. "Your sister den will in dis—how you say?—bouleversement be draggedt! Pauvre dame! Allongs, parlongs frongçais, madame. Ça c'est moings difficile pour moy." His French was little better than his English. "Mais voulez-vous en aller tout de suite, vraimong?"

"S'il vous plaît, votre Majesté."

"Ça ne me plaît pas, mais cela me fait plaisir pour vous faire plaisir. Alors, *auf Wiedersehen*, Lady Mary."

She backed from the Presence. Two silver-clad pages flung open the door. Passing through the Ante-room she gained the red-carpeted staircase. Tall pier-glasses reflected ornate vistas of gilded panelling, of crimson velvet curtains, of duplicated flunkeys in scarlet and gold; of herself, childishly slender in ivory brocade fashioned to fall in wide gathered folds over a whale-boned hoop. From the close-fitting bodice her bare bosom and throat rose, lily-white, unadorned save for a necklace of pearls. Her mouse-coloured hair, drawn back from her forehead, showed to their fullest advantage her eyes, widely set in the curled fringe of her lashes. At one of the mirrors she paused to peer closer. Not a woman in London could boast of such wondrous long lashes as hers, extolled by Pope, admired of the King! . . . Then as she proceeded down the staircase she recalled those disquieting remarks concerning Mar. She had guessed from the letters Frances wrote her from Scotland that trouble was brewing over the Border, stirred by the Jacks and 'Bobbing John'. What if Mar should raise his standard and an army to fight for the Pretender? A fine disgrace to bring upon the Family and sink the King's admired Lady Mary—eyelashes and all —into the dust!

"God curse the treacherous fool!" she muttered. "May his head be stuck on Temple Bar for his misdoings." She had spoken through her teeth, her face anything but lovely, disfigured by a scowl glimpsed in those mirrors. She swept it away in a smile when, as she proceeded down the stairs she saw coming up, Mr. James Craggs, the King's henchman.

She knew much of Mr. Craggs and little to his credit. Charm he had in plenty for the ladies, which he had turned with some success on that painted old harridan, Countess Platen, mistress of the late Hanoverian Elector. The King had brought his father's favourite page, young Craggs, to England as his Cofferer, and he and Mary halved the distinction of being the only British subjects of His Majesty to dine in private at the Royal board.

A good-looking, blue-eyed, not highly intelligent but highly self-opinionated gentleman was Craggs, who possessed besides unlimited ambition, a schoolboy sense of humour that leaned towards puerile practical jokes. His manners, culled from the beer-gardens of Hanover and the gay old Platen's gatherings at 'Monplaisir', were scarcely in accordance with those of the blue-blooded British aristocracy attached to the Court of George I.

Meeting Mary on the staircase Craggs bowed very low, then clicked his heels in the way they had in the German army. True, he had never worn a uniform nor carried a commission, but he had attended numerous parades and, as an admiring spectator, had watched the orderly high-stepping march of the Electoral troops.

"Why, madam, how is this? Do you leave us, and so early? The very lights are dimmed at your withdrawal."

A footman was snuffing a branch of wall-candles that had guttered down to their sockets. Mary, squeezed against the baluster, for Craggs had blocked her way, said:

"Pray, sir, let me pass. I have the King's permission to retire, and beg that you do not detain me. I am already overdue for a previous engagement."

She could have bitten out her tongue for that, having pleaded, as excuse, indisposition. He would certainly go blabbing to the Schulenberg, if not to the King, that she had lied.

"You can have no engagement," protested Mr. Craggs, "that is prior to the King's command. You, who grace his Court, to deprive us and me, a late arrival, of your presence, is ungenerous. I speak for the King."

And he gustily emitted a breath of sour wine. His eyes were too bright, his speech was too careful, his face very flushed. Thought Mary, decidedly he's drunk. Then even as her foot touched the lower stair, he took three steps in his stride, snatched her up in his arms and, despite her shrieks and the shocked faces of the flunkeys, raced with her to the Ante-Room. There he set her on her feet, dropped on one knee, and rapturously kissed her hand.

"Odso!" she cried, white with rage and terror, "have you run mad? My husband will demand satisfaction, sir, for this."

She addressed the empty air. Mr. Craggs had vanished. The grinning pages who had ushered her out now sprang to attention and ushered her in, with treble-voiced announcement, to the Presence. Those grouped about the King's chair, raised their eyebrows. The Schulenberg, hiding astonishment, expressed her satisfaction that her ladyship had changed her mind. Compelled to advance, she bobbed to His staring Majesty; was raised, her hand patted.

"Ach! La revoilà!" cried the King.

There were titters all around her. The Schulenberg was smiling to split her face in two; while Mary, forgetful of her manners and Court etiquette, anxious only to put herself right who appeared to be wrong, quavered: "Lord, Sir! I have suffered such a fright—I must tell you!" And on a note of hysteria she told.

The King and his Germans listened amazed. She was encircled. Guttural ejaculations spurted from all sides. *Gott im Himmel!* Such unmannerly behaviour in the castle of the King could not unpardoned go! The pig-dog who this infamous assault had on the noble lady perpetrated must instantly punished be! Then, in the midst of the *jas* and the *nas* and the '*schrecklichs*' and '*dochs*' and the hubbub, the doors flew open again and Mr. Craggs was announced.

He seemed unperturbed and excessively sober as he made his obeisance to the King who, pop-eyed, exploded: "Mais commong donck, Monsieur Craggs, est que c'est l'usage du pays de porter des belles dames comme un sac de froment?"

Dumbfounded at this unexpected attack, Craggs stood for a moment speechless; then, recovering composure, he bowed again, and, with guarded insolence, replied: "Sire, cela ne se fait pas, mais je n'hésite devant rien pour la satisfaction de votre Majesté."

The King's bulbous nose twitched; his eyes narrowed; he chuckled, burst into loud laughter, slapping his thigh with a puffy red hand. "Alors! Si vous tournez tout en plaisanterie Lady Mary must you forgif. *Auch* will we you forgif, Monsieur Craggs, for you to me de Lady Mary bringk ven she has bidt me au revoir. Now you will not again us leaf, Lady Mary. You will mit us stay. *Nicht wahr?*"

She was left with no alternative; she had to stay, turning a chilly shoulder upon Craggs, who tacked a threat with smiling spite, to his apology.

"I have no excuse to offer for my inexcusable behaviour, other than that your beauty inflamed me to madness. Madam, no worm could be more abject that I who crave your pardon, but—" his voice behind that smile was dangerously smooth—"take heed lest the tale you have told to my discredit does not redound—to yours."

There was no reading of the *Iliad* that night. When, on the stroke of twelve, the King withdrew and Mary was free to go home, she found on her arrival that Pope had gone. Edward, returned from the House, was glumly dispensing drinks to Addison and Steele. Still smarting from her undiminished indignation at the incredible conduct of Craggs, she treated the gentlemen to a highly coloured version of the episode, punctuated by magniloquent assurance from Steele that he himself would demand a just revenge. And as if to prove his chivalrous intent, the gallant knight bounced from his chair, drew his blade, and was only restrained from rushing forth in search of Craggs when Mary darted after him to catch at his coat-tails, entreating:

"Sir Richard, don't be rash! Harm enough has already

been done by my tactless tale-bearing to the King. Craggs will never forgive me—so for heaven's sake put up your sword. I'll not be the cause of further mischief."

"Faith, lady! Am I not pledged," vociferated Steele, perilously flourishing his weapon, "to exert my rights as champion of beauty in distress? I'll seek him out, and run him through—with this!"

"No, no!" Still tugging at the tails of his coat, Mary, between peals of laughter, dragged him from the door. "I'll take your goodwill for the deed—so don't do it. Edward, I'm exhausted. I must have a glass of wine."

"As must I too, sir," blared Steele, "to drink damnation to the misbegotten punk—craving your ladyship's pardon."

Edward, who of the three gentlemen had appeared to be the least affected by Mary's recital, replenished the glasses, half filling a goblet which he passed to his wife with the curt reminder: "A mixture of drinks at this hour when you should be abed, is not advisable."

Reddening, she snatched the glass from his hand to say, high: "Have you counted the dregs of the bottle you grudge, as you count every penny in your money-bags?" And could have struck the words from her lips when she saw how his glance slid away from hers with something in it of contempt, but more of hurt. To Steele, such transitory conflict was the froth of married life; to Addison it was a revelation.

Coldly aloof, save among his intimates, he seemed, as Pope had cattily said of him, 'to preserve his dignity much'. Yet the simple honesty that underlay the cynical thrusts of his wit was warm in his heart for his friends. And ever since Edward's boyhood in Paris, Addison, the impecunious celebrated scholar, had been his good patron and friend. So now he, who lived in the world, as he naïvely confessed, 'rather as a "Spectator" of mankind than as one of the species', dispersed with a cock of an eyebrow, a wave of his slender white hand, that darkening moment between these two, once lovers, who stood before him there as strangers to themselves.

"Dick, you are not the only champion of this incomparable lady. Tell her—for you can tell it better than I—" Better than he, the most delightful talker of them all? "—how Pope

173

related to us a verbatim account of his 'most horrid and barbarous revenge on Edmund Curll'."

"Why? What's this?" Mary turned from Addison to Steele, who was only too ready to tell, despite his host's pointed look at the clock that was chiming the hour of one.

Taking his stance on the hearthrug, Steele set his glass upon the oaken mantelshelf and, as if he faced an auditorium, began:

"We have only Pope's word for the incident, you understand, and which closely concerns you, Lady Mary."

Edward abruptly got up from his chair.

"But does not," he said, "concern me."

"How, sir? Sure, there is no matter which may involve your good lady that is not also her husband's concern. Sit ye down and fill me up." Dick reached for and held out his glass. "Me tongue's dry as a lime-kiln."

Edward reluctantly opened the last of six bottles with a surly: "Help yourself."

Steele helped himself, and remarking, "A fair wine to middling, but 'twill serve," gulped, refilled, resumed. "Pope, so he says, overheard at Button's certain talk of Lady Mary's poems about to be published."

"Never!" Mary started from her seat. "There's no question of—"

"Wait now, will ye?" Dick wagged a solemn finger. "No question at all—without your permission—that's granted. But question enough there was between Curll who, for your knowledge, Lady Mary, is a bookseller——"

She nodded. "I know that."

"And do ye so?" said Steele admiringly. "Between Curll, as I was saying, and Roberts too, another of his ilk, who by some means unawares to Pope, but more foul than fair beseeming, had learned you had written these verses and—bad cess to um both—did propose jointly to print um!"

"But this is beyond all belief!" exclaimed Mary. "None knows of, nor has seen my verses, not even my husband."

"None?" Edward's look pierced her. "Surely one, but not I, admittedly, has seen them?"

"No. I swear." She crushed her hands together till their knuckles whitened. "Yes, 'tis true I have read excerpts of the first draft to Mr. Pope, and he——" she panted slightly—"you remember—as I told you—he thought well of——"

"Ah!" The interruption cut through that pause like a slap in the face. "You have read them to Pope. This is news to me."

"Your memory is short." She had regained her breath and her composure. "Pray go on with your story, Sir Richard—or Pope's."

"Pope's it is," Steele's eyes were on the bottle; he twirled his empty glass, but his host ignored the hint. "Pope's it is," continued Steele, "as I was saying, how that he having overheard this talk of Lady Mary's verses to be printed, met Curll by appointment at the Swan in Fleet Street and brought with him one of his publishers, Lintot, who, Pope swears, will—if called upon—stand witness to the case."

"Case!" cried Mary, blenching. "What, Sir Richard, may you mean by 'case'?"

"Sure, 'tis naught but a figure of speech. The case, if case it were or was to be, is settled. Pope, having gathered his two guests together at a table, calls for wine and fills the glasses and Curll's glass last of all, and, says he: 'So I hear you'll be printing a set o' verses entitled "Town Eclogues" by an Anonymous Lady o' Quality, Curll?'"

"Who on earth," breathed Mary, "could have told him?"

"That," said Steele, wagging his finger again, "is what Pope wished to know. 'And who,' he asks Curll, 'may this Lady o' Quality be—between ourselves?' 'And she must remain between ourselves, that is to say, between *my*self and Roberts,' chirrups Curll with a twitter like a bird's; yet 'tis too nice a simile for one that's black-hearted as Barabbas, being as he is a publisher, of lower sort, who draws from his authors their blood-sweated labour to be mauled by those petty students of syntax, our critics. God A'mighty," roared Steele, "that these fifth-rate gentlemen judges should dare to pass sentence of death on the trifling slips of a penman, whose prose or verse compared to their gross overladen hyperboles —which they never can put into print at more than a ha'penny a line—flaunt as sweet as a rose on a laystall! Well, our excellent Pope, who takes pride in nothing but to snap and snarl at the failure of his fellows, has marked

Curll his victim in vengeance for his dastardly vandalism of your cherished work, Lady Mary. And he—hoorooh! hah-hah!" A torrent of laughter broke into Steele's speech. He stood convulsed and shaking, to put Mary in the giggles, and Edward in a scowl.

"But, pray, Sir Richard, don't suspend your story. What," cried Mary, "did Pope do?"

"Do? Why the devil he did! And the devil was in it—" spluttered Steele—"to dose Curll's wine with a powerful emetic that sent him staggering up from the table with his hands to his belly, his face like a lemon, and himself—hah-hah!—laid out for dead!"

"Oh!" Mary gave a shiver of disgust. "How dreadfully mischievous of Pope!"

"Not at all," Steele retorted. "And not near so much did Curll get—the impenitent pimp—as he deserved. You should be grateful, Lady Mary, that your verses are rescued from Curll's piracy."

"My wife may be, but I," said Edward in his crisp cool voice, "confess myself *un*grateful to know that her name, which is mine, can be bandied among carrion printers and scribes in Town taverns."

"You have me wrong!" Dick's Irish temper, drink inflamed, was up. "The lady's name, nor yours, was never spoken. I'll vouch for that on Pope's most solemn oath."

"The oath of a Jacobite Papist bears no weight with me."

"Be damned, sir!" Steele's hand was at his sword-hilt. "There's weight enough and plenty in the saving of a lady's honour."

"You exaggerate the incident, Sir Richard, which should not have been repeated in the presence of my wife."

"'Od's Soul!" burst forth Steele, "I could offer, but will not, in my host's house, reply to that."

"Sir," Edward jerkily bowed, "my reply to you, in my house, is—goodnight. My wife and I do not keep such late hours."

"Not late." Addison came forward to stand between the two, and with his easy smile said again: "It is not late, 'tis

¹ *Town Eclogues* were piratically printed by Curll in 1716, in the name of 'A Lady of Quality.'

176

early. Look! Through a chink in the shutters stole a grey whisper of light. "Here, like a little cold bare-footed girl, comes the morning. Lady Mary," he bent to her hand, "there's not a man alive who would not defend you with his sword, or with his pen. Your servant, madam. Dick, come on, and souse your head. Edward, to you—good-day!"

Long she lay in that grey dawning, sleepless while her husband slept. Her slight indisposition, attributed to undigested German food, was now causing her considerable malaise. She wished she had listened to Edward's advice against taking a mixture of drinks which, she presumed, would account for the pain in her head though not for the pain in her body. In every limb she ached, and as if a little demon had sat himself between her brows to strike each lagging minute with careful hammer blows, so her temples throbbed in tortured rhythm. And when the first sun-rays probed between the curtains to steal from the room its night shadows, she raised herself upon an elbow to tell Edward, "I feel awful."

He grunted, but he did not wake.

Gazing down at that placid face beside her, so cameo-fine of feature and so still, she leaned over him in sudden fright lest he were dead, and put her lips to his to feel the reassurance of his quiet breath upon them . . . And lying there before the household stirred, with a fire in her forehead and cold shudders in her spine, her thoughts raced back along the years of her impassioned youth that had led her into marriage. With what poignant longings, what emotional abandon had she loved him, first as child, then as girl, but . . . had he loved her? That was the question which recurred again and cruelly again, yet never with such pitiless insistence as now when she lay racked and ill—of a rheum, of the plague, or some hideous contagion, God knew what! Yet her mind was clear enough to search that guarded borderline between life lived and life envisioned.

She remembered painfully those empty months at Hinchinbroke before the coming of her child; her impatience, her querulous self-pity, her peevish small suspicions, that like maggots had wormed destructively among the tender fibres of possession . . . She was startled. Had she been too possessive then, too certain he was hers, who by sheer persistence had won him to have and to hold until . . . No! Nothing, not death nor never life should part them. But she must fairly admit herself at fault in her attempt to mould him to her life's pattern, even as her father before her had superimposed his will on hers. Maybe, in some secret unconsciousness, she had sought in her dominance of Edward, whom she knew to be the weaker, a reprisal for those petty tyrannies that had discoloured her young girlhood. She recalled how that soon after her marriage she had scratched with a diamond on a window-pane: 'Let this great maxim be my virtue's guide. In part she is to blame that has been try'd; he comes too near who comes to be deny'd.' Yet when had she denied him?

And as she yearned above his sleeping face, that without the familiar frame of its wig looked like the cast of some forgotten Caesar, the hair receding from the temples and ever so slightly grey, a rueful pang shot through her. She had not seen nor known his hair was grey. There must be much she did not know of him, or he of her. My dear, my dear, she said, why do we draw apart who should be one? I love you . . . love you. Why should we let these little goaded nothings trample down the ramparts on which our lives are built? Yet although she believed she had spoken aloud, not a word escaped the clamour of her thoughts; and still he slept, and still that little hammer in her temples beat its devilish tattoo, until:

"Your ladyship's chocolate," she heard.

Grace with a breakfast-tray stood over her.

"I have been dead," her voice was hoarse to rasp her throat, "and like Lazarus have . . . come to life again." And she turned to find her husband gone, and was told she had been sleeping late, and the master had ordered that she not disturbed.

"But I haven't closed my eyes! My head . . ." she put her hand up to it, "is in torment."

"Your ladyship will be better for your chocolate."

"No, a drink of water. My mouth is parched. Why do you look at me? What do you see?"

178

The maid's homely pock-marked face was bent above her own. "I see my lady in a fever. I will send for Dr. Garth."

"Yes, I think . . ." Mary clutched at that comforting arm. "What have I? Not the measles? I have already had the measles. Can one take it twice?"

" 'Tis possible, my lady," Grace soothed her. "Why, madam, your shift is soaking wet. You have sweated well. That will rid you of your rheum."

"Yes." Mary nodded. "A rheum. I knew it was no worse than that . . . Water, for the love of God!"

And when Grace gave her to drink she sipped and flung aside the glass and, clapping her hands to her head, rocked herself whimpering, "No worse, no worse, no worse . . ." over and over in the mounting frenzy of the fever that roared about her blinded sight, and cast her down.

★ 10 ★

THERE came a day when those formless shadow shapes that touched to lift and tend her and bore no resemblance to anything human, were dimly recognizable; no longer were they troglodytes, emerging from vast cave-like recesses, maliciously a-grin, with their hot fœtid breath in her mouth; nor were they elongated, haloed in a glory, never speaking, only sorrowfully looking, to fade from her ghost-like and wigless. "But you are only thirty-eight," she said. "You should not be grey at thirty-eight. Don't leave me, never leave me. Am I dying?"

"Dying? Tut! What talk is this of dying?" Another, pigeon-chested, stout, who brought with him an aromatic odour, raised, tapped, plastered her, and laid a cooling bandage to her eyes . . . Her eyes! How they smarted, itched and burned.

"I cannot see. . . ."

"You can, and now you may."

The sheath was unfolded; the room, sun-filled, returned to her in welcome, with Dr. Garth at her bedside, his fingers on her pulse and a broadening smile on his face.

"Good, very good! You are well out of your trouble, my dear. A mild attack, but obstinate. The fever has been high. Drink this."

She drank that; a bitter tasting cordial, and asked: "What fever? I know I have been sick. I have the itch!" She scratched. "But I am better."

"Indeed you are. Miraculously better." The doctor gave his low-voiced orders. "Keep the curtains drawn against the light—strengthening nourishment, beef and chicken broth, white meats, broiled fowl, and a dose of the physic twice daily. I shall not visit her ladyship tonight. Glove her hands. She must not scratch."

He went out.

"Come here," called Mary feebly. The maid came. "Have I been ill of a contagion? Where is my boy? Where *is* he?"

"As a precaution merely, madam, he has been sent away and is now in the care of his Grace."

"His—my father! Has——?"

"His Grace has himself called or sent every day of your illness, to inquire of your ladyship."

"Did he so?"

She lay back upon her pillows. "I must have been sick unto death for my father to—Grace! What has ailed me? What have I had?"

But Grace quietly had left the room.

Wondering and anxious, Mary's glance travelled in that gentle half-light from one familiar object to another. All was as before; the walnut tallboy between the windows, the convex commode at her bedside; the table with its phials of physic, a dish of oranges, a bowl of roses, fragrant, multi-coloured. Pinned to the velvety petals a card: 'From your affectionate Father my Grandson is with me a fine Boy.'

Slow hurting tears gathered behind her lids. At last she was forgiven—and about time too! Then fresh panic seized her. No matter Dr. Garth's prevarication or the soothing answers of her maid, she knew she must have been snatched from death's door for her father to show himself so friendly. As her hand reached out to replace the card, the loose sleeve of her nightgown disclosed her bare arm and a rash of red pustules upon it. She sat up in bed to tear aside her shift, staring down at her chest horror-stricken to see clustered there, a putrid and scab-like excrescence.

Her hands flew to her face, her eyes to the mirror on her dressing-table. It was gone.

Shrieking for her maid, she flung off the covers and struggled out of bed; and so Grace found her, stumbling round the room in search of a looking-glass.

"I must see myself! Why do you hide the mirror? Give me a mirror!"

She was got back to bed and lay there sobbing wildly. "My face! My face . . . The smallpox! Don't lie to me. I've had the smallpox."

Edward came and took her hand and kissed her eyes. "My dear, you'll not be scarred. There's scarce a mark."

"You tell me that for comfort, but I know!"

"You cannot know. I swear you have had, as Dr. Garth corroborates, the mildest attack."

"Lord's sakes! If this be mild, what is strong? A mirror! Why won't you give me a mirror?" But as he leaned over to kiss her again, she pushed him back. "No, no! You'll take the sickness. Keep away."

"I have no fear. Am I not sworn to be beside you in sickness or in health?"

She wept, she screamed, she fought, imploring that he bathe himself from head to foot in vinegar, nor to come near her till all risk of infection had passed.

"Too late for that," he told her lightly. "If I am to take it I am already infected, for I have been with you day and night these three weeks."

Then he took from Grace a cup of broth and sat spoon-feeding her as if she were his child.

Her return to convalescence was retarded by the shock she received when they could no longer keep her from a looking-glass.

Dazedly incredulous, she saw herself a crop-haired boy, an urchin, peaked and pale, whose face was blotched and crusted, and whose unwinking eyes stared back at her, pink-rimmed, bereft of lashes. Horrible!

"My eyes!" she whispered. "What is amiss with my eyes?"

Though the smallpox would leave her skin almost un-scarred, she had lost her eyelashes, her precious eyelashes! And Dr. Garth, impatient of her wailings, had told her brusquely they would never grow again.

What a cruel dispensation of divine injustice that she must go through life hereafter with eyes unshaded, glassily staring. Why, she asked a hundred times a day, should she have been singled out to undergo such monstrous penance for the petty sin of vanity? Yes, she had been vain, she admitted, of her eyelashes, but of all her other manifold attractions, her wit, her beauty, lauded to the skies by Mr. Pope, admired of the King and the King's son, and every other man on whom the light of her countenance—before this vile smallpox came to darken it—had shone, she had cared not one iota. And now a dire visitation had descended to punish her for her one conceit.

It was during the interval that must elapse before visitors could call on her without fear of infection, that she wrote the sixth of her *Town Eclogues*: 'The Smallpox'. In this, the only one of the set that can with any certainty be ascribed to Lady Mary as her unaided work, she gives us:

> '*The wretched Flavia, who on her couch reclined,*
> *Thus breath'd the anguish of a wounded mind.*

>   . . .

> "*How am I changed! Alas! How am I grown*
> *A frightful spectre, to myself unknown!*
> *Where's my complexion, where my radiant bloom,*
> *That promis'd happiness for years to come?*. . . .
> *There was a time (Oh! that I could forget!)*
> *When opera-tickets pour'd before my feet;*
> *And at the Ring, where brightest beauties shine,*
> *The earliest cherries of the spring were mine.* . . .
> *Adieu, ye Parks—in some obscure recess,*
> *Where gentle streams will weep at my distress,*
> *Where no false friend will in my grief take part,*
> *And mourn my ruin with a joyful heart;*
> *There let me live, in some deserted place,*
> *There hide in shades this lost inglorious face.*
> *Plays, operas, circles, I no more must view,*
> *My toilette, patches, all the world, adieu!*" '

A succession of friends, perhaps not quite so false as 'Flavia' would have them, came with their good wishes or condolences to call on Lady Mary.

Frances was the first, down from Scotland, and too full of her husband's latest exploits to pay much attention to her sister's 'wounded mind' and tearful query:

"Tell me the truth. Am I hideous?"

Maddeningly, Frances hesitated to reply before she told her: "N-no, not hideous. Peculiar."

"There's a bitch you are to taunt me!" Mary sprang at her, and they were back ten years ago in time's dissolving, as if time had never been. "How you crow at and gloat on my misfortune!"

"Well, you asked me for the truth," retorted Frances. "I can't honestly admit that you're improved. And do keep your hands to yourself! You was always spiteful. One would hope you had outgrown your filthy temper. If you fly out at Edward like a wild cat, you'll be losing him—so mind your ways."

"All I can hope," snivelled Mary with her knuckles in her lashless eyes, "is that you'll never take the pox, small or great—with Johnnie Mar!"

But that remark, luckily for Mary, Frances had not heard. "I have troubles worse'n yours," she said; and taking from the dressing-table a bottle of perfume she liberally soaked her handkerchief, then carelessly dropped the flask.

"Now see what you've done!" cried Mary. "That's Eau sans Pareil. A whole guinea's worth lost to me—spilled on the carpet!"

Frances swung round.

"Lord! What's the loss of a bottle o' scent or your precious eyelashes, compared to mine? *I've* lost my husband."

"What!"

"Yes, *what*! You're so taken up with yourself and your face that you haven't a thought for my troubles. I'm half crazed with the worry of John. He must be mad to do what he is doing—and has done." And Frances fell to sobbing.

Mary had a flash of recollection. Was it not the night when Craggs had made a fool of her before the Court, that the King had spoken of some pother to do with John Mar?

Stupefied, she listened to the rigmarole Frances recounted. Mar, it seemed, had left London on the second day of August, five weeks since. He had attended the King's levée the night before—"and never a word to me, fancy that!" sobbed Frances. "Such deceit—and making excuse he must see his agent in the North, he embarked from Gravesend in a collier, dressed as a Jack-pudding in rags. I can tell you, Mary, what I wouldn't tell to any other person else, so swear that you won't breathe a word of this to Edward."

"I swear," said Mary, much alarmed. "Go on."

Frances went on. "I know this for gospel fact. Johnnie has been in correspondence through Bolingbroke with the Pretender!"

"Good God!" Mary's eyes looked to be starting from their sockets.

"Yes. Don't stare like you was seeing ghosts. I know you can't help it but it terrifies me. Is Grace about?" Frances crept to the door, peered out into the passage and came back whispering, "I don't want to be catched and hanged as the wife of a traitor, though heaven knows I'll hang myself if they should take him, and what Papa will say or do when he hears of this I dare not contemplate."

What England will say or do, Mary thought, would be more to the point. She was white to the lips. "Where is Mar now?"

"In the Highlands," blubbered Frances. "He wrote me from Fife to say he is attended by Hamilton and Hay—hot as hell Jacobites, the pair o' them! All London's ablaze with it."

"And yet," Mary said indignantly, "you told me not to breathe a word to Edward. Why?"

"Because he's the last one to hear, with his head in the air, and I'll wager when he does he'll go nosing round to pick up every dirt to bring Mar down. He hates him."

"He does not!"

"He does so. Your Edward, my dear, is the most intolerant of Whigs against the Jacks, except those hell-cats around the Princess—Adehilda Shrewsbury and the Roxburgh woman and Sarah Marlborough—the snite—how she and all of 'em spit at me! You'd want to die, as I do, for my shame."

" 'Tis no shame of yours, my dear." Mary slid an arm around her sister's heaving shoulders. "You're not responsible for John's abominations."

"I am! I am! Are we not one? I'll take full share of whatever lies in store for us. Only that I dread," wailed Frances, "they'll bring him to the block when he's been tried by his peers. They say he's raised the standard of James the Third—as they call him—at Braemar. And what do you think, Mary? I've a letter from John written in the battle line. They're fighting like mad dogs up there, those Scots, and he says the Highland Chief forecast ill-bodings because a gilt ball perched on top of the pole that flew the Stuart's flag bounced off it and fell to the ground. Then they consecrated the standard with their prayers to save the Cause—and the last I've heard is that the whole country north of the Tay is with Johnnie. I wish I was dead!"

Concealing her horrified dismay at this recital, Mary strove to reassure the sobbing Frances. "Don't lose heart, love. This revolt is certain to be quelled and John brought to his senses."

"Or the gallows," said Frances with another gush of tears.

"No, they'll never hang a peer. At the worst they'll execute or maybe extradite him," was Mary's doubtful comfort. "Give over fretting. What's the good? You can't help him that way. Bestir yourself, girl! Or I will—yes, I'll speak to the King and get a pardon for Johnnie when my hair grows again and my wretched face clears. It's still full o' the pox."

"It isn't. It's lovely. My darling!" Frances rushed to hug her. "What a beast am I to tease you. I've always been jealous that you're prettier than me. Your eyes are more wonderful than ever—cross my heart they are. You *will* speak to the King for Johnnie, won't you? Everyone knows he adores you—the King I mean, not Johnnie. I'm for ever quarrelling with John because he says you're so blown out with yourself that one of these days you'll burst."

"Does he?" cried Mary. "The dirty rebel hound!"

"Hound is it? You puffed up unchristian snip-snap—eat your words!"

They were at it again; Mary now the fiercer of the two since her sister's news had overwrought her. Better than Frances had she gauged the significance of Mar's rebellion. And after his lachrymose Countess had left, Mary went in search of Edward. She found him in his study. The door was ajar, and he conning a speech. Unperceived, she watched him, hard put to hold her laughter at what she heard and saw.

He stood before a mirror with his back to her, a paper in his hand, and his face well reflected in the glass. Each sentence, carefully pronounced, as if he were an actor rehearsing his part, was punctuated with deliberate asides.

"May I remind the honourable member (raise the eyebrows) that Mr. Walpole's violence and impudence is censored by all Whigs but those (a meaningful glance at the Opposition benches)—um—but those who depend upon the Court, except one or two who are not—(a shrug of the shoulders and a smile) *not* reckoned among men of good judgement. Had the King taken the opinion of the principal members of the House before any business had been proposed of moment—which was (hem!) the method constantly used by King William, the affair would certainly have been better managed (No—I must score that out. They'll not stand for criticism of His Majesty)——"

"And nor will I!" tittered Mary from the doorway.

Edward rounded on her, the scroll crumpled in his fist, his colour rising.

"What do you here? You should be at rest."

"I have rested all day. Dear heart, you have missed your vocation. You should be on the boards. Recite me your speech."

"It will never now be spoken." His chilled face drained the warmth from hers. "You should know that I resent intrusion. This is my private hour. Leave me to it."

"How you carp! Must I not seek you out when I'm in trouble?"

"I think," he said, "that I've been told of your trouble *ad infinitum*. You have dwelled too long and foolishly on your supposed disfigurement. Employ yourself, pray, in more profitable manner than in constant harping on what can't be helped. Be thankful that our boy has not taken the sickness, nor myself. Now leave me."

"Boo, boo, boo!" Mary pulled a face at him. "You talk like you was a beadle. Nor am I come to dwell on my disfigurement, as you so kindly call it—much you care! My sister Mar, if you must know, has been here with a tale. That's *her* trouble—and mine too, since I needs must take it to myself. More fool am I!"

"Yes?"

She gritted her teeth.

"Edward. Have you heard, or am I the only one who *hasn't* heard—until today—of Mar's rebellion?"

"Possibly."

"She told me not to tell you."

"Oh?"

"You knew?"

"I did."

"And you didn't tell *me*?"

"Why should I?"

Her lower lip slackened and from it broke a sob. She knew she was behaving like a child, but for the life of her she could not help herself. She felt weak and ill; she must be humoured. "Edward, what will they do to Mar?"

"Who do you mean by 'they'?" His tone was one of gentle weariness. "Marlborough has the case in hand, and in due course will deal with it."

"But Marlborough is not in the Highlands."

"He has no reason to be in the Highlands. Marlborough can disperse a pack of rebels from headquarters here in London. Do not distress yourself in this concern, which—" relentlessly he took her hands in his and kissed her fingers— "which is no concern of yours. Now go to rest."

"There'll be no rest for me," Mary flung at him, unsoftened, "till I have interceded with the King on Mar's account."

"The King!"

There was a decisiveness in the ejaculation. He stood, biting at his inner lip, a trick he had when deep in thought. "Yes." His hands tightened on hers, "you may—and you

must intercede with the King. But not on Mar's account,"
he said, "on mine!"

* * *

The remainder of that year was an anxious time for Mary
when Frances, half-demented after John's defeat at Sherriff-
muir, sought sanctuary with her. Yet even while news filtered
through of daily desertions from the weakened rebel ranks,
a pale, tall, and lanky gentleman landed at Peterhead amid
enthusiastic welcome.

This excitement of the loyal clans was not, however,
followed by the victory and crowning of their King. John
Mar, the irrepressible, found himself repressed, and his
forces, which had swelled to eleven thousand strong,
miserably dwindled to six hundred. Thus the claimant to
the Throne of Great Britain returned dejectedly to France
whence he had come; and Mar, who saw himself a Hotspur,
full of fealty to repeat his mad adventure and win hands
down with the Stuart's standard up, raced after him to plan
a fresh attack.

In January and February and well on into March, London
talked of nothing but High Treason. Death sentences were
passed on all the followers of Mar with a price upon the
heads of those in hiding. But although some dozen pleaded
guilty, two only paid the penalty on Tower Hill.

So soon as secret information had been conveyed to
Frances that John was safe in Paris with his Sovereign Lord,
she went to join him. Mary saw her go with much relief.
She had matter of more moment to occupy her mind than
her 'Sister Mar's' hysterics and Johnnie Mar's disgrace.

Her husband's future, indeed his whole career, hung in
the balance of a slender chance which none but she could
turn to his advantage. She would never know what it must
have cost him to sink his pride and come to her with an aloof
appeal disguised as a command. It behoved her to approach
the Throne on his behalf. It had reached his ears—never
mind how or through whom—(Addison, she rightly guessed)
—that a major Embassy in the Near East was about to
become vacant, and in view of the fact that he spoke fluent
French——

188

"But surely," she broke in, "you would not wish to be a mere attaché to the Embassy in Paris? Besides, you are too old. Such appointments are given to youths with a diplomatic future."

"I said," corrected Edward stiffly, "the Near East. Think again."

"I can't. Why speak in riddles? What have you in mind?"

What he had in mind was so stupendous that imagination reeled before the opportunity which opened out before him, but which she doubted would be his to take.

"Why?" He refused to be dashed. Was he not equipped with all the essentials required of a diplomat? Not any other man of his acquaintance spoke such knowledgeable French as he, unless it were Joe Addison; but his poor health would never stand the climate. Besides, he was about to marry Lady Warwick, who would certainly not be a suitable wife for an —Ambassador.

"Edward!" And as the full portent of his conception dawned on her she flung herself into his arms. "If I have misjudged your ingenuity, your competence—if ever I believed you indolent, a dormouse—may God forgive me that I've wronged you! Tell me more."

There was little more to tell; more to do. "And this," he said, "is where I turn to you. Bring your wit to bear on this one end." He spoke with unusual intensity, his eyes a-shine as if some inward flame had lit them. "The only end," he repeated, "to which I dedicate my life. Mary, you shall approach the King for me. He will listen when," he gently emphasized, "*you* talk."

"I?" Her hand sprang to her mouth. "How can *I* talk? What am I to say? Who am I to ask the King—make my husband an Ambassador for me—the Court Fool! Besides, have you considered what construction may be put to such a—" and at his gimlet look she flushed, and faltered—"such a request?"

His head turned slightly.

"Caesar's wife——"

"Yes," and she was smiling, "I'll remind you of that sentiment when you reproach me with your sneers at my interest in men of fame and parts." Then, fearing a wrangle, she

189

hastened to resume, "but you have not yet told me what Embassy, other than Paris, requires such knowledge of French."

Edward walked to the window and with his back to her said:

"French is the language most commonly used by all the diplomatic services in . . . Turkey."

* I I *

'Additional instructions for our trusty and well beloved Edward Wortley Montagu, Esq., whom we have appointed to be our Ambassador Extraordinary to the Grand Seigneur. Given at our Court at Hanover this twenty-first day of December, 1716, in the third year of our reign.

George R.'

AND IN the fourth year of her marriage Mary attained the highest peak of her ambition.

How much Edward owed to her energetic or his unob-trusive endeavours to achieve his promotion is debatable; but that, to the envy and amaze of his associates, he secured this Ministerial commission has made history; not his.

It was Mary's Embassy, her triumph, her greatest of adventures to bear her away upon a magic carpet in which the colours are as fadeless still, and fresh as on the day when she set forth upon her pilgrimage through Europe.

Edward, to be sure, did, from the first, raise the objection —hotly refuted by Mary—that the voyage and its trials, the climate, the heat of that semi-barbaric and almost unexplored country to which he was bound, would be no place for her. There were scenes; there were threats. If he, who owed his promotion to her influence at Court, should refuse her the right to share in his success, then would she use her power to intervene again and snatch his laurels from him, to defame him—destroy him! Go she would and, moreover, their son would go with them.

Vainly Edward fought this last suggestion. She stood

unshaken. She would not leave her child. nor would she leave her husband to go careering off alone to strange heathenish lands. Must she be tossed aside like rotten fruit while he reaped the harvest she had sown for him? Never! . . . And so on and on, till, for his peace and sore patience, he gave in. Having won her point, Mary took upon herself to superintend all arrangements for departure. While Edward paid a farewell visit to his father at Wortley, she stayed behind to engage a secretary, a surgeon, a chaplain, and a retinue of footmen whose 'twenty liveries,' she informed her husband, 'will cost a hundred and ten pounds' . . . To her own personal equipment she gave the least attention. Any new gowns she would need could be bought in Vienna. They were to travel overland through Holland, Germany and Austria. Mary studied maps, marking the chain of cities they would visit, every port of call, each posting-stage. The Hague, Cologne, Nuremberg, Ratisbon, Belgrade, and down the Danube to . . . the Golden Horn!

In the year when Wortley Montagu became Ambassador for Britain at Constantinople, war was raging between Austria and Turkey. Since the Triple Alliance that linked France and Britain with Austria demanded a cessation of hostilities, it behoved King George's 'trusty well beloved' to persuade the representatives of the two belligerent countries to lay down their arms and call a truce. That Edward, with no previous experience to guide him, should have been chosen to undertake so difficult a task, might have staggered a more hardened diplomat than he—but not Mary. With her to jog his elbow she entertained no doubt of his success.

On August 1, 1716, the newly appointed Ambassador, his wife, his son and his suite, sailed from Gravesend to Flushing pursued by a violent storm. If Edward's sudden elevation had a little turned his head, the turbulent seas quite over-turned his stomach. While, abased and groaning, His Excellency lay abandoned to his agony below, Mary, in a seaman's surtout, walked the deck. The sea held no terrors for her. The ship was a stallion, fierce and splendid, plunging into battle with the waves. And as the heavily churned waters crashed upon the bridge, where, to the consternation of the sailors, she had clambered to avoid a drenching, she shook the spray from her eyes and screamed above the yell of the winds for sheer joy in this orchestrated chorus of the elements. It seemed as if the forces of nature had combined to herald her voyage to the unknown, with a fanfare of trumpets and white flags flying.

And if Mary is to be believed, she was the only one aboard, not excepting half the crew, unaffected by that fearful visitation. 'We were all Sunday night tossed very handsomely,' she boasts to Frances. 'I never saw a man more frighted than the Captain. For my part I have been lucky neither to suffer from fear or sea-sickness.'

Soaked to the skin but undaunted, with her face full of health, her eyes full of light, she tripped ashore at Rotterdam and packed her pale Edward off to bed.

Then, as none of her attendants was in fit case to go with her, she changed her clothes and explored the town alone, to marvel at Dutch cleanliness. Not a speck of dirt could be seen in the streets, 'where the maids wash the pavements with more application than ours do our bedchambers . . . Nor is one shocked with those loathsome cripples so common in London, nor with the importunities of idle fellows, and wenches that choose to be nasty. . . .'

In short, everything she saw, every person she met, delighted her, 'even the common servants here are more nicely clean than our ladies.'

Posting through Holland, however, was for Mary a deal more fatiguing than the handsome tossing she had sustained in the North Sea. Bumping over rough roads on the spring-less seats of hired chaises till she was black and blue, choked with dust and grit, sickened by the smell of sweating horses, dung, and the dirty straw that from its powerful stench had seemingly never been changed, 'was nothing,' she complained in a letter to one of her friends, Lady Rich[1] 'to what I suffered yesterday!' (dated August 15).

When they came to Stamal, some thirty miles' distance from Cologne, the over-driven horses that had brought them from Niemeguen collapsed, and as no fresh conveyance

[1] Lady-in-Waiting to the Princess of Wales.

could be found they were forced to lie the night in a 'wretched lodging no better than a hovel'. After one shuddering look at the flea-bitten beds—how different from the spotless Dutch inns was this!—Mary decided to sit up in a chair, fully dressed, while Edward, too tired to be fussy, slept as if he never meant to wake.

They accomplished the remainder of the journey to Cologne in three hours, and with no mishap. Mary, unattended still, went out in the bright sunshine to look at the 'old-built town' and its churches; and was received 'in a very complaisant manner by a handsome young Jesuit', who, unaware of her identity and despite his priesthood, 'took a liberty in his compliments and railleries' to her great diversion . . . He showed her the images of silver saints ornamented with a profusion of rich jewels that Mary much admired, and confessed she had 'wickedness enough to covet St. Ursula's pearl necklace'. Her handsome young escort, loth to let her go, further detained her by exhibiting for her wonder and amusement, a shrine heaped with the skulls of eleven thousand virgins who had died for their Faith at the hands of the infidel Moors.

"What! Eleven thousand virgins!" cried Mary. "Why, Father, that speaks ill for the manhood of your citizens fifteen hundred years ago!"

The Father, who had naught to say to that, gave her his blessing and something more besides, of less value.

At Nuremberg, after another five days' travel, she was astonished to see in one poor little Catholic church, unobtrusively hidden away amidst the more stolid sobriety of Lutheran places of worship, 'an image of Our Saviour over the altar, in a full-bottomed wig, very well powdered'.

From Nuremberg they went by easy stages to Ratisbon, where Mary caught a fearful cold; a calamitous misfortune. Ratisbon was the general headquarters for the envoys of various states, and here for the first time since she had left London, she attended social functions as the wife of the British Ambassador. To summon gracious smiles and extend, between sneezes, a vice-regal hand to be kissed by curtsying ladies, did not induce that proper dignity demanded of her high position. Moreover, she was vexed to find that those who held no right to be addressed as Excellency, 'which they all pretend to', claimed equal rank with her. And it seems she put these forward ladies in their places, to make herself thoroughly unpopular, for: 'It is publicly whispered, as a piece of impertinent pride in me, that I have been *saucily civil*!'

Lectured by Edward on how to behave with the wives of junior officials, she was thankful to leave Ratisbon and her cold behind her, for the journey down the Danube to Vienna.

Vienna! . . . Joyous scope for her unflagging pen was this lovely little city, lying like an ivory casket at the foot of azure mountains, ringed around with pine-woods, watered by the blue sun-dimpled Danube: a city of strange contrasts where the luxurious magnificence of white palatial houses over-topped the crowded tenements that lined each narrow street; where Fashion, in gay colours, jostled poverty in rags; and where even in the starving, poorest quarters of the town sweet music could be heard, and song.

Mary's initial attendance at the Imperial Court was delayed for lack of a suitable gown. She ordered several, 'which certainly', she wrote to Frances, 'show the shape and neck . . .' And showed hers to such advantage that the Emperor, Charles VI, was moved to entertain her 'in a most obliging manner', that may have atoned for the disobliging dress into which she had to be 'squeezed', to give her a stitch in her side. Then, to be ultra-modish, Her Excellency was constrained to carry on her head 'a thing they call a *bourle*, too large to go into a moderate tub. . . .'

The Viennese women, in Mary's opinion, had as little to commend them as their dress. 'All,' she declares, 'are liberally endowed with a natural ugliness.' All, that is to say, except the Empress, who conceded private audience to the wife of the British Ambassador. Mary was ravished, but maybe as much by the honour conferred as by the Royal lady's beauty. 'Her neck! Her hands!' she rhapsodizes. 'Till I saw them I could not believe there were any in nature so perfect, and was almost sorry my rank did not permit me to *kiss* them . . .' But if no kisses were permitted, the smiles and the whispers that passed between the Empress and her little English guest, who, her Imperial Majesty insisted, must sit beside her while

194

she played at Quinze, almost compensated for more fervent demonstration.

According to Mary, Vienna was 'a paradise for old women, who until the age of five and thirty are looked upon as raw young girls!' Still, one cannot believe that all the 'old women' she met were as plain as she paints them, since 'it is the custom,' she informs her pet gossip, Lady Rich, 'for every lady here to have two husbands, one that bears the name and another that performs the duties.'

To this same correspondent, who Mary did not doubt would hand her letters round to be read by all her circle, including Mr. Pope, she demurely records her own conquests. Vice Chancellor Schönbrunn invited her to dinner . . . 'perfectly fine and well-ordered and made still more agreeable by the good humour of the Count . . .' They strolled in the garden, where the strains of flute and viol drew from leafy branches the nightingale's song to break a throbbing silence, to suspend a whispered word . . . And there was yet another Count—they all were Counts—a younger Count, whose name, circumspectly, is withheld. He, with appropriate persuasion, suggested she might pass her time in Vienna 'more agreeably were she to engage with him in a little affair of the heart'.

' "My heart" (answered I bravely enough)'—thus Mary to Lady Rich—' "does not engage very easily, and I have no design of parting with it." '

'He sighed', and confessed his mortification, saying he was 'utterly charmed and devoted to her service, but if she would let him know of any other more deserving of her choice he would undertake to manage the affair to her entire satisfaction'.

These confidences, racily recorded, may have come, as doubtless was intended, to the ears of Mr. Pope.

Distance lent enchantment to his person, and his pen. No matter he was dwarfish, humped, a monster in her sight, he feared no rival when it came to 'talking upon paper', as he put it; and at exaggerated length proceeds to talk. . . . Could she not imagine how desirous he must be of a correspondence with one who had taught him long ago that it was 'as possible to esteem at first sight as to love'?

There are pages of it, ending with a wicked little jealous dig at Edward.

'May that person for whom you have left all the world be so just as prefer you to all the world . . . May you continue to think him worthy of whatever you have. May you ever look upon him with the eyes of a first lover . . . In a word, may you receive from him as many pleasures and gratifications as even I think you can give. I wish this from my heart.'

*　　　*　　　*

Before resuming their journey to the Porte, Edward heard from his King, on holiday in Hanover, that he was commanded to call upon His Majesty for further instructions.

Not without regret did Mary from the window of the chaise take her last glimpse of Vienna where, even without the assistance of the amorous young Count, time had flown too fast and never for her so 'agreeably'.

From Vienna to Prague, through the desolate kingdom of Bohemia, they journeyed for three days and nights. The accommodation offered at the inns along the way was even more inferior and comfortless than any hitherto encountered. Mary, who after her experience at Stamal, had provided her own bed, refused to set it up in a room where horrors crawled on walls and ceilings, and icy blasts came whistling under doors. Nor did a common stove in the public parlour, shared by swineherds, tramps, 'and filled with all sorts of ill scents', provide any better alternative. Edward, already half asleep, would have willingly stretched himself out on the floor, but his wife would have none of that. She insisted they return to the chaise and go on till they came to some proper hostel.

She had reason to regret her decision when, after several hours' hard posting, not a village and no sign of any hostel did they see. With her son in her lap and Edward at her side, fast asleep, Mary, who slept not a wink and was bruised in every limb from heavy jolting, watched the moon rise strong and full above those rugged canyons dividing Bohemia from Saxony.

The mountain pass, hewn from solid rock, that towered to immeasurable heights above and sank to fathomless depths below, was so narrow that the wheels of the coach were within a bare inch of the precipice; and far down, in a cleft of the valley, the river Elbe, like a thin translucent snake, threaded its winding course . . . Then, while the horses tore round the bends at full gallop, she saw by the bright staring disc of the moon that the weary postilions were a-nod in their saddles. Clutching her child she wrenched open the door of the chaise, screaming at the men, "For God's sake watch where you're going—we'll be killed!" Edward, awakened by her cries, leaned over to pull the door shut and peremptorily to tell her, "Keep back and keep still!" And, as he peered from the window he muttered, nothing to lessen her panic, "Ecod! I've crossed the Alps five times, but have never seen any such abysmal slope as this. These fellows will have us in the Elbe before they've done!"

Mary said her prayers, rained despairing kisses on her unresponsive boy, and: "At least," she whispered, "my treasure will die in my arms with me. Edward," she nudged him, "hold my hand. We three will fall together."

They did not. No crushing disaster, no hideous end overtook them or the sure-footed beasts that knew every inch of that rough rock-strewn way, to bring them safely down to Dresden in the morning.

There, although 'heartily tired of twenty-four hours' post-travel without rest or refreshment', Mary found time to remark and record her impressions of 'the frailties of Saxon ladies, who have,' she allows, 'pretty faces . . . yet they would think it a mortal sin against good breeding if they spoke or moved in a natural manner. They all affect a little soft lisp and a pretty pitti-pat step . . .' She wished her husband's business would have permitted him a longer stay in this 'neatest' of German towns, but they were bound for Hanover, where His Majesty awaited them.

And here, in King George's second capital—which he secretly regarded as his first—Mary was received with royal gush. She and Edward were given sumptuous apartments in the Palace. No hedging round the honour of her title now, where all the King's ladies must follow his lead. Basking in the beams of magnanimity she dined at the King's table, was plied with Rhenish wine, toasted in German, ate deliciously of pineapple for the first time in her life, and was entertained by the King's French comedians. His Majesty rolled in his chair at the jokes which Mary could not understand but pretended she did, and with her Royal host laughed heartily to the immense disapproval of Edward . . . He did understand them.

It was now November, but despite Edward's insistence that she return to England rather than endure the hardships of the long winter's journey across Europe, Mary refused to go back. 'While my husband is determined to proceed in his design,' she wrote to Lady Rich, 'I am determined to follow him.'

Follow him she would. Edward held his peace. He knew better than to argue with her whose headlong spirit and indomitable will defied danger.

Their baggage was packed and bundled on the wagons; Mary bade farewell to gracious Majesty, cloaked herself in sables, wrapped her son in coney-skins, and bowing right and left in regal fashion to minor envoys lined up to see her go, she stepped into the chaise. Edward grimly followed. The Portuguese Ambassador, who had a roving eye for her, wafted a kiss; she waved her hand. The postilions cracked their whips, the leaders sprang forward, and out at the Palace gates, out of the town, kicking up a dust-cloud behind their heels, they went.

The Turkish adventure had begun.

★ 12 ★

From Alexander Pope to Lady Mary Wortley Montagu
[undated]

'Madam,
If to live in the memory of others have anything desirable in it, 'tis what you possess with regard to me in the highest sense of the words. There is not a day in which your figure does not appear before me, your conversation return to my thoughts . . . If I hear from you I look upon it as little less than a miracle or extraordinary visitation from another world. . . .

You tell me the pleasure of being near the sun has a great effect upon your health and spirits. You have turned my affections so far eastward that I could almost be one of his worshippers . . . What may we not expect from a creature that went out the most perfect of this part of the world and is every day improving by the sun of the other!

I make not the least question that you could give me great éclaircissement upon many passages in Homer, since you have been enlightened by the same sun that inspired the father of poetry. . . .

I send you, therefore, with this, the third volume of the Iliad. Among the rest you have all I am worth . . . my works.

For God's sake, madam, send to me as often as you can . . . Tell me that you are well, that your little son is well, tell me that your very dog (if you have one) is well. Defraud me of no one thing that pleases you, for whatever that is it will please me better than anything else can do.

I am always yours,

A. Pope.'

From Lady Mary Wortley Montagu to Alexander Pope

Adrianople,

April 1, O.S. 1717

' . . . I am at this present moment writing in a house situated on the banks of the Hebrus which runs under my chamber windows. My garden is full of cypress trees, upon the branches of which several couple of true turtles are saying soft things to one another from morning till night. . . .

The summer is already far advanced in this part of the world; and, for some miles around Adrianople the whole ground is laid out in gardens, and the banks of the rivers are set with rows of fruit trees, under which all the most considerable Turks divert themselves every evening; not with walking, that is not one of their pleasures, but a set party of them choose out a green spot where the shade is very thick, and there they spread a carpet, upon which they sit drinking their coffee and are generally attended by some slave with a fine voice, or that plays on some instrument. . . .

The young lads generally divert themselves with making garlands for their favourite lambs, which I have often seen painted and adorned with flowers, lying at their feet while they sung or played.

I read over your Homer here with an infinite pleasure . . . It would be too tedious to point out all the passages that relate to present customs. But I can assure you that the princesses and great ladies pass their time at their looms, embroidering veils and robes, surrounded by their maids, in the same manner as we found Andromache and Helen described . . . The snowy veil that Helen throws over her face is still fashionable; and I never see half a dozen old bashaws (as I do very often), with their reverend beards, sitting basking in the sun, but I recollect good King Priam and his counsellors. . . .

The eastern manners give a great light into many Scripture passages that appear odd to us, their phrases being commonly what we should call Scripture language . . . and I am very glad I have it in my power to satisfy your curiosity by sending you a faithful copy of the verses that Ibrahim Pashá, the reigning favourite, has made for the young princess, his contracted wife, whom he is not yet permitted to visit without witnesses, though she is gone home to his house.

"Turkish Verses, addressed to the Sultana, eldest daughter of Sultan Achmet III

The wish'd possession is delay'd from day to day,
The cruel Sultan Achmet will not permit me
To see those cheeks, more vermilion that roses.
I dare not snatch one of your kisses.
The sweetness of your charms has ravish'd my soul.
The wretched Ibrahim sighs in these verses;
One dart from your eyes has pierced thro' my heart.
Ah! Sultana! stag-eyed—an angel amongst angels!
I desire—and my desire remains unsatisfied.
Can you take delight to prey upon my heart?
Turn to me, Sultana—let me gaze on thy beauty.
Crown of my life! Fair light of my eyes!
My Sultana! My Princess!
Adieu! I go down to the grave.
If you call me—I return.
My heart is hot as sulphur;—sigh and it will flame."

You see I am pretty far gone in Oriental learning, and to say truth I study very hard. . . .'

The effect upon Pope of her studies may be seen from his answer to this and to other transcriptions in similar vein.

From Alexander Pope to Lady Mary Wortley Montagu
[undated]

'I could quarrel with you quite through this paper upon

200

a period in yours which bids me remember you if I possibly can. You would have shewn more knowledge both of yourself and me, had you bid me forget you if I possibly could. When I do, may this hand (as the Scripture says) forget its cunning and this heart its folly . . . I fancy myself, in my romantic thought and distant admiration of you, not unlike the man in the Alchemist, that has a passion for the Queen of the fairies; I lie dreaming of you in moon-shiny nights, exactly in the posture of Endymion gaping for Cynthia. . . .

I write as if I were drunk . . . I think my letters have nothing in 'em, but I am sure my heart has so much that I am vexed to find no better name for your friend and admirer than

Your friend and admirer,
A. Pope.'

The journey from Belgrade to Adrianople had not been undertaken without hardship; nor, so Mary in a careful account of it to the Princess of Wales declares, 'by any Christian since the time of the Greek Emperors'. A gross inaccuracy this, that the Princess was charmed to believe.

The fatigue and miseries of that seven days' rough going through almost impenetrable Servian forests—'deserts' Mary calls them—was soon forgotten in the wondrous scenic panorama presented through the windows of their coach. Attended by a guard of five hundred janissaries, the Ambassadorial procession came to Nissa, once the capital of Servia, a land of 'fruitful soil and great plenty'; but a 'plenty' that the natives of the country were never allowed to enjoy. Hounded to their labours in the fertile vineyards, the starving peasants shrank beneath the overseers' whips, a prey to the arrogance and cruelty of their masters, and reduced Mary 'to tears every day' . . . The impression given to Her Royal Highness is that of a compassionate Niobe, heartbroken to see 'the wretches that provided twenty wagons for our baggage from Belgrade, sent back without payment, some of their horses lamed and others killed . . . The poor fellows came round the house weeping and tearing their hair in a most pitiful manner without getting anything but drubs from the soldiers . . .' Nor anything from Mary. 'I would have gladly paid them their money', she adds, 'but that it would only be giving so much to the Aga who would have taken it from them with no remorse.'

A wise precaution, doubtless endorsed by her husband's regard for his pocket.

After another four days' travel over mountain passes, but none so alarmingly precipitous as those they had crossed in Bohemia, their Excellencies' caravan, with its mules and asses, wagons, and its fierce bewhiskered guards in sheepskin tunics, arrived at Sofia. Mary was enchanted by the city and its beautiful surroundings. 'It is hardly possible to see a more agreeable landscape. Here are hot baths very famous for their medicinal virtues . . . This theme would carry me far.'

Too far indeed, for prudence to disclose to the Princess of Wales, but not too far for Lady Rich, who may possibly have wished it to go farther.

In her salon at St. James's, to an audience composed of Pope, Congreve, Steele, and the gently smiling Addison, Lady Rich read Mary's letter relating 'a remarkable experience' and how the amatory Steele restrained himself to hear it may be better imagined than described.

At Sofia they had halted for a day and a night, and though Mary urged her husband to stay longer, he would not. 'So zealous was he in the service of His Majesty', he must hasten to Adrianople, the Sultan's Seigneurial Court; no time to be wasted in explorative excursion: only time, insisted Edward, to refresh themselves and rest. But Mary, accustomed now to sleeping in a post-chaise, had taken all the rest that she required, and after an unappetizing breakfast left Edward to his slumbers, hired a coach, and went out.

'Not at all like ours'—nor like any other vehicle ever seen by her, was this. Lined with silk, fringed and embroidered, its seats were covered in scarlet cloth, its framework painted in arabesques of flowers with Turkish love mottoes entwined. And instead of windows a pair of wooden lattices provided veiled ladies opportunity to peep.

In this delightful conveyance Mary drove, unattended, through the sunbaked streets to the Bagnio: the Turkish Baths.

The entrance to the Bagnio, a stone-built rotunda, was guarded by a species of female Cerberus, into whose outstretched paw Mary slipped a crown piece on which the portress spat with a glowering suspicion, divided between King George's head and the riding-suit in which Mary chose to travel.

Passing through the first room, paved and benched with marble, she came to an apartment steaming with sulphurous fumes of such insufferable heat that she hastily withdrew to the adjacent cooling-room. There her gentlemanly habit caused an immediate sensation among the host of ladies restfully reclining, and all completely nude.

Her first shock at the sight of a crowd of naked women lounging upon cushions sipping sherbet, and 'without any beauty or defect concealed', turned instantly to admiration.

It was a veritable rosary where every tint of creamy flesh, pearl white and softest pink, rose-shaded, mingled with the buff and coffee-coloured sheen of slaves. And they, like their mistresses, were covered in nothing save the long silken fall of their hair. 'I had wickedness enough to wish,' reflects the startled Mary, 'that Mr. Jervas[1] could have been there invisible. I fancy it would have much improved his art!'

These houris appeared to be equally as charmed by the English lady's dress as she by their lack of any. Adoringly they gathered round her, fingering her habit that proclaimed her sex only by the trailing velvet of her skirt looped over her arm to reveal her legs encased in knee-top boots. Sibilant whispers flew between them: 'Guzél, pék guzél'. (Charming, very charming.') But when by their gestures they begged her to disrobe, she laughed and shook her head at them. Yet so desirous were these pretty creatures to see her as they were, they needs must unfasten her habit and strip her to her stays. Then they stopped to stare, and to signify with little nods and smiles that they would no longer urge her. They fully understood. It was her lord, who, very properly, had locked her into this mechanical contrivance for her safety, since, unlike themselves, Englishwomen were permitted to walk abroad unveiled, the desired of all men.

Reluctantly she left them and returned to the inn where

[1] Pupil of Kneller, famed for his portraits of women.

Edward, in a scold, was about to send a search party to find her. Where in the devil had she been?

She told him. He was horrified, and sternly forbade her to go off alone again. What! To exploit herself in the public baths among a crowd of naked heathens! Had she no regard for her position or for his? Was she devoid of all decency and shame?

If to revel in such loveliness were shame, she answered sweetly, then she was.

Her interest, however, was not wholly claimed by lovely Turkish ladies. A fresh focus for her tireless attention was provided by the Turkish Government over which the army held supreme command.

'The Grand Seignior with all his absolute power, is as much a slave as any of his subjects, and trembles at a janissary's frown!' And, should any dare to criticize tyrannical autocracy, the house of the offender would be razed to the ground and he and his family put to the torture. 'Here are no huzzaing mobs, senseless pamphlets, and tavern disputes about politics; and none of your harmless calling of names . . .' Yet, if the Minister should press authority too far he, in his turn, would be over-ruled, his person seized, his arms and legs bound, and, like a trussed fowl, would be dragged, howling, through the streets. Were he unlucky, not only his hands and his feet, but his head would be cut off and cast at the gates of the Seraglio as a warning to the Sultan who, nothing reassured by cringing subservience, cowered, terror-struck, in his apartments awaiting a similar doom.

'This is the blessed condition of the most absolute monarch on earth,' observes Mary; and suggests that 'our Parliament send over a shipload of your passive obedient men to see arbitrary Government in its clearest, strongest light, where it is hard to judge whether the Prince, the People or the Minister are most to be pitied.'

A curious anomaly, in view of the Sultan's submission to administrative power, was the ultra-extravagant pomp that attended him inside and out of his Palace.

From her window at Adrianople Mary watched His Sublimity, Achmet III, pass on his way to the Mosque. First in procession came a guard of the janissaries, their scimitars shining like a row of crescent moons, their turbaned heads sprouting white feathers. Behind them rode the Horse Guards, whose uniforms and breastplates were a blaze of golden light, their prancing Arab steeds gaily caparisoned and hung with silver bells. The Royal gardeners in solemn file followed, in so rich a variety of colour they 'appeared like a parterre of tulips', Mary said. Immediately after rode the Aga of the Janissaries, in purple velvet lined with silver tissue; beside him, and not the least imposing figure, walked, or rather waddled, the Kyzlár-Aga, Chief Black Eunuch, a swollen balloon-like monstrosity in a sugar-loaf hat and a sable-edged brocaded yellow pelisse.

Then, arrayed in all his glory, mounted on his beautiful white charger, came the All Highest, descendant of the Prophet, gowned in green and spangled with diamonds, emeralds, rubies, as if a hive of jewelled bees had swarmed upon him there. Almost as splendid as the Sultan's raiment were the trappings of his horse, the gem-studded bridle and golden saddle-cloth. Similarly decked were the six pure white Arabs, led by six courtiers all a-glitter in the sun. Last in the procession marched the Royal Cup Bearers carrying the gold and silver coffee-pots; and in the rear a slave who bore upon his head the silver stool for His Highness's convenience.

So in a shower of light passed the Sultan, 'a handsome man of forty', Mary notes. And in his passing he drew rein and for a moment halted. Those before him halted; those behind him halted, while the eyes of His Sublimity, 'very full and black', gazed attentively up at the lattice where stood the British Ambassador's wife, gazing down.

Too attentive was that glance to go unheeded. . . .

In Lady Rich's salon six months later, so slowly did news travel, it was hinted, to the gnashing of Pope's teeth, that Achmet III, the Grand Seignior, had thrown the handkerchief to Lady Mary.

*   *   *

The glowing oriental spring sped swiftly on to early summer in a brilliant pageant of ever changeful scenes and extraordinary adventures, brushed with magic.

Beyond the walls of Adrianople, a distant ridge of lilac-tinted hills melted, fainting, on a misty sky; and from the summit of those grassy slopes to the pastel green valley lay a carpet of flowers: the death-scented asphodel, dancing white narcissi, jonquils, anemones, hyacinth, rose—always the opening buds of the rose—to overflow each garden, great or small.

Their fragrance drifted in at Mary's window while her pen ran riot to seize upon and cherish a bouquet of impressions, culled from her daily journal and sent to all her friends; to Pope, to Frances, 'a record that reads, you will say,' she tells her sister, 'too like the Arabian Tales. You forget . . . those very tales were written by an author of this country.'

Yet she does not so much dilate on the beauties of 'this country' as on the beauty of its ladies, more particularly one: Fatima, wife of the Kyhaïá, aide-de-camp to the Grand Vizier.

Accompanied by a dour-visaged Greek interpretress, Mary paid a visit to the Kyhaïá's harem. Two enormous, fat negroes received her at the door, both identically dressed in red and green with conical-shaped hats on their woolly black heads and a mouthful of grins on their faces.

"A droll pair of butlers, to be sure," whispered Mary; and was instantly corrected.

"Not butlers, Madame, eunuchs."

Mary blinked. She should have known; but there was much she did not know, and much to learn in a land where the passing of a thousand and one years had not changed the tradition of A Thousand and One Nights.

Through a series of apartments roofed in gold, the walls inlaid with china from Japan and ivory from India, the eunuchs led the way into a marble gallery. Here on either side were ranged a line of girls, white as lilies and all exactly dressed alike in silver threaded damask. Mary confessed herself 'sorry that decency did not permit her to stay and consider them nearer' . . . But all thought of these pretty young creatures was lost when her guides brought her to the threshold of a porphyry pavilion. Across its high domed ceiling a fall of painted flowers perpetually tumbled from their golden painted baskets. Through the open gilt-framed windows could be seen a garden girt about with tall trees, planted so close to the casement that their shade defied the sun and cooled the room. The scent of jasmine and honey-suckle mingled with the perfume of a fountain that sprayed its crystalline sweet waters into alabaster basins.

At the far end of this fairy-like bower stood a dais strewn with Persian rugs; and there, cushioned on a sofa, the Kyhaïá's lady rested. At her feet sat two little girls 'lovely as angels, dressed perfectly rich'; yet nothing so lovely were they as their mother.

'I must own,' raves Mary, 'that I never saw anything so gloriously beautiful. That surprising harmony of feature!— That exact proportion of body!—The unutterable enchant-ment of her smile!—But her eyes!—Large and black!—' and so on.

The exquisite Fatima returned her admiration with almost equal rapture and, laying her hands on her heart in Turkish fashion of salute, bade her honoured guest be seated.

Mary sat—in a corner of the couch—and wonderingly gazed upon her hostess. She wore a *caftan* of gold brocade flowered in silver; her shift, a provocative veil of gauze, revealed more of her breasts than it hid. Her finger-tips were hennaed coral-red, as were her nipples, glimpsed through their flimsy sheath; her waistcoat, or short tunic, was wrought in green and silver; her black glossy hair, roped with pearls, fell, straight as rain, to her knees; diamond bracelets flashed upon her arms; her girdle was of diamonds. From head to foot she glittered.

Graciously she plied her guest with sherbet and a jelly-soft sweetmeat that stuck to the teeth and tasted of rose-water, honey, and almonds. "*Rahet Lahoum,*" smiled Fatima.

"Which is to say, Madame," the sour Greek interpreted, " 'giving sweet ease to the throat' ": to be known the world over as Turkish Delight.

But there was still more delight than this to come.

Nestling closer, Fatima slid her hand in Mary's and coaxingly whispered in her ear.

"What," asked Mary, blushing, "does she say—or does she want?"

The Greek lady gave a little cough.

"Would your Excellency wish to see the dancers?"

Yes, her Excellency would; and her Excellency did—with her eyes popping out of her head.

Twenty young slaves in the sheerest of shifts, came forward at a signal from their mistress. Four of them, armed with stringed instruments, sank to the ground and sitting cross-legged began to sing. The others danced—and how they danced! 'Nothing,' Mary hysterically reports, 'could be more artful *to raise certain ideas*. The tunes so soft!—the motions so languishing!—accompanied with pauses and dying eyes! The coldest and most rigid prude on earth could not have looked upon them without thinking of *something not to be spoken of*!'

So there she was in a Turkish harem, with the lovely Fatima beside her, and damsels bearing silver flasks to spray her with attar of roses; then down on their knees to touch the floor with their foreheads and serve her with coffee in cups of carven silver . . . And the dancing girls gyrated and swayed and swung before her, wriggling their pretty little hips, interweaving patterns to the music, softly singing; while the great pot-bellied eunuchs clapped their hands and wagged their heads in rhythm, showed their glistening white teeth, and cried in women's voices for more and more of it . . . And Fatima leaned nearer, caressingly to whisper: *"Guzél, guzél, Sultana—derdinden oldum zabun,"* ('I am sick with love'), which the Greek interpretress grimly translated, indicating it was time to go.

Fatima was desolate. *"Must the Beautiful One leave her?"*

"Yes," prompted the interpretress, "she must."

"But not without all the gifts of my heart."

"What does she say?" asked Mary, apprehensive.

"She has a present for you, Madame."

Not one, but a hundred presents. Two slaves were sent to bring a silver basket filled to overflowing with embroidered handkerchiefs. Mary, who had learned to know the significance of handkerchiefs, wondered were it circumspect to take them. Fatima, seeing her hesitate, implored:

"Take the richest for yourself and give the remainder to your woman." Or so the Greek lady construed it; and departed with her goodly share.

Then with the same sweet ceremony of her hands upon her heart, Fatima bade 'the Fairest of the Young' farewell.

No wonder Mary 'could not help but think she had been in some Mahomet's paradise . . .' A paradisiac delusion that dogged all those sun-dazzled days.

While Edward, fully conscious of his dignity, interviewed and was received by the Sultan's high officials, Mary ecstatically pursued her explorations, studied Turkish, and bought a Turkish dress. For the envy of Frances she sent her an elaborate description of herself in native costume, in which she sat for her portrait, 'and vastly,' she said, 'does it become me.'

She is seen in long silken drawers wrought in silver, and a smock that 'shews the shape and colour of the bosom very well.' The *antery* or waistcoat of white and gold damask, trailed its sleeves to the ground and was confined at the waist with a girdle of diamonds or, one may believe, of paste, since it is unlikely Edward would have lent his purse to any such extravagance. For cooler weather she wore the *curdee* or brocaded fur-lined mantle, and, to complete the astonishing ensemble, a jaunty little cap, the *talpock*—in velvet for the winter, silver tissue for the summer, was perched on one side of her head.

In this attire, accompanied by her Greek attendant, Mary roamed the town; but when she drove out she must go in state, together with the French Ambassadress. A chattering, lively young person was she, and 'so delighted,' Mary scoffs, 'with her guards, her four and twenty footmen, her gentlemen ushers and her damsels, y'clept Maids of Honour, that she would rather die than make me a visit without them'.

Because Edward had urged her 'be agreeable and forthcoming to the Parisienne. Relations between France and England require carefullest negotiation,' Mary strove to humour but not to suffer gladly this 'silly little ostentatious fool'. Not with Madame 'Chou-chou', as privately she called her, were Mary's excursions through the city to be shared. She would have much preferred to go alone and unattended

but that her 'studies', though they ran to verse, had not so far
perfected her in the Turkish language that she could understand one single word of it.

Adrianople, the European seat of the Ottoman Empire,
lay as if flung at the foot of a low mountain range intersected
by the ancient river Hebrus, renamed the Maritza, which
collected all the refuse of the city's open drains and stank
to heaven. In her Turkish dress and thickly veiled, Mary
joyed to mingle with and watch the mosaic crowd that
strolled along the river banks or thronged the seething
streets.

It was a city of surprises, an endless masquerade, where
women were so effectually disguised that their own husbands
could not know them beyond the harem walls; a city of
intrigue, where lovers met in Jews' shops, as in London they
met in the India houses, and whose owners, East and West,
made their fortunes from discretion; a city where the
splendour of the Orient outshone the lurking poverty of
narrow fœtid ways, unseen by Mary. Not for her the sight
of huddled victims of Ottoman oppression who writhed in
rat-infested dungeons, lacerated by the sabre thrusts of
savage guards, their gangrened wounds a feast for flies . . .
Beauty, cleanliness, and always some fresh novelty, was
presented daily for her delectation. She loved to linger at
her window when a Biblical, slow-moving frieze of burdened
camels, long-necked, spongy-footed, uncouth, yet proudly
disdainful, passed on its way to Bagdad, led by a driver on
an ass; or there would come the beasts that drew the plough-
shares, great shaggy buffaloes with a tortured glint in their
patient eyes, a black cloud of insects round their heads, and
their frontal tufts and tails dyed vermilion . . . And the
horses! Never were seen such magnificent horses: not for
labour these, cared for, petted, bred for spirit were they.
Mary had a white one, small and dainty, arrow-swift. 'I
would not part with him on any terms. He prances under
me,' she boasts, 'with so much fire you would think I had a
great deal of courage to mount him . . .' But of all the
pleasure that the city had to offer she most enjoyed to visit
the Bazaar.

Neither the eroticism of Fatima's fantasia, nor the white-hot throbbing colour of the streets with their purple-shadowed painted wooden houses, could bring to her so vividly the essence of the East as that vast arcade of merchandise, the pulse of the Moslems' trade. Here the highest and the lowest in the land came to barter at three hundred and sixty-five stalls.

In this huge market-place every nationality, Russians, French, Italians, Arabs, Jews—and mostly Jews—yelled their wares in unison. Turbaned dark-skinned vendors displayed bales of shimmering stuffs to be fingered by an Aga's jewelled hands, or filthy hands, or ladies' hands—all sorts came to buy, and some, who looked the poorest, concealed beneath their tatters bags of gold. There were rugs from Bokhara, ruby-red or pale as a fading rose; flower-like carpets from India; carpets from Turkey, thick as moss and richly patterned, hawked about by greasy, evil-faced Levantines. There were *papoushes* — slippers — rows of them, gold-threaded, pearl-encrusted, gleaming; and boxes of cedar wood, of inlaid ivory and beaten brass; combs and brushes, tooth-picks of tortoise-shell; necklaces of coral, uncut turquoise, every kind of semi-precious stone. And wherever Mary strayed entranced to pause at one or other stall, she was jostled to its neighbour with cacophonous enticement.

She bought madly. "I'll be ruined!" Oh, but she must, she positively must have this Turkish love-letter. Was there ever such a curious, delicious thing? All said in symbols, enclosed within a small partitioned casket, and in each division lay a token with a little verse attached; a pearl, a clove, a strand of hair, a jonquil, a grape, a rose, a stick of cinnamon. "There is no flower, herb, nor pebble, no fruit nor feather, weed," her guide explained, "that has not some amorous significance. You may quarrel, send letters of passion, or make a proposal of marriage without even inking your fingers."

Mary bought one from an Arab to send to Lady Rich.

The Jewish marketeers were the most insistent. Undeceived by her costume, they followed at her heels to beguile her in pidgin English. "Dis vay, dis vay—*tchelebi*!" Tempting her with oil of roses. Broussa gauze and table rugs, or balm of Mecca to beautify the face. Mary instantly purchased a jar of it, unheedful of the warning: "Madame, this is not balm of Mecca. It is mutton fat, perfumed."

Thereafter she was pestered by bearded Israelites entreating: "Vat you vish, *tchelebi*—vat you vish?" She wished for everything she saw, from the gilded festooned pillars that supported the dome, to a flea-bitten pariah puppy urged upon her by a Hindu. Yet although the heat in there was almost insupportable, Mary found the booths and pavements of the vast Bazaar infinitely better kept and cleaner than any in London's New Exchange. Layers of fine muslin protected the stalls of the confectioners and butchers from the ravages of flies. White-clad sellers of sherbet shoved their bubbling glasses in her face; but when she would have quenched her thirst, her guide again restrained her. "Your Excellency must not drink from public vessels. The plague is rife, Madame, in the Bazaar."

"The plague! Good heavens, I should never have been brought here!"

The Greek was a fatalist. "Allah holds your Excellency in His hands."

"No doubt," retorted Mary, "and if Allah wills I may have sickened now. But why do you speak the name of Allah? Are you not a Christian?"

In the treacle-black eyes of the duenna lay all the wisdom and the sorrows of the ages; with a furtive glance around her shoulder she hushed her voice to say:

"Though my heart is with the Christ our Lord, Madame, I am of a conquered race and my will is not my own. It is the Saracen's."

"But surely you Greeks are permitted to follow your faith in your Orthodox Churches?"

"Excellency, there was a time when my father stood as high in his own land as does your father in his. Now he lies low, buried deep beneath the stones of a dungeon. So much are we permitted."

"Oh!" Mary caught her breath. The Greek lady's head lifted as if to challenge sympathy.

"Let us not speak, Madame, of what shall not be spoken."

"Yet you speak," Mary said with a dampness in her eyes, "such perfect English. Where did you learn my language?"

"From my English nurse and governess, Madame, when I was a child. One does not forget."

"But what I do not understand," pursued Mary, pushing aside a grinning Asiatic with a hookah—"Lord! does he expect me to buy *this*? What I don't understand is why these Jews are tolerated here. Never did I see so many Jews. They seem to comprise half the population."

"That is so, Excellency, for they have drawn to themselves the trade of the Ottoman Empire. Every Pasha has his Jew, his *homme d'affaires*. And as all merchandise passes through their hands, so they may worship where they will. Yet we, Madame, whose race is as old as that of the Hebrews, must be serfs."

The motley crowd had lost its charm, the scene its glamour. A wretched object, huddled in the rags of a striped burnous, whined, grovelling for alms, at Mary's elbow. His features were thick and leonine, ghastly; his hands and chest a hairless dreadful white.

"A leper, Madame," said the calm duenna.

Mary shrieked. *"Bon Dieu!* First you scare me with the plague, and now with lepers. Let me go!"

Weaving her way through that clamorous gesticulating mob, she hurried out; and when safely in the coach: "But of all your talk of lepers and the plague," she said, "I have seen few signs on any face of smallpox here in Turkey. Why is that?"

"That," was the imperturbable reply, "is the secret of the Turks, Madame."

There comes to most of us a moment of significance when the whole of life converges to one point upon the compass of our destinies. Thus in a second and with no premonition, Mary's future was decided; not as Toast, not as Beauty, nor Ambassadress, nor Scribe, but to resound throughout the chronicles of science. Such are the naïve compulsions that control the laws of accident, a trick-light thrown across the path of chance to seize upon and follow—or ignore.

All history is founded upon trifles: a game of bowls, the blind eye of a sailor, the necklace of a Queen; by these slight indications great dynasties are fallen, great victories are

fought, great names remembered. So, if Mary had not asked
a certain question; if her vital curiosity had not been
aroused by an evasive answer; or if she had not seen, as once,
upon occasion, in a harem she did see, an old witch of a
woman . . .

But why speculate?

The fact remains that what she saw and noted sets a land-
mark to her journey; lights a beacon on her way.

*   *   *

Before she left for Constantinople, Mary paid a round of
farewell visits to the harems. The beautiful Fatima mourned
her departure with tears, and offered for remembrance a
casket containing—of all things in the world—a lump of
coal.

"Lud! Is the creature insolent?"

"No, Madame, affectionate," the unsmiling Greek corrected. "The gift of a coal is a symbol of love in this country,
and means 'may I die and all my years be yours.'"

"Very delicate I'm sure. But what am I to answer?"

"You must answer, Excellency, *'Sen ghel ben chekheim
senin hartsin,'* which is to say, 'All my fortune is thine.'"

Mary bade her lady: "Say it for me, and God send she
don't keep me to your word!"

The hen-faced duenna said it for her; whereupon Fatima
bowed her head, laid her hand to her heart and gabbled,
weeping.

"And now what's the fuss?" inquired Mary.

"She fears she will never see your Excellency, whom she
names 'The Lovely One', again."

"Tell her we will meet in Constantinople."

This reassurance, however, was doubted. Fatima, sighing
deeply, pointed to her breast and then to Mary's.

"She asks you for the rose you wear, Madame." And which
when given was received with expressions of joy and
smothered in rapturous kisses.

"For the rose," said the Greek, "is also a symbol of love,
to signify 'may you be happy and your sorrows mine.'". . .

Nothing so exotic as her farewell to Fatima was her visit
to another lady on her list: the wife of the Grand Vizier.

She, a quiet modest fifty, having passed the age of her lord's delight, gave herself to prayer and not to pleasure. The furniture of her apartments reflected her devotions. No lavish ornamental extravagance was hers. The lady confessed she had neither the money nor leisure to spend on 'super-fluities'. True, she had upon occasion invited the British Ambassadress to dine; yet so dreary were these pious gatherings, so numerous and highly spiced the dishes, all of which Mary had been forced to eat lest she offend her hostess, that she suffered indigestion for a week. This formidable feast had been followed by the customary performance of the dancing girls—but how different from that charming exhibition with which Fatima had entertained her. The slaves of the Grand Vizier's wife, who excused their want of skill by saying she had not the time to teach them any better, lacked everything of grace and beauty, and were dressed in shifts that resembled more an English spinster's nightgown than the tantalizing veils of Fatima's pretty maids.

"So should she invite me to dine with her today," Mary whispered to her lady, "you must say I have a previous engagement. If I eat with her again I shall be dead."

She found her hostess hideously dressed in olive green, with some dozen of her friends, all elderly and fat, clustered round her.

"I am happy your Excellency calls at so opportune a moment," translated the interpretress, "I beg you to be seated."

"Why," asked Mary, sitting, "is the moment opportune?"

"Wait, Madame," she was told, "and you will see."

An air of expectancy prevailed among the guests as they murmured together, casting sidelong looks at Mary. The slaves had withdrawn to a corner of the room, and through the open windows a chill wind drifted. Mary shivered and was offered a *curdee*, or mantle, ermine-lined. The ladies became more animated, volubly chattering and glancing at the door.

"They seem to be excited. What are they saying?"

"They are pleased, your Excellency, that the weather is turned cooler, for this is the last day of spring."

"But why should that please them? There have been other days of spring as cool as this." And when the Greek remained silent Mary was beset with fears. What if these barbarians should be hatching plots against her? As the wife of the British Ambassador she represented a hostile country, since Austria, ally of Britain, warred with Turkey. Surely Edward had been rash in his insistence that she pay this duty call to the wife of the Sultan's First Minister, particularly now, when the Ottoman armies were encamped outside the town, preparing an advance upon the Austrians. There was no knowing what horrible revenge these apparently gracious but sinister women, chattels of their masters, might perpetrate on her whose husband had not yet succeeded in effecting any approach to a truce. Only the week before Mary had witnessed the fanatical enthusiasm of the volunteers who had joined the Seigneurial troops. From her lattice she had watched—and watching almost fainted—to see pass beneath her window those who had begged of the Sultan the honour of serving him. Naked to their waists, their heads and arms stuck over with arrows, their faces streaming blood, they marched through the streets, singing, shouting, bespattering their way with crimson drops; and as they passed the windows of their women they slashed at their arms and chests with knives till the blood spurted afresh, to indicate they were as eager to die for the love of a lady as for His Sublimity himself . . . So what now, she wondered, as her hostess and the other guests reclining on their cushions, rolled back their sleeves and looked markedly at her!

"I do not like their gestures," Mary muttered. "I am going."

The Greek lady shook her head.

"Have patience, Madame, and you will see a miracle."

"I do not care for miracles. I know their Turkish miracles. Send for my footmen."

"Madame, recollect. No man may enter here."

"Be damned to that! I demand protection in his Excellency's name."

"Hush, Madame, you will frighten these good ladies."

"I hope I do—and trust you're not in league with them."

But even as she rose to run, the harem doors were opened by two eunuchs, and into the apartment hobbled a black-robed, mummified figure. It paused upon the threshold, flinging back its veil to reveal a face, brown and wizened as a medlar, inconceivably malign.

As Mary, sick with terror, stood uncertain, her hostess gently urged her back upon the cushions and spoke to the interpretress.

"Your Excellency is requested to see the engrafting."

"See the—*what*?" shrieked Mary.

Permitting her grim features to relax into a smile, "A Turkish custom, Madame," the duenna said. "You are fortunate to be confided with this secret; the only secret of the Turks," she added in a lower voice, "that is not ungodly. You asked me once, you may remember, why you had perceived no sign of the smallpox here in Turkey. You will now know why this is, Madame . . . So watch."

That evening Edward, returning to the palace where, of the Sultan's courtesy, they lodged, found a breathless wife awaiting him. Her eyes were bright; her hands hot as fire clutching his.

"Edward!"

"Well?" Coolly he detached himself to say: "You are quite overwrought with your endless excursions."

"Edward, listen!" She threw off her *caftan*. She was in her Turkish dress, which, in total disregard of her husband's disapproval, she continuously wore. "To-day I have made a discovery—an astonishing discovery—that should render me a benefactor to mankind."

He started, stared, took her hand again and felt her pulse. "You're in a fever. A touch of the sun, I suspect."

"You rile me," said Mary, "past endurance. Will you listen! I have witnessed to-day with these eyes that have been so monstrously disfigured from the scourge, a lasting cure for it."

"Exactly so," soothed Edward. "Go you to bed, and I will send for the doctor."

"I won't—and you shan't!" She came close to him, her face uplifted, glowing. "Edward, you have known me foolish,

217

you have known me vain, and self-willed, maybe, but I have always held within me here," she tapped her breast, "the certainty that some day, somehow, I would make my mark; not as versifier—God forbid!—not even as your wife, though I'm proud," she snuggled up to him, "to name myself as such."

"Since I am become," he said with coldness, "an Ambassador?"

"Unworthy!" She wrung a finger-nail fighting for control. "I could retort to that, but what I have to tell you is above all petty wrangles." She drew a breath. "And what I've seen is truly, as my guide did say, a miracle."

Edward walked to the door.

"Come back!" she shrilled at him. He turned: she coaxed. "Come, love, and sit beside me."

He was beguiled to a sofa where cross-legged she sat on cushions, slid her arm around his neck and said: "Don't scoff, you disbeliever. All I beg is that you'll listen. To-day I was at the house of the Grand Vizier, where his wife entertained a parcel of monsters, fat and bloated, dreadful. I was frightened. I thought they were come there to do me a mischief, so mysterious and whispering were they! Then came limping in what I took to be a revivified mummy . . . No, Edward, I'm not mad, nor sick, nor sun-struck. I am sane—" her voice ran down in laughter. "How Steele would scold at me for this alliteration!—and as scientific as any pompous medico or Dr. Garth, for I swear, as God's my judge, I have found a remedy to cure the spread of smallpox!"

Edward got up. "You are not yourself, my dear. Go to bed. I will send for the——"

"Say it again and I'll scream!"

He said it again; but Mary did not scream. She folded her arms, looking impish.

"Very well, send for the doctor. And I will tell him what I'm going to tell you."

Mr. Maitland, apothecary-surgeon, courteously styled 'Doctor', was a nervous little man in a tie-wig and suitable black relieved by impeccable white. Brought from England to attend upon the Embassy, he had never before been invited to their Excellencies' private apartments. Sherbet and a sticky sweetmeat in a silver casket were offered by her ladyship; these Mr. Maitland declined. He wore a denture. Her Excellency did not wear a denture; her pearly teeth were all her own. She munched at ease while Mr. Maitland indulged in a rosy perspective of higher honour yet to come. Such marked preference indicated, surely, a promotion; he might even be appointed Apothecary-Surgeon to the King, when he should return to his unappetizing wife and the practice he had left in Chelsea village.

"Sir," requested Mary, "will you feel my pulse?"

The apothecary's vision faded; he had been too optimistic. His visit was professional. Neither more nor less. He pulled in his lips, pulled out his watch, laid his fingers on her wrist and pronounced: "A trifle rapid, but not indicative of fever."

"His Excellency fears I have a sunstroke."

"Does your Excellency complain of the headache?"

"No, I don't."

"And a thirst?"

"None at all. Pray be seated, Doctor. I was about to tell my husband of my experience today in a harem, which I advise you to investigate. While I sat with the ladies an old woman arrived, holding in her hand a nutshell——"

Edward sniffed.

"And in this nutshell," Mary said, speaking slowly, clearly, "was collected the pus of the most virulent species of small-pox."

Mr. Maitland put his head to one side, looking like a very startled sparrow.

Mary shrugged a shoulder.

"I can't expect you to believe me, for what I tell is true, beyond belief. This old hag—I saw her do it—opens up a vein in your arm or your leg with a needle, and into the scratch she passes no more of the pus than will lie on the head of a pin. Then she binds the wound with a hollow bit of shell that it may not be exposed to the air. In this way is the sickness engrafted, as they call it, and thus is the patient rendered immune from——"

"I have never heard of anything so utterly preposterous!" passionately interrupted Edward. "I am astonished you can be deceived by such a trick. Unless, indeed, you are deluded."

"I am not deluded. Doctor, do you think I am deluded? Is not this—if you will bring your sense to bear on it—a possible method of allaying the disease?"

"Ha-hum!" The little man began to sweat. He thought her Excellency was, if not deluded, exceedingly gullible, but he would not care to say so. Instead, he sought to compromise. "I have heard, your Excellency, that—a—that a form of witchcraft is practised in heathen countries as a cure for—hem!" He floundered.

Mary nodded, smiling.

"The physicians of the West may yet learn from the East, where all medical knowledge derives. You have only heard the prelude to this witchcraft. Hear now its sequel. Within a few days, those who have been engrafted take the sickness."

"Ah!" Edward twisted his nose.

"The sickness," Mary repeated, glancing daggers at him, "with slight symptoms of the smallpox."

"In other words," Edward scathingly addressed the flustered doctor, "they give themselves the smallpox to prevent it. Remarkable!"

"Yes!" Mary started up. "Remarkable it is. They *do* give themselves the smallpox, or the semblance of it, which causes no distemper worse than the running sore where the pus-pointed needle has entered. And that very sore is proof that the sickness has been taken and the patient, after three days of mild fever, is guarded—for life—from its recurrence."

Mr. Maitland was leaning forward, his hands on his knees, his whole attention riveted upon the speaker.

"For life," Mary emphasized. "Think of it! No scar is left, no disability. Thousands here in Turkey undergo the operation twice a year—in the spring and autumn. So *that*," she spoke half to herself, "is why they were in such twitters at the coolness of the day. From now on until October there will be no more engrafting . . . Look around you, Doctor. Have you not observed how in this city none but the poorest, and few enough of them, bears any mark of the scourge that attacks three-fourths of our people in England? Scarce a

220

family with us that has not suffered either death or disfigure-ment from this dread disease. Take my case alone. I have lost a dear beloved brother, and my eyelashes. Yes, Doctor! You have never seen my eyes as they were, only as they are, unshaded, bursting from my head. I'm conspicuous—a woman without eyelashes. A figure of fun!"

"Your Excellency's eyes," stammered Mr. Maitland, "are the more beautiful for——"

"Fiddlesticks! You know, or you should know, how in this frightful sunlight glare my eyes are weakened, pouring water. You should prescribe me spectacles of blackened glass. Not rose-coloured—" she smiled—"for so perceptive is my sight it should be shielded, lest it uncover more unlikely secrets. So that, sir, is my story—in a nutshell! You may take it, you may leave it. But I shall *never* leave it, until," she spread her arms, "I have retold it—to the world!"

★ 13 ★

When 'the world', understood to be that exclusive area bounded on the south by the Palace of St. James's, on the north by Leicester Fields, had been duly apprised of Mary's 'story in a nutshell', it was mildly amused. Passed from mouth to mouth in ladies' drawing-rooms, her 'astonishing discovery' created less disturbance than her account of her visit to Fatima's harem, or of herself in Turkish dress.

Mr. Secretary Craggs, who had not forgotten an occasion when a harmless little joke he had played on Lady Mary had been wrongfully retailed for the King's displeasure, nursed a sour grievance while awaiting sweet revenge. That His Majesty had long forgotten his bêtise did not decrease his rancour. But for Lady Mary's malice Mr. Craggs believed that he, and not Wortley Montagu, would have been Ambassador at Constantinople.

Disquieting news from the Porte had been pounced upon by Mr. Craggs. All hope of mediation between the Austrians and Turks appeared to have receded. Belgrade had been captured by Imperialist troops under Prince Eugene, with enormous loss of men and arms and money . . . For how long, was Mr. Craggs' suggestion to the King, could Austria bear the burden of this needless expense, which sooner or later His Majesty's Government would be called upon to subsidize? Was not the purpose of his Excellency's mission to avoid the furtherance of war? Yet it would seem . . .

Mr. Craggs produced a cutting from *The Daily Courant*. Dragged from nostalgic memories of Herrenhausen, whence he had recently returned, the King was moved to ask:

"*Was kann das sein?*"

"An account, Sire, from a journal recording a visit paid by Your Majesty's Ambassador at the Porte to the camp of the Grand Seignior at Philippopolis."

"*Nein!*" The King's sagging head jerked as if pulled by a wire. "My Ambassator to visit de enemy's camp? Pas possible!"

"The Turk, Sire," gently corrected Mr. Craggs, "is not Your Majesty's enemy—yet. Indeed, so anxious is his Excellency to placate him, that this ceremonial entry into the Sultan's arena—" the Secretary spoke with studied care that the King's reddening ears should miss no word of it— "was manoeuvred with much ceremonial magnificence, according to this news-sheet's report. And so impressed by such gratifying homage from Your Majesty was the Grand Vizier, who I understand in all matters politic ranks higher than the Sultan, that he ordered his Excellency's tent to be placed beside his own."

"*Du lieber Gott!*" The King's pouchy eyes, so like a pair of boiled gooseberries, were bolting. "And dis newss is after how moch time—tree munts—by de courier come. Not?"

Craggs nodded agreement.

" 'Tis stale news in the Porte by now, Sire, but—three months at least, maybe four."

"*Ach! Scheusslich!*" exploded the King. "And vat is since dis come—*nicht*? On whose side does mine Excellency work? From us—or from de Sultan?"

"Shall we say, from an overweening, but, alas," sighed Mr. Craggs, "misplaced sense of duty, hoping perchance—" A thoughtful pause and stroking of the chin preceded the words—"that by an obvious placation a truce may be achieved."

"Not so! Na, na! Dis is not de vay to act de—how you say?—de pandar to de Turk?"

Craggs masked a grin.

"Sire, his Excellency's policy is that of peace at all costs. Nor in his zeal does Your Majesty's Ambassador spare his wife, the Lady Mary. She too——"

Again Craggs paused with a simultaneous folding of his lips and the paper in his hand:

"She!" The King clutched the arms of his chair. "Vy speak you of she? Is *auch* de Lady Mary at de camp?"

"No, Sire. I understand her Excellency is under the impression that it is more tactful to adapt herself to the native custom of feminine retirement. She visits nowhere save in the harems and," Craggs glanced carefully aside, "in Turkish dress."

The King wetted his lips. It needed no great effort of imagination to visualize her Excellency in her Turkish dress.

"And," continued Craggs, laying balm to his festering canker, "I am told that so appealing does the Sultan find her ladyship's attire that he has thrown the handkerchief—that is to say, Sire, invited her Excellency to visit his Seraglio."

"Diable!" Although the King's English was limited, he understood sufficient of this dulcet innuendo, gustily to burst forth into French. "Mais! C'est incroyable! Je sais bien que miladi est une originale, *aber* dis is trop fort! Too moch! We are dégouté!"

Sadly Mr. Craggs inclined his head.

"The Court of Vienna, Sire, labours under the—we hope erroneous—assumption that his Excellency acts in the interests of Turkey rather than our own."

"Evidamment!" The King's mottled chins shook with his fury. "If mein Ambassador permits his wife to—na, *doch*! We vill not dis horreur belief."

Mr. Craggs was beginning to enjoy himself.

"The Austrian proposals, Your Majesty, that the Turks render up Wallachia, Moldavia, Bosnia and Belgrade," said the bland Mr. Craggs, "have been refused. Hence the siege and prolongation of the war. His Excellency's efforts on Your Majesty's behalf would appear to be as wasted as— misplaced."

The King rose up, his short dumpy figure squarely set. Disregarding the unpleasant implication against his much admired Lady Mary, he, nothing if not conscientious, lent Teutonic thoroughness to bear upon the point. Since Austrian alliance was essential to British foreign policy, so His Majesty's not over-ripe intelligence foresaw, and if the Treaty should be severed by mistaken mediation, then:

"De cause," he said, "of dis mistake shall be—removedt!"

           *   *   *

Meanwhile Mary, unaware of serpentine insinuations in her 'Mahomet's Paradise', had come by Marmora's seaboard way to Pera at Constantinople. The Embassy, a palace perched on a hill, overlooked the city that rose, tier upon white tier, above the Golden Horn; and as the opalescent morning mists unrolled from those fervent blue waters, so the sun's revived strength would reveal a proud forest of masts.

Flanked by the domes and minarets of the Magnificent Suleiman's Mosque, the Sultan's ships, like swans of gold, floated amid gaunt native craft. There, with damp brown sails spread, merchantmen returned from the Aegean Islands or the lands along the Danube, disgorged their cargoes of timber, fruit, and oil, spices, wine, while busy little caiques ferried back and forth, fetching passengers and goods from bank to bank. Beyond that glistening diadem of palaces, of Saracenic temples, domes and cupolas, the cypress-girdled mountains ringed the sky to Asia; and farther still upon the Turkish side, a snow-capped spur, touched with swords of fire, lifted up the shredded clouds to Heaven . . . Mount Olympus.

Mary waxed ecstatic when she first surveyed 'this crowded city where summer reigns with one eternal smile', thus she eulogized, in verse of seven pages, which she sent to Mr. Pope to be received with the rapture he bestowed on her *Eclogues*.

'These gilded leaves,' he wrote, 'are opened with no less

veneration . . . and like them locked up and concealed from profane eyes.'

But summer in Constantinople, its 'eternal smile' notwithstanding, proved uncomfortably warm. After a month of it Mary, fearing the effect of the heat upon her son, carried him off to Belgrade Village, a fashionable Turkish coastal resort. There, fanned by the Black Sea's breezes, she stayed till the advance of the Austrian troops drove her back to the palace at Pera. During those few weeks of her retirement her letters reveal unmistakable signs that the highly coloured, highly flavoured East begins to pall . . . 'I am sometimes weary of this singing and dancing and sunshine, and wish for the smoke in which you toil.'

At the palace casement she watched her small son playing in the garden where the dappled shadows of overhanging trees enclosed the noonday sun, and nameless flowers scented, heavy-sweet, the air. And as she watched his listless movements, Mary, worried by his pallor, called:

"Come in, my love. You should not stay too long in the sun . . . Bring him to me."

His nurse, an Armenian, brought him.

An unchildishly silent little boy was this younger Edward, with his father's light hair and finely modelled features, and nothing of his mother in his face. As she brushed back a limp elf-lock from his moist forehead, Mary's heart narrowed, conscience-stirred. She should never have dragged him to this unnatural climate, but how could she have left him for five years, or maybe more?

"Are you happy here, my darling, or would you rather be in England?"

"Yes."

That might have been an answer to both questions. His eyes, full and clear, gazed through her into space. A surge of love welled up and overswept her. She enclosed his slight body with her arm, pressing his head to her breast. "Would you wish to go that long way home without me?"

Puckering his mouth in a grimace he freed himself.

"I want a ship."

"A ship, sweetheart?"

"To sail on the sea." He pointed vaguely outward.

"I will take you for a sail in a ship along the Bosphorus."

"No, not with you. Alone." Savagely he struck at a mosquito with his battledore. It was as if he had struck her.

"Give him a cooling drink," she bade the nurse. "You must not allow him to play in the sun. Put him to rest."

Without a word or backward look he went.

Even there in her latticed room, the heat rising from the sun-soaked marble floor, was too intense for comfort. A distant rumble that might have been thunder or the murmur of the sea beat in her ears like a drum. And as she leaned from her window to listen she heard her boy's voice, shrill, querulous, commanding: "You must do as I say, not as *she* says. I won't rest!"

An obstinate, difficult child. Again her heart misgave her. She was wrong to have uprooted him. These alien surroundings and incessant blinding sun might ill affect his future. She turned to go after him and assure herself that the nurse would obey her orders and not his; but as she reached the door a faintness came upon her; the room wavered, the walls rocked and dipped. Giddily she sought to keep her balance, and groping for a chair sank into it . . . The suspicion of the last few weeks was now become a certainty. She struggled to her feet and summoned an attendant . . . "Fetch the doctor." It were best to have a medical opinion.

A brief examination dispelled all lurking hope that she had been mistaken. In February her baby would be born.

* * *

'Give me, great God, said I, a little farm,
In summer shady and in winter, warm. . . .'

How often in those dragging months did Mary offer up that prayer while she awaited the coming of her second child, conceived in the passionate Levantine spring; and although in all her letters she made light of it, she by no means welcomed her 'uneasy situation' . . . 'In this country they have a notion that whenever a woman leaves off bringing forth children it is because she is too old for that business, whatever her face says to the contrary . . . When they are with child they hope God will be so merciful as to send them

226

two this time!' . . . Two. Twins. A devastating thought that would never do to dwell upon, yet despite herself she did, and was filled with misgivings for her safe deliverance. She yearned for the England she had left, and the far familiar home life of her kind.

'I am now sitting, this fourth of January, with the windows open enjoying the warm shine of the sun while you are freezing over a sad sea-coal fire! . . .' Gladly would she have exchanged the sunshine and the flowers, the jonquils, roses, carnations, fresh-plucked from her garden, for a whiff of London fog. Seeking new diversion to pass her weary time, she 'bespoke' a mummy, made a collection of doubtful Greek coins, and visited the *Hanns* (monasteries) to watch the dancing Dervishes at their devotions. Faster and faster, in maniacal frenzy, they whirled to the wail of pipes, swaying, stamping, shouting 'Allah! Allah-hou!'—to cease on one long-drawn triumphant howl: *'There is no other God but God, and Mahomet is His Prophet!'*

But not even this extraordinary sight, which Mary found ridiculous, and not a little touching; nor the lavish hospitality of harem ladies could compensate her for the sameness of her days, catalogued as 'Monday—setting of partridges. Tuesday—reading English. Wednesday—studying the Turkish language. Thursday—classical authors. Friday—spent in writing. Saturday—at my needle. Sunday—admitting of visitors, hearing of music.'

Edward is not included in this routine, to which, from a surfeit of Turkish women, customs, climate, she had turned. Or maybe she blamed herself more than she blamed him that in her avid explorations she had seen so little of her husband. "If I were not so confident of your scruples," she quizzed him, "I would believe you also had adopted Turkish fashion and kept a harem of a dozen other wives."

A remark that went unheeded. Edward, more morose of late than she had ever known him, prowled, fidgeting, about the room, fingering an ornament, sniffing at a rose . . . "I am sick of roses!" she cried petulantly. "Roses in January! What would I not give to see a snowdrop."

He said, with a thin, haggard look:

"Next year you may."

"What ails you?" she asked him. "Are you ill?"

"No." And avoiding her eyes, "Mary," he asked, "would you care to go home?"

"Home!" Her face lightened. "Would I not! But—" with a delicate instinctive gesture she laid her hand against her body, "no matter how much I might *care* to go home, how can I?" Then as she saw words hover on his lips she added quickly: "Is there some purpose in your suggestion other than," her voice broke, "than that you see at last how I am wretched—dreading this event? I must wait till it is over, and then, if I live, I must wait nine months more. Would you have me travel with a suckling at my breast—or maybe two?"

He stood stock still.

"I have had a letter from Addison. He—did I mention this before?—has now become First Secretary of State."

"So I have heard, but not from you. From one or other of my correspondents who fill me up with London news." And, at that look of his that slid from hers, her heart gave a dive. "What of Addison?"

"Nothing of Addison." Edward's lips tightened. "He writes me as a friend. He *is* my friend."

"But we know he is your friend!" she cried, and rising from her seat she went to him; he had sunk into a chair, a cumbrous walnut English chair left over from the furnishings of Sir Robert Sutton, his predecessor at the Porte. "What—" she took his hand; it was clammy—"what do you hide from me? Does Addison's letter bring bad news?"

He offered her a folded paper, "Read it." A muscle moved in his jaw as if he were biting his words. "Friend Addison, First Secretary of State, has an admirable diffidence in his choice of language to prepare me for a pending blow."

Leaving the cool shadows for the sunny window's light, Mary read the letter, read it twice again, how that:

'. . . I find myself obliged to communicate to you, not as Secretary to the Ambassador, but as an humble servant to his friend . . . Our great men are of opinion it would be more agreeable to your inclinations as well as for the King's service which you are so able to promote in Parliament, rather to return to your own country than to live at Constantinople.

For this reason they have thought of relieving you by Mr. Stanyon, who is now at the Imperial Court, and of joining Sir Robert Sutton with him in mediation of a peace between the Emperor and the Turks . . . I find by His Majesty's way of speaking of you, that you are much in his favour. . . .'

"His favour!" She crimsoned. "So great is His Majesty's favour that he sets Addison to pave a pretty way for—" her laughter was brittle as glass in her throat—"for your recall!"

Edward caught her as she swayed.

"It was wrong in me to tell you," he muttered. "I should have had more consideration for your state."

"You had every right to tell me." She left his arms and, with forced composure, said: "I trust I shall be given time to bear my babe before we are turned out. I would not wish . . ." Her words trailed off, her quick breathing stirred the laces at her breast; but when he came close to slide an arm round her shoulders she moved sharply away.

She did not see the hurt behind his eyes.

*　　*　　*

Early in March Mary was gaily writing to Frances to say she was the mother of a daughter five weeks old. 'I don't mention this as one of my most diverting adventures, though I must own it is not so mortifying here as in England.' Never to Frances, nor to anyone else, would she reveal how deeply she resented the shame of her husband's dismissal; and in her silent brooding she came to regard his recall as more her own failure than his. From the first she had mistaken his potentialities, had buoyed herself on images to find her disillusionment, too late.

Secretly at night, while he slept beside her, she sobbed into her pillow, hurling abuse at him, unvoiced. A clumsy-headed mooncalf, a fine diplomat was he! And she the greater fool to have believed in him. Had she not been warned of his inherent instability, with his letters blowing hot and cold— enough to fill a volume, year in, year out, until—her cheeks burned to admit it, she had dragged him by the ears to run away with her? She had been an emotional romantic, absorbed in dreams and too possessive. He had asked for a slave, a gentle wifely creature, and she had given him a mistress, or a master! Yet she would have been malleable and loving too, had he shown himself more kindly in those early days of marriage . . . Look how for months at a time he had left her while he followed his 'Business' in London with no thought for her, buried in the country. "And I loved you so," she whispered. "You were my whole life."

Memories hovered around her as she lay face downwards, stifling her sobs. Nature, that old harridan, had stolen a march on her, betrayed her to herself. She, the once hopeful, expectant 'Laetitia' who had set 'Sebastian' on high to make a saint of him, saw him cruelly disenchanted. She had given him her body and—she believed—her soul; and that, too, with a cynical grimace, she recognized as 'blarney', as that awful Mr. K. would have had it . . . Dear Lord, she said, had I heeded my father and taken that one, I could not have done worse than take a puppet and enshrine it—for my prayers.

And Edward snored.

"You too," she raised her head to tell him, "may have sought escape from the nothingness of life in a new heaven, or new earth. Must we *wait* for heaven? . . . Where are people matched? Or do we come together as in a country dance when hands are strangely given, strangely taken, till at last all meet their partners when the jig is done?"

"Wha-ah?" Edward woke with a start. "Wha's time?"

She leaned over him, brushing his cheek with her hair.

"Long past kissing time—no time to kiss again."

The back of his head in the moonlight revealed a bald patch like a tonsured monk's. She gazed at it pitifully; a tear rolled down her nose and dropped; and as if a fly had touched him he shook himself and bubbled in his sleep.

She rose, unrefreshed, to watch the dawning spread a ruby mantle on Olympus. Yet another day!

A week of days, a month of days slid by, and all too slowly. She was impatient to be gone, even though she 'trembled' at the thought of the journey, 'with a little infant hanging at my breast', so flippantly she wrote; but trembled more at the prospect of the feline salutations that would greet her return after such a surprisingly short absence. Addison's kindly gilding of the pill, with the suggestion that the King could better spare Edward's service in an Embassy abroad than in Parliament at home, did not for one moment deceive Mary; nor her husband.

If she had shown some sympathy in his disappointment instead of dwelling on her own, with the biting reminder that she 'hoped the news was less of a shock to him than it had been to her', even then she might have saved their marriage; but it was not in Mary to dissemble. She had made it clear that by misplaced administration he had lost himself his post and ingloriously failed. No more was to be said.

Nor did she know that she had said too much.

* * *

As the day of departure drew near, Mary appeared to be in highest spirits; but while she kept her word and spoke no more of Edward's dismissal, her very avoidance of the subject was a perpetual reproach. Her attitude toward him now was one of cool indifference that bordered on contempt. In April she took the children to Belgrade Village, ostensibly to escape the heat, but actually to have her boy 'engrafted' for the smallpox. Not till the deed had been done did she write to tell Edward, and forestalled objection by adding: 'He is at this time singing and playing, and impatient for his supper.'

Back again in Constantinople she employed herself in making an itinerary of the places they would visit on the journey home in which Edward had no choice, nor voice. She decided they would take a boat to Tunis—for she positively must see Africa—calling at various Greek islands on their way; thence to Genoa and overland to Paris, where she would meet the Abbé Conti and her 'Sister Mar' . . . And she would hope to find a French nurse for the baby.

They embarked on the evening of July the fourth in the *Preston*, a British man-o'-war.

She stood on deck to watch the westering sky spend its glory on the mountains beyond the Golden Horn. The barges, caiques, and merchantmen had taken to their moorings. The air was cool, the water's silence broken only by the cry of gulls, a sailor's song; the creak and groan of canvas swelling to the breeze. Fiercely the light deepened, folding purple scarves and saffron hoods about the hills; the city's domes and minarets were tipped with crimson fire; and as the ship skimmed out of harbour and over the wave-ruffled sea, that shining land sank with the last of the sun between night and the ended day.

★ 14 ★

DICK STEELE was entertaining friends to supper at his house in St. James's Street, the lease of which he had precariously held on and off for the last three years.

It was November. The autumn had been mild, to pay the penalty in fog—and what a fog!—on this night worse than ever. It came slinking into corners and drifting down the chimney, to damp the sparking logs and tease the eyes and rasp the throat, and tarnish Dick's high spirits and his wife's best silver dishes laid for company. And: "Dear to goodness," fussed Prue, "what man in his senses would venture out in this to kill a cat?"

"They'll venture, never fear, through worse than fog—an earthquake—for a sight of your sweet face," said Dick, tenderly taking from under each arm a bottle to set on the sideboard. "That's six, and there's another dozen o' the same below. And now for the Porto and Canary—and the punch-bowl, me darling. Will ye fetch it out the cupboard?"

"I will not. Am I your serving-wench to fetch and carry for you? So weakened as I am from my lying-in, with nothing more to show for it—" Prue sucked in a shaking underlip— "than a dead babe."

"Nay now, my soul!" Although he was holding two more bottles round their necks, Dick managed to clasp her. "What a green-toothed rat am I to put so much upon you! But you're strengthening," he pleaded. "Tell me—aren't you? Doctors Garth and Woodward report a great improvement. You've some colour to your cheeks—or is it paint?"

Lifting up her chin Prue retorted: "Paint it is. Am'nt I

cadaverous without it? Much you care, *Sir* Richard——" She bared her teeth at him, unsmiling. "And look you, that bailiff's man. I will not have him to bring in the gentlemen, bowing round like a flunkey and drunk as a lord. No, I will not. May I die."

"Never say it!" Dick rid himself of bottles to stretch his arms for her again. "You wring me heart."

"I will wring your neck!" Prue coughed and beat her chest to beat the fog away. "Will you keep your hands to yourself —for ever fumbling."

Dick's broadened smile fled. "Must I not touch what's mine, paid for in honest marriage licence?"

"Which is all that is paid for honest in this house, see." She flounced to the door, "I will to my bed and stay there, while you fill yourselves with sirloin of beef and chicken fritters, that I, not *you*, have paid for out of that I put by in my stocking back in Wales while you were pot-housing in Edinbro'. Yes! And I was out in this plaguy fog this morning early, to bespeak a hare——"

"A hare!" With the return of Dick's grin his eyes almost disappeared in the up-roll of his cheeks. "Was there ever such a woman, priced above rubies, to buy me a hare? Will ye jug it in claret?"

"It is jugged." Prue scowled at him. "And stinking high."

"Stinking high! O, excellent wife—and well seasoned with cloves and the leaves of the bay, and a soupçon of pimento as I like it?"

"Go then," screeched Prue, "and be your own scullion, and baste the joint yourself, and me up to the elbows in pig's blood, as am I half the day, making a black pudding for Joe Addison, knowing him partial to it. So!"

"Hear her, will ye?" Dick addressed the ceiling. "A thought for all. A black pudding for Joe and a hare for me. Is she not a treasure beyond——"

"By damn!" With her hand on the door-knob Prue turned. "If I have not forgot today is Friday, is it, and Mr. Pope a Papist and not so much as a fish-bone in the house!"

"Send the bailiff's bum to buy a salmon," Dick called after her, "and tell him to bring it all alive and kicking in me well-boat!"

But as the door closed the laughter faded from his face; his prune-dark eyes were moist . . . When a week ago he had returned from Edinburgh, where he had been busy with a finger in the pie of the Commission, he had seen, and seeing feared to see so swift a change in Prue. Her throat showed hollows; her lovely breasts had shrunk, and her skin had a greenish-white tinge due, he declared, to the purges and emetics prescribed by Dr. Woodward; but though the dance had gone out of her step there was dance enough to her tongue, Lord be thanked. For while she could scold, Dick reflected for his comfort, she'd not sicken.

If only he could clear himself of debt! He owed that black-livered usurer, Minshull, twelve hundred guineas for an advance on a share in Drury Lane Playhouse, and this beery devil who hung his hat up in the hall was baneful reminder of the fact; or if he could see his ship come home, his well-boat, his prime invention—the 'fish-pool' he called it—full of salmon all alive-o, his fortune would be made— yes, and a good six hundred *that* had cost him too! Yet at least he had seen his 'fish-pool' launched at Temple Mills where she was built, and go rolling down the river to the sea. True, no sizeable salmon had so far been inveigled in her tank to be delivered swimming to the stalls at Billingsgate, but time would show the worth of his fine patent. What though Grub Street split its sides with laughing, and dangled lampoons limp from the press in his face as he walked out? What though his enemies would gladly see him sunk with his sloop in Thames mud, Dick's unswerving optimism kept his ship afloat to stave off his creditors with the promise of riches to them and himself. And then there were those seven plays he had been commanded to produce for the King at Hampton Court; all would bring in money to pay Minshull, and the eight hundred Prue declared he owed her, and the boy's schooling and Betty's, and the doctor's bills and what not—and the sea-coal merchant and his wig-maker, and then, dear God, he would buy that sorrel mare he had seen at Tattersall's, and a pearl necklace for his Prue.

A rat-tat below sent him limping—he was gouty—to the window. The fog had thinned enough for him to discern the ghostly shapes of houses opposite, and the flare of a link-boy's torch hazily lighting a sedan, that, even as he watched, was raised and borne away by two shadows in cocked hats. Dick closed the shutters to keep out the fog and to keep in the warmth, heaped logs on the fire and set chairs to rights around the table—he was short of two. A dish of walnuts beside a red glass bowl of fruit took his fancy. He cracked a nut between his strong white teeth. And now what of walnuts had he lately heard? At Button's —was it yesterday?—some fantastic tale to do with Lady Mary home again from foreign parts. Pope would know if there were any truth in the talk that was going round the clubs, since, if Pope could be believed, the lady had written him a dozen or more letters in a year.

Then, at the sound of Warren's footsteps in a hurry down the passage, Dick gave a look at himself in the glass to admire his peruke with those few grey hairs that he had ordered to be threaded through the black. Lepine, his tailor, had made a good job of that alteration to his coat, another inch—God's mercy!—to be let out around the middle. Pulling in his belly, Dick adjusted his sword-belt and with studied negligence awaited his first guest.

"S'death, what a night! I'm fairly perished." Pope hobbled to the fire, spreading thin little hands to the blaze. "Yet when I left Twit'nam the sun was daffodil bright in the sky and the birds sang in the hedges, and I saw a rose unfolding in my garden."

"At Twickenham!" cried Dick, holding out a glass. "Drink this to drown the fog. What did you at Twickenham, and why do you speak of your garden? I didn't know you had a garden."

"I shall have very soon, my dear—and a house." Pope swallowed his wine. "I am about to buy a long lease with five acres of land, if I can get it at my price."

"What's this?" cried Dick, with envy.

"And a temple in the grounds, with a bowling-green, a hothouse, and a vineyard." Pope set down his glass, rubbed his palms and chuckled, pleased as and looking like a wicked little Punch.

"And all from the *Iliad*. Well—" Dick gave the crooked

back a hearty slap—"I'll say that you deserve it. 'Tis rare that genius reaps reward in wealth."

"Hum!" Pope sniffed sideways, and pulling out his handkerchief blew a trumpet-blast to clear his nose. "You flatter me, Dick. I know myself. I am no genius—but I take pains. 'I was not for courts or great affairs. I pay my debts—' " Dick reddened at the cut—" 'and say my prayers.' Amen. And who, to bear me company, is this?"

'This' was Addison. Dick rushed to welcome him. "Joe! I hardly dared hope ye'd come all the way through this porridge soup from Kensington!"

Addison, married to his Countess, lived in luxury at his stepson's century-old manor, Holland House. Dick passed him a bumper. "This will warm your bones. How's the asthma?"

"Comme ci, comme ça." Peeling off his perfumed gloves, Joe seized the glass and drained it.

Trying not to look as anxious as he felt, Dick saw Joe a very sick man. His face was lined, but not with age; his eyes were puffy round the lids, yet the womanish weak mouth could still smile, bitter-sweetly; and his hands, though darkcorded with veins, were eloquent and sensitive as ever. He was laughing now to tell them how Dr. Garth had called him from across the room at Button's with latest news of Lady Mary.

"Yes," Pope interrupted meaningfully, "and news blows hot to tell us more than that. Is it true that Wortley Montagu has sold the Treaty to the Turks?"

Addison shot a cool long stare to freeze Pope's grin, and said: "As true as that you'd sorrow if it were. No, it is not. And that which Garth was full of is as tall a story as any our tongue-wagging Walpole may tell, in or out of Westminster Hall. The Doctor had a thing to say of Lady Mary, who, on her journey home, kept guard—with a deal more care than she guarded her jewels—of a casket of walnutshells."

"*That's* what I've been chasing in me mind!" exclaimed Dick. "There's been a mort o' chattering of walnuts and Lady Mary to put to shame me fish-pool for invention."

"Not invention," drawled Addison. "A discovery, which

the lady claims to have brought from Turkey, to annihilate the smallpox."

"The Doctor will be here tonight," said Dick, "weather permitting; and he'll tell us what 'tis all about, though I cannot see that nuts can cure the smallpox. Thousands of us eat of walnuts daily, and yet—" he took up a handful and searched for the crackers, "there may be something in it if you eat enough."

"I could tell you—" Pope stood, back to the fire, warming his scraggy calves—"I could tell you the gist of that tale, which is not of walnuts but of what their shells contain, to raise a wind that will blow the College of Physicians to the skies."

The door opened as he spoke. Dr. Garth, unwinding himself from his cloak, strutted in. "Am I late?"

"No, sir." Dick gave him a hand. "Let me have this, and your hat." He threw both on a settle. "You're in time to demonstrate your medical opinion upon a knotty problem—" he pronounced it 'nutty' in the fashion of the day, with a sidelong grin for Addison's frown. "Let it pass, Joe, Let it pass. Have you not said yourself that the seeds of punning are in the minds of all men, and will shoot up even when doused by good sense?"

"Zounds!" The Doctor was twisting a foot. "I'm pricked with pins and needles. How's this? A problem? I'll give you one to solve. What is it, as Doctor Honorificicabilitudintatisbusque will have it, that although it be much of a midget or sizeable, contains a mighty something of great use, and is a powerful good medicine which all men may carry in their pockets as antidote against ill humours? You don't know? You can't guess? . . . Well, I could show you a sample had I with me my pharmaceutical assistant who produces in a trice this *coticula*, or touchstone, as 'tis called in layman's parlance."

And having delivered his monologue with the utmost professional sobriety, the Doctor sat down amid laughter to rattle the roof.

"There's two more yet to come." Dick looked at the clock. "Gay and Congreve."

"Not Congreve." Garth screwed an eye at the bottles on

the sideboard. "He has a carbuncle. I left him lying on his front with a plaster on his— Yes, sirs. But Gay will be here, late as usual. I ran into him in Arlington Street. He was waiting on the Duke and the little Duchess. Gay delights her."

Pope sniggered. "Gay will lap strawberries and cream with dukes and duchesses when he is twanging the lyre up above among the cherubim. There's Prior's Kitty[1] who loves his little tricks and—what d'ye call it."

Steele guffawed and Addison sighed wearily; and the Doctor, who, though he liked his bit of bawdy, was a stickler for fact, asked Pope how much his hand or Arbuthnot's had to do with Gay's *What d'ye call it* which ran for eleven nights. But before Pope could tell him that, beyond writing letters round to all the critics to ensure a warm reception, neither his hand, nor certainly Arbuthnot's, had aught whatsoever to do with Gay's farce,—or its failure—the author of it, announced by a slatternly Warren, burst into the room.

"Dick! Will you lend me a shilling for the chair? I have forgot my pouch."

A shilling was handed to Warren with the hissed injunction: "Wipe those smuts from your face before you wait at table. Has the fish come?"

"Yes, Sir Richard."

"Is it cooked?"

"'Tis cooking."

"Tell her ladyship to send up for Mr. Pope's first course what is left of the stewed eels that we had for dinner, and let the gentleman below stairs help you with the dishes. Put your mob straight, girl. It's over your ear . . . So now, sirs," as Warren scuttled, "to the board!"

They did full justice to it. Wine flowed as freely as the talk, led by Gay, who, although born in the same year as Pope, looked at least five years younger than he.

John Gay was jocular, round as a ball, slightly slovenly in dress as in verse, very musical, and full of quips at no one's expense but his own. Having picked clean the bones of the hare and eaten more than any of roast beef and chicken fritters, and drunk six glasses of Burgundy, two of Canary

---

[1] Duchess of Queensberry.

and the better part of a bottle of Oporto, he fetched his flute from his overcoat pocket, and played to the company notes as sweet and melodious as a thrush's song.

"And that—" he paused to tell his audience, all of whom had a tenderness for Gay—"is the theme of a Newgate pastoral that Swift has suggested I should write. So now I'm writing it, but God knows when 'twill be finished. I'll sing you a ballad that goes:

> 'How happy could I be with either,
> Were t'other dear charmer away'."

It was almost impossible, when Gay was present, to steer the conversation toward anything that savoured of the serious. Everybody loved him—for his artlessness, his laziness, his greediness, his modesty, his ineffable good humour. Even the peppery Dean of St. Patrick's ceased to rage at life and turned to laugh with Gay. His success offended no one. He had never been heard to speak slightingly of his more gifted colleagues; all men were his friends and all women were angels. So when he took his flute from his mouth to put more food and wine into it, and the name of Lady Mary and her conquest in Paris in connection with a certain Monsieur Rémond, circulated as the port went round, Gay said: "No!" and "No" again, very solemn, who was never solemn save in drink. "I'll not hear a word to the detriment of that delicious creature. Rémond—tcha! I've met him. You remember—" he jogged Pope beside him with his elbow —"the Abbé Conti, a ponderous ass, but scholarly, brought him over as a kind of gentleman valet when the Abbé was in London chasing Newton."

Pope shook his head. "I've never heard the fellow's name."

"You will," said Garth. "Her ladyship, who writes such charming letters, if a trifle indiscreet, invites Monsieur Rémond to England in the spring." He brushed a crumb from his cravat and smiled as he murmured: "In the spring the youth of primy nature, forward not permanent, sweet, not lasting'—to a Frenchman's fancy."

"Now be easy! Sure to God," cried Dick, "you medical gentlemen are as glib for gossip as the ladies. Too much acquaintance with the bedside puts their words into your

mouths. Lady Mary meets a Frenchman who admires her—
as well may be. And so the Abbé gnaws his thumb, and so
the lady writes to this one and that pretty dear, to have them
jump at conclusions that it's cuckolds all awry. Shame on ye,
Doctor! Fill your glass."

Lady Steele, in her bed above, listened to the uproar down
below. They were knocking on the table now, and speechifying, singing songs, with Mr. Gay at his flute—a blithesome
tune—and me, moaned Prue, with naught but a haddock for
me cheer.

"Mrs. Keck!" she called, and pulled the bell-rope. "Mrs.
Keck, will you take this tray?"

Mrs. Keck, the shapely, well-spoken, managing wife of
Robert Keck of the Inner Temple, had volunteered to run
the house for her good friend, Lady Steele, during her con-
finement, and she ran it still. The grand spread offered to
Sir Richard's guests was, it must be owned, of Mrs. Keck's
providing. She, not Prue, had gone that day to market, had
jugged the hare, had bought and cooked the salmon steak
for Mr. Pope. It was Mrs. Keck who had given a cast-off suit
of Sir Richard's to the bailiff's gentleman that he should be
presentable for company, and had bade him shave his chin
and take the dishes up and wait at table; and Mrs. Keck who,
at her lady's summons, came to say with a purr in her voice:

"You'd best settle for the night, my dear. They'll be at it
till morning."

"I will not settle. Look you, an you love me, go put your
ear to the door down there and give back to me what they
are saying."

Mrs. Keck folded her arms and tucked in her chin.

"No, i' faith! I'd be shamed to hear them. You know how
'tis when wine's in and truth's out, to blister the tongue of a
Piazza trull."

"Then I will go." Flinging off the bedclothes, Prue
snatched up a dressing-gown. "The Doctor is here to keep
them steady."

"Not he," said Mrs. Keck. "He's as raddled as the rest of
them. And what he lets forth—" she raised her hands—"is
full of drollery, pertinent to his profession, but none the less
libidinous."

"See now," said Prue, slant-eyed, "if you be squeamish I am not." And she was out of the room and down the stairs before Mrs. Keck could stop her. Bending to the keyhole, she laid her ear against it.

"Lady Rich—" Prue recognized the doctor's voice, high-toned and measured. She nodded to herself. Lady Rich! A nose-up-head-up-cut-me-dead party, red as a fox, or myself, said Prue, and not dyed in the wool as I am, whatever but—dyed.

"Lady Rich reports that the air of Paris has agreeably affected Lady Mary's health and spirits."

Hah! The Lady Mary, was it? Prue might have guessed how she, returned to Town, would fill the mouths of all the gentlemen, by damn.

"The French ladies—" Prue heard—"are, so Lady Mary says, monstrously painted and wear powdered heads that they look as they were capped in white wool."

And would you believe that a Doctor of Medicine and rare poets, withal, marvelled Prue, would stoop to such very small talk? She removed her ear from the keyhole, put an eye to it and saw a vignette of Mr. Pope's face attentively turned to the speaker.

"She has met the French King and extols his good shape——"

As so she would! muttered Prue.

"I too have had a letter from Paris," Pope was saying. "Lady Mary tells me everybody stares. Staring is à la mode in Paris. She has met her sister and of course the Abbé Conti."

Prue pouted. As lively as a snail on a cabbage leaf was this.

"Has her ladyship mentioned anything to you in her letter—" Prue ducked her ear again, for Dick was speaking—"of that which she claims to cure the smallpox?"

Before Pope could answer the doctor put in his word.

"Not to cure—to prevent it."

"Is that possible?"

"Emphatically, no! There is no preventive known to medical science that can stay the spread of contagious disease —smallpox or whatever—more than the precautions which we doctors suggest, but cannot enforce, such as washing in vinegar after contact with a case, or inhalation from a pomander. Cleanliness is as good a guard against disease as any."

"Then you do not believe," it was Gay who spoke now, "that by injection of the smallpox pus the patient is immunized—have I coined that word—for life, from the sickness? I am told that Lady Mary has 'engrafted', as she calls it, her five-year-old son."

"Yes. And 'tis a wonder he survived. I tell you," the doctor thumped his fist on the table, "if Lady Mary should attempt to introduce these dangerous practices here in London, as I understand is her intention, I and my fellow physicians will fight it, tooth and——"

Prue strained to hear more, but no more came, for the Doctor's vehemence ended in an oath when his gesturing hand swept over a bottle of wine——

"To ruin my best damask!" Prue sprang up from her knees and, forgetful of her dressing-gown, dashed in upon the company.

The gentlemen were on their feet, Dick barring the door. "Sweet! We are joyed to see you but——"

Prue thrust him aside.

"A napkin, quick, and clear the table. I must have that cloth in soak."

"To break me party," moaned Dick, "for a drop of spilled wine."

"God's sakes! You can drink without a cloth. Take these bottles, gentlemen—and help me."

They helped her with a will, stacking empty dishes on the sideboard, while Prue gathered up her damaged cloth and hurried out.

Mrs. Keck was waiting for her on the stairs.

"See this!" Prue flung at her the tablecloth. "Go put it in a pail, if you please. I paid three guineas at Mr. D'Oyley's for that last week, with my monogram embroidered fine, and look you what is done to it!"

"Salt will remove the stain. Don't fash yourself, my dear. Men, men," sighed Mrs. Keck, "what they cost us in hard cash, to say nothing of hard labour. Let them bear our pangs —and would they sing?"

"They would not." Then, as Prue made for the door of her room she wheeled round, for the gentlemen were roaring out a toast. To whom? To her?

With a girl's brightness in her face, though she was forty, she ran back again to listen.

"A Toast!" It was Pope's voice, shrill and cracked, that called. Prue clasped her hands and waited—to hear the glasses clinking and the echo of: "A Toast—to——"

"Lady Mary!"

Prue stamped her foot to jerk her knee, and took herself to bed; and when, two hours later, Dick, swaying, tumbled into it:

"To hell with you," cried Prue, "and Lady Mary."

*　　*　　*

Lady Mary! . . . From the Palace of the King to the felons' cells at Newgate, through the chocolate-houses, coffee-houses, boudoirs of St. James's, her name rang. There may have been a dozen Lady Marys in Society, but of only one did London speak. Those of her intimates invited to attend her morning toilet, came away full of envy and wonder at her Turkish dress, her Italian coiffeur, and her little black page brought from Tunis.

"A eunuch, my dears, and so fat—his belly wobbles! And she allows him to bathe her in rose-water. Can you fancy it? The perfect lady's maid, she says."

And then there was a mummy—what a thing!—swathed, embalmed, and laid out on a slab in her bedroom—'So daring.' And such tales as she told of the harems and the dancing girls and lovely naked women—not to be repeated. And although she flatly denied that the Sultan had pressed her to visit the Seraglio, she spoke with too much rapture of his handsome eyes and looks to be believed.

Gossip spread like fire to embellish Lady Mary with jewels from the Sultan's coffers; emeralds the size of turkeys' eggs, pearls twice as large and of finer quality than even those of the Duchess of Marlborough. And if the little daughter born had not been flaxen-haired and white as snow—but truly it was fortunate the baby looked so English.

While innuendos rippled on the tongues of Mary's dearest

friends, the more serious and privileged had been allowed to see a copy of the Koran, irrefutable proof that she, as rumour gave it, had adopted the Mohammedan religion. And then the journey home—all the way to Africa to see the ruins of the aqueducts of Carthage, where the natives, as Mary described them—to convulse her audience—'differed little in their sitting posture and the colour of their skins, with their lank black hair falling either side their faces, from their country people, the baboons.'

Of the ex-Ambassador the ladies had the least to say, but they said it with pitying looks. His hair had fallen out and his mouth had fallen in, having lost all his teeth, poor man, from drinking those bad waters, according to his wife. But everyone knew the truth of that! He had pined himself sick at his recall. All very well for Mr. Addison to offer, as very lame excuse for it, that the King could not spare his service from the Commons. What service more than his hardly won seat for Huntingdon, which he had resigned to his senile father, had *he* ever rendered to Parliament? And not even a knighthood to show for his pains. *Quite* a failure. As for her—she was mad as a puss at his downfall. They were scarce on speaking, and not certainly on bed terms. He never would forgive her—and rightly too—for the engrafting of their son against the smallpox without his knowledge or permission. 'Twas a mercy the child didn't die.

While Mary's account of her Turkish adventures had been taken with a modicum of salt, her 'story in a nutshell' was swallowed whole by the members of the College of Physicians, to regurgitate in abusive controversy.

Led by Doctors Arbuthnot, Garth, and Woodward, the Faculty rose to a man, and with every contradiction known to *materia medica* condemned out of hand this insalubrious fad, introduced to the gullible by an unqualified person.

When, shortly after her return, the more daring of her feminine acquaintances had, with timorous giggles and shrieks, submitted their arms, or, if they feared scarring, their legs to Mary's needle, the medical profession ignored, as beneath their contempt, this latest craze of Fashion. To them it was of no more consequence than the taking of snuff, in which whimsical habit ladies were wont to indulge.

But after a very few months the doctors could no longer disregard Lady Mary's pernicious activities, practised not only on her friends but on the lower orders; in fact it was evident she believed herself to be a pioneer. She infected the credulous who flocked to her salon with her own enthusiasm. She had all her answers ready. "There is no example," she asseverated, "that anyone has died of the treatment, no, nor suffered any ill result from it." If she had doubted the efficacy of so wondrous a preventive against recurrent epidemics, would she have endangered the life of her son?

The doctors met in consultation. This injurious campaign must not be permitted to influence an ignorant public against all accepted and preconceived theories. What evidence other than the de-Christianized thaumaturgy of harems, had Lady Mary to offer as proof of her 'engrafting'?

From the pulpit the clergy took up the cry, to descant on the impiety of those who questioned the laws of Divine Providence. It was the duty of God's servants, who had been called to follow in the steps of Luke, the Beloved, to advise. It was God's will alone to cure or kill—and so forth.

But not even the opprobrium hurled at her by the Church or the College of Physicians could deter Mary from her purpose. She would prove herself right and them wrong. And among all those who decried, only one supported her: Maitland, the loyal little apothecary-surgeon, who, though he stood to lose his practice and the patronage of his more distinguished colleagues, enrolled himself her assistant and disciple. At her instigation he inoculated those of the poorer classes willing to take a chance on the experiment, and few enough were they.

Apart from the clergy and doctors, the most obstreperous of Mary's opponents were to be met with in the streets of London. On one occasion, in the autumn of 1719, when driving alone on her way to the opera, her coach was held up by a mob of screeching women. Dark threatening faces crowded to the carriage windows, led by a toothless drab with a gash of a mouth who shook her fist at and cursed her for an 'in'uman unnatural mother that would risk the life of her child for the teachings o' the devil!' Then, as the driver's whips lashed out, a welter of maddened crowd-moiled bodies hurtled to the doors of the coach.

The footmen jumped down from their stands, striking left and right with their batons; mud was slung at the windows, and a stone that struck with a shower of splintering glass to graze Mary's stockinged instep. A crimson stain spread; she sat still. Her courage was high, her blood warm with hate and disgust in her heart. She kicked aside the fallen stone and had all to do not to pick it up and sling it back, when, on an impulse she lowered the window to be greeted by a torrent of yells: "Take the damned crank of a witch to the ducking-stool. She'll swim, I'll warrant! A fine madam, she—with her lewd practices!"

"Fools!" Her voice rang out above the din. "Would you sooner die o' the 'pox or be saved from it?"

In a second she regretted she had spoken. The rabble, who for the most part were gin-sodden and out for a brawl, flung themselves at the horses' heads to start them rearing; and while the coachman tugged at the reins there came an interruption in high-pitched, well-loaded invective.

"Ha' done! You dirty three-ha-porth o' sows' udders—misbegotten sisters to a pimp—ha' done!"

Mary peeped. It seemed she had an ally; a stout, rosy-cheeked, buxom wench, with wild black hair and a wide white grin to prick at memory as of someone known or seen before . . . Surely not!

"Let the lady bide, you whiffling, piddling, lousy brood o' night-walkers—be off to Southwark Ditch where you belong!"

This gentle peroration was received with cat-calls and shouts of "High-ti-tiddly-Betty-calling-kettle-black," and "Night-walker yourself, all tricked out! Have a care o' your face, strumpet, lest you be branded next session and whipped round the Town at the cart's tail! Yes, *you*—who was whelped in a kennel!"

The attention of the ladies, thus diverted from Mary, turned to the newcomer, who vigorously laid about her with her fists, until a purposeful tramping and cries of 'Break! Break!' announced the arrival of the constables.

Like rats disturbed in a cellar, the crowd scattered; of them all only one remained.

Adjusting her bodice which had been wrenched off her shoulders, she sheepishly approached the window. A footman shoved her away, but:

"Stop!" Mary bade him, "I will speak to her. Come here, girl. Your face is familiar. Who are you?"

"Your ladyship should know." She dabbed at her nose; it was bleeding. "That pig's offal what stoned you—she got me a beauty, but I'll have the hide off her back in return for't."

"You're hurt."

"No, sweetness, proud—to be of service to your ladyship, and 'tis not the first time, although long since. No matter."

And before Mary could hand her the gold piece she had ready, the woman was gone.

It had been a distressful experience, but from it came one good result. Mary was now more than ever determined to bring the medical faculty to its worthy senses, and this mob that had attacked her, to heel. She would have them eat dirt for the dirt they had slung; she would show them and the world she was a benefactor, to bring their curses down in blessings on her head.

She summoned Mr. Maitland to assist her and advise. "How can I convince these imbeciles that what I have to give is for their everlasting good?"

Mr. Maitland rubbed his chin, put his head on one side, looked all ways at once like a sparrow, and said: "Madam, there are in Newgate Gaol at this present six criminals condemned to death. I am acquainted with the Governor of the prison, and if he will permit that I engraft them——"

"Ah!" Her eyes lit up. "That's the solution. If these felons have to die in any case, what though I kill them? But I won't. You and I between us have treated at least a hundred persons with no ill effect, and look you, sir—" she turned to him sparkling, "you must ask your friend the Governor to procure for these six—if they recover, as we know they will— a free pardon from His Majesty the King!"

*　　　*　　　*

A few weeks later Mary received a visit from a Mr. John Hervey, a young gentleman-in-waiting on the Princess of

Wales. He was come, he informed her flattered ladyship, at the command of Her Royal Highness, who had heard of the successful engrafting of six Newgate prisoners committed to the gallows, and to whom, in consequence of their recovery from the operation, His Majesty had graciously granted a reprieve.

"This, madam," said young Mr. Hervey, whom Mary noted lacked nothing of self-confidence nor of personable looks, "this is but the precursor of my intrusion."

She inclined her head and, begging the gentleman be seated, assured him that his call was no intrusion. "For indeed, sir, I have known your mother, Lady Bristol, since my youth, but have not had the previous pleasure of your acquaintance. During my life abroad—" she spoke as if her one year of absence from Town had been ten—"you have grown from boy to man." Enchantingly she smiled.

"It is my regret," Mr. Hervey replied with an answering smile, "that so many years until this moment have been wasted."

Certainly a charmer, with something in his bearing and his face that distinguished him from other 'pretty fellows' of his age. He was delicately featured with a skin like a girl's and a blush that might well have been rouge; yet the foppishness of his attire and appearance did not detract from, but seemed rather to enhance the ironic twist of the small, severe mouth, and the quizzical glance of those clear, light blue eyes that looked upon her boldly, to admire.

Mary offered him tokay, which he airily declined. "Spirituous liquor is poison to me. I am strictly dieted to ass's milk and flour biscuits." Then, before she had recovered from the shock of that, he announced a further reason for his coming. "Madam, Her Royal Highness desires that you wait on her at noon tomorrow—with your needle."

"With my——?"

"Needle," repeated Mr. Hervey. "I am fully convinced that you would prefer to go camping in jack-boots than to curtsy in a drawing-room where grey-headed fribbles in gauze will cheat you of a guinea at ombre; for you, Lady Mary, enjoy what you will. I don't enjoy what I may."

She began to wonder if this young man were in full

possession of his wits, and, surprisingly, as if he read her thought:

"You consider me eccentric?" he suggested. "I am, and would sooner be so than one who, like a looking-glass, returns its every image, even though he be worth a hundred such as I who will paint or polish till there is nothing more of nature in my words than there is in my complexion."

Decidedly, considered Mary, he is droll and—most engaging.

"Sir," she reminded him, "you were speaking of the Princess."

"Who, in short—" he got up—"Your eyes are so astonishingly beautiful and odd without their lashes, that I had forgot what has brought me. Her Royal Highness requests you engraft the Royal children for the smallpox."

"Sir!" Mary too was on her feet; her hand upon her heart. "If there be paint or polish and naught of nature or of truth in your words, then leave me, pray, for I am that sort of a virtuosa who loves not copies but originals."

"Indeed, madam, I am with you, and I find you inexpressibly diverting. You will receive more implicit instructions in due course. My duty, Lady Mary, and your very humble servant. We will meet again."

They did; and often at the house of his mother, the Countess of Bristol; not so often at the Court of the Princess. While Mary's much discussed enterprise had won her the patronage and favour of the First Lady in the Land, the King, whose open quarrel with his son and his son's wife was common knowledge, inclined to the view of his physicians. It was one thing for Lady Mary to experiment on six Newgate felons, but, "*Gott im Himmel!*" the King blustered, "ça c'est autre chose!" when the same operation was repeated on his grandchildren.

The Heir Apparent, having been ejected from the Royal Palace, had established himself and his Court at Leicester Fields. His three young daughters, Anne, Amelia and Caroline, who, the King insisted, must remain at St. James's, were smuggled thence in secrecy to their mother's house for Lady Mary's engrafting.

When news filtered through that the young princesses

were her latest victims, the King had a brain-storm; Mr. Craggs a brain-wave. Supported by the Schulenberg, lately promoted to the Duchy of Kendal, and who much resented the King's *Schwärmerei* for Lady Mary, Craggs contrived to let her ladyship know that her presence at the Palace was taboo. But she had gone too far now to retract. Certainly the admiration of the Prince of Wales did somewhat atone for the loss of his father's good-will; yet while Mary knew better than to discourage the Prince's advances, she gave no thought to him other than as a strutting, overdressed, imperishable bore. She much preferred his wife, but Her Royal Highness who—none could tell why—passionately loved her absurd little ogling Prince, extended Lady Mary chilly welcome to her Court. Nevertheless, she was so besieged with entreaties from friends, eager to be in the fashion set by the Princess of Wales to engraft their children, that she confessed herself sick of the whole business. 'I would never have attempted it,' in after years she used to say, 'had I foreseen the obloquy and persecution that it brought me. . . .'

Her father had been among the first to denounce her. When his kittenish Duchess begged Mary to 'prick' her little girls—'your half-sisters, my dear, and so pretty as angels—' the Duke stormed.

What! Would he stand by and allow his children to be murdered!

"But Evie, darling," pleaded his Duchess, "if the Princess sees fit to approve——"

"I forbid it. As for you—" he turned to his daughter, who had brought her small son to visit his grandpapa, and had bid him speak up nicely—"As for you, I had hoped to see you bettered by your travels, bled of your folly and endowed with commonsense. I was mistook. This caps all that's gone before. You have made yourself notorious in prison stews, and a target for mud-slingers in the streets. A fine heritage you leave to him!" He grabbed Edward, who was sitting on a stool at the feet of his mamma. "Show me the marks on your arm where your mother scratched you."

With a mutinous look at the large, red-jowled face bent above his own, Edward sullenly took off his coat and rolled up the sleeve of his shirt. The Duke approached nearer, exclaiming, "Adso! A scar the size of a shilling. Much good may it do you. Give me a kiss."

"No," Edward wriggled. "You smell."

"God's blood! So do I!" roared the Duke and cuffed him smartly.

Edward howled. His mother seized him by the hand. The Duchess screamed with laughter.

"La! A nasty ill-conditioned child as ever I did see! Never will I let him play with my angel babes, his aunts!"

"Out!" The Duke hustled the scowling, pale little boy to the door. "Take yourself off. And you, madam," to his daughter, "go with him. Not a penny—yes! A shilling, to match the 'pox on his arm, is all that you and your brat will get from me."

So Mary had definite reason enough to regret her 'patriotic undertaking'. In future, she decided, she would send prospective patients to Maitland to be treated; and in order to secure herself from importunate approach, she gave out she was sick of the quinsy and had been ordered rest.

Edward had secured, at an absurdly low rental, the lease of a house in Cavendish Square; and for the next few months Mary attended no routs nor assemblies; her doors were closed to callers. The buying of curtains, carpets, and sundry new furniture occupied much of her time. Edward had stated the sum he would allow her to spend on the removal, which she declared to be wholly insufficient. He said she must do with what he allowed her. He was not made of money.

"But that is just what you are!" she flashed. "Money is your god, and you have created yourself in its likeness, as once I thought to create you in mine."

He stared at her reflectively, saying: "Then why blame me if all goes wry with us?" And with disconcerting inconsequence he added: "Who writes you from Paris?"

"From Paris?" she echoed, and thought: So he is spying, and, "You should know," she told him carelessly. "My sister Mar."

"It is not your sister's hand that addressed the letter I saw on the salver in the hall this forenoon."

"If it were not her hand it must be another's. I have a dozen or more letters every day. How can I remember or account for every one?"

Edward unpleasantly smiled. "Your correspondence," he said, "has always been prolific. This Monsieur Rémond—" He paused.

She controlled herself to answer lightly, "Ah, yes, Rémond. He has written to tell me he will be in London at Christmastide, visiting the Abbé Conti."

Edward's smile was caught back on a dry tooth. He made as if to speak again, when, glancing at the clock, she reminded him: "That is slow, and you have invited Sir Richard to dinner. Poor soul, I fear he is not the same man since the death of his wife. Will you excuse me if I do not come to table? I have a miserable headache."

"But of course."

Nothing could have been more courteous, more cool, and more unloving than the look with which he bowed her out.

In her room she sat idle at her window, gazing at the naked trees, stark against a dusky sky. This house, which for the next few years must be her home, was situated on the fringe of Mary'bone marshes, where mansions newly built encroached upon a dreary swamp, the haunt of wild water-fowl and duck-shooting squires. Even now as she watched, a party of them, loud-voiced with drink, and followed by their dogs, red-tongued and panting at the horses' hooves, rode by. A chair, preceded by a link-boy's torch, deposited Steele at the door. He was less stout than formerly, and still in black for his wife who had been dead a year. His step had lost its buoyancy, and in the lanthorn's light Mary saw the ravages that grief had wrought upon his face. Lines, deep carven, ran from mouth to heavy chin; there was a slowness in his speech as he queried the fare and paid it without murmur. And watching him, she thought: There goes a great lover, who, bereft of love, is like a child that is starved of the breast . . . Steele had suffered not only the loss of his adored Prue, but six months later, of Addison, friend of his boyhood, with whom at the last he had quarrelled over Sunderland's Peerage Bill, which Steele had attacked in his pamphlet *The Plebeian*.

Addison's reply to this in *The Old Whig* of March 1719, a vituperative cut at the 'instability of friendship', declared open war between the two, until, unknown to Steele, Joe lay dying, strangled in the grip of his old enemy, the asthma.

Torn with remorse and contrition to know that he had tormented the last hours of one he had loved as a brother, Dick may have grieved more for the death of Joe than for his Prue. Who could tell? . . . Mary too had grieved for Addison, and could not believe him gone, who had stood in the background of her life from its beginnings. Edward had never spoken of Joe's death, yet she knew that it had left a hollow in his heart.

How far from Edward had she travelled since they had set out together on their hopeful voyage to Turkey! Memory groping among the ashes of the past, gathered up discarded fragments: his letters, his first kiss behind the curtained windows of a coach; that joyous mad escape in the dawn of her bridal day . . . A sob broke from her, and tears fell; not for him, who had taught her the dark witchery of passion and all of passion's emptiness; and not for her wounded love, but for that young, that lost 'Laetitia', her dream within a dream.

★ 15 ★

IN THE spring of 1720, Mary emerged from her temporary retirement notorious, though less for her charm or fading beauty than for those accursed nutshells she had brought from the Near East.

To her sisters, Evelyn and Frances, who were visiting their aunt at Chelsea, she confided, while they sat around the tea-table: "No longer can I claim to be, as Pope is pleased to have it, a 'female wit' but a female apothecary."

"Or," Evelyn suggested nastily, "a quack."

"As you say," agreed Mary, unwontedly meek. "I am become indifferent to abuse or inquisition. Believe it or not I have been forced to submit—maybe 'tis an honour, take it as you will—to submit to a Government inquiry. Hear this——"

And with little sympathy her sisters heard, how that four 'Magi' from the College of Physicians had been authorized by Parliament to watch her at her 'tricks'.

"Yes, they insisted—can you conceive how—that they should stand by when I engrafted my own little infant, God bless her! And I'll swear," said Mary ragefully, "they were willing her to die. For three days and nights these poke-nose disbelievers stood by the cot, turn about, in pairs. I could not leave her alone with them one second, for fear they should do her a mischief. But even though she showed scarce a symptom of the sickness, and was eating and crowing and kicking her legs at them all of the time, they departed unconvinced and black as hell."

"'Tis lucky you was not born a hundred years ago," Frances said, "or they'd have burned you at the stake."

"As they would now an they could—and may yet; for what they'll not forgive me," smiled Mary, "is my sex."

Evelyn, a slow, lazy-lidded girl, looked startled. Frances sniggered; Mary sighed. "Oh, yes! And were I born again two hundred years ahead you would see these same wise gentlemen not spitting, but sitting—at my feet! For the time will come, mark me," her lashless eyes shone with a sudden fierce intensity, "the time will come when women, who have more to give men than their bodies, will be accepted—not as man's plaything and not as his whore—no, nor even his 'female wit'—but as man's equal." And saying that, as if to shake away a shiver, she shook herself and laughed. "A grey goose passed over my grave as many grey geese will before they scratch up the earth from my coffin, to raise a tablet in commemoration of me and of my works."

"The girl's crazed." Frances stole a glance aside at Evelyn who, drawing in her lips, supplemented readily:

"And wanton, to speak so lightly of 'bodies'. As for being the equal of man, that is palpably impossible, or if such a thing should come to pass it would be an end of man's respect and chivalry to us."

"Fine chivalry it is," retorted Mary, "to pursue and flatter

254

us, that they may gloat upon their conquests in every club and ordinary to befoul our names."

"You've befouled your name yourself," put in Frances, sharp as knives. "I could tell you for your good——"

"Pray don't," and again Mary smiled, over-sweetly. "There's naught you can tell me for the good of one that's damned to the world—and everlasting."

"How you talk!" Frances reached her hand for a dish of caraway cakes and tasted one, grimacing. "Zooks! If my pastrycook baked as poor as this I'd have him in the stocks. I was thinking I should tell you—shall I tell her?" Again she glanced at Evelyn, who nodded prim assent. An indeterminate blonde, Lady Gower was possessed of one weakness, a passion for cards. Her losses at the gaming-board had brought about a breach between herself and her husband who refused to pay any more of her debts. Having borrowed from Frances up to the hilt, she had turned to beg from Mary, a fruitless appeal in view of Wortley Montagu's parsimony; and so, "Yes, tell her," Evelyn said with inward relish. She had little love for Mary, and since the recent elder-sisterly rebuff she had received when Mary had spoken her mind to say: 'Search the green baize for some greenhorn to tap, but not me!' she loved her less. "Yes, let her know," Evelyn passed her cup to be refilled, "what London —*and* Paris—is hinting."

"Surely more than hinting?" Mary held her smile fixed while she poured the boiling brew from the tea-urn beside her. "I am fully aware that London—*and* Paris," she mimicked Evelyn's drawl, "has it pat that my heart is broke for pretty Mr. Hervey who has got himself secretly married to Molly Lepel, which is a secret no longer. She has catched him—and wait!" She handed Evelyn her cup. "That's not all. My husband is mad as jumping beans—dear Lord! I wish he were—that I've cuckolded him with my Parisian beau, Monsieur Rémond."

"Heavenly powers!" gasped Evelyn, showing the whites of her eyes, "are you lost to all shame to admit it?" Her jaw dropped; and Frances, crunching a biscuit, said:

"This is stale. Does Edward cut your household purse so low that you must serve us with last year's stuff! ... Evelyn,

shut your mouth, do. You look exactly like a landed codfish."
Then, as Evelyn made to retort, Frances went on coolly:
"As for her shame, you should know by her admission that
she stands self-vindicated. Though her thought may have
mothered the wish to cuckold her stick of a husband—who
wouldn't?—she'd never in her senses stoop to Rémond.
Have you seen him? Lud! He has a nose like an elephant's
trunk."

"But he writes," said Mary gently, "such very charming
letters."

"Better burn 'em." Frances got up, smoothing out her
gown. "These panniers! They may be modish, but they're
the deuce to crush. Come, Evelyn, we must go. I'll call upon
my milliner and have her bone my petticoats."

"And I," said Evelyn glumly, "will take mine to a Jew,
for my gowns are all I have to sell, since I must raise some
cash somehow."

"You can always," Mary smiled, "sell yourself—at a low
price."

And with the utmost affection she kissed them both
goodbye and waved from the window as they drove off in
their aunt's coach. But no sooner had the clatter of hooves
and wheels died away on the cobbles, than she was at her
bureau hunting for a letter she had hidden—where? "God
blight those chattering fools!" she cursed, "where in Hades
did I put it? Ah! Praise be." She snatched the paper,
smoothed it out, and, as she re-read it her face cleared. He
could turn a pretty phrase in French, and none *too* compromising . . . Yet not to Monsieur Rémond did Mary give
her thoughts as she sat with his letter in her hand. So! The
rumour of Hervey's secret marriage to Mistress Lepel, the
loveliest of all the Maids of Honour, then, was true! She
had suspected as much and had been piqued to probe: "It
is said, sir, that you are resolved to renounce your vows as
a celibatarian—" which he had neither denied nor admitted,
but had answered with subtlety, epigrammatic, to leave her
in doubt—and in hope.

"Madam, should I resolve never to eat because the thing
I love best is out of season?"

That was all; an interchange of banter in a crowd at

Leicester House. 'A stinking, sweating, pushing, greedy, senseless crowd,' he called it, with that disturbing hooded glance of his and head upraised, reminiscent of a snake about to strike. And he had shot a particular venom at a cluster of women rigged out in flaunting finery, squeezing their way to the gilt chairs where the little red-faced, staring Prince of Wales sat with his stout and still beautiful wife.

But Mary had seen Mr. Hervey's eyes stray more than once to a sprig of a girl standing demurely in attendance on the Princess, bending her head to take a whispered order, gliding past the thronging guests to brush Mary's slippers with her skirts as she went; a gentle brief apology, 'Dear Lady Mary!' A billowing bob and away, sweet and fresh as a drift of the flowering hawthorn . . . That was last month, since when Mr. Hervey had neither called nor sent a note nor book of verse to Lady Mary; nor did he ride as he was used to do, to meet her carriage in Hyde Park. So why go chasing moonbeams when here at her hand for her choice was another, confessed of his passion, and if less bewitching, more ardent . . . *pour passer le temps.*

*   *   *

It had been a joyous spring, spun with blossom, where every street in this King George's London ended in a glimpse of green; where the squares and gardens of St. James's sprayed a foam of petals, pink and white, on the heads of passers-by; and sun-bewildered plane trees traced an intricate pattern of leaves on pavings that rang to the mincing steps of beaux in powdered wigs and silken foppery.

From his lodging obscurely off Long Acre, with a temporary address in care of Mr. Warner, Goldsmith, hard by Temple Bar, Monsieur Rémond of Paris, on a May time afternoon, was carried in a sedan to the house of Lady Mary.

This was not Rémond's first visit to London, yet he never ceased to wonder at these streets of red-brick houses, unpretentious, graceful, much of a sameness, with flat high windows and three steps up; nor at the smells of the soot-begrimed city, a medley of sewers, pastures, oranges and cats; and then the tumult of these narrow ways, the incessant cries of vendors. Épouvantable! and these English women—

gauche, above all—pas de chic, with the teeth, bon dieu, of a horse! Their hands, their feet, by example, grossières. As for the cuisine of these English—abominable; their King, quel horreur, their politicians, pas mal, Monsieur Rémond conceded—this Walpole, in fine, with the face of a pig, who, to Rémond's chagrin, had opposed, but happily without effect, that admirable project launched by a company of the South Sea to pay les dettes nationales de l'Angleterre.

The proposals of this Company to augment British Funds to the tune of eight millions as a douceur to the Government, had brought Rémond to London to enjoy a little flutter on the Bourse. At the suggestion of his patron, l'Abbé Conti, seconded by Lady Mary, he had judiciously bought of these stocks. He was greatly in need of financial support; his affairs were more than usually unsettled, and the response to the letters he had written to the lady encouraged Monsieur Rémond to write more.

When, two years since, he had first met her in Paris he was sure he had vanquished her heart. A correspondence ensued and continued, to titillate his interest and increase his admiration. Lady Mary's advice in this business of the South Seas had proved her to possess a solid head; an intellectuelle, in Rémond's estimation, pas légère, and of sufficiently good mien—but amorous? As to that, he doubted. She was demi-vierge, this one. He knew the type, in love with love and with herself, but not with him; a Narcisse, veritably. Eh, well, we will see, complacently reflected Monsieur Rémond; and favouring the back of his foremost carrier with a glare of exceeding repugnance—what species of crétins, he inquired, were these that marched with the gait of a slug? Had he known the distance was so far he would have promenaded in a carriage.

From the pocket of his grey velvet coat he took a gold-framed mirror too small to see more than one eye at a time. Minutely he examined each in turn. If miladi lacked lashes he assuredly did not. His were long, thick, and liberally treated with mascara. He must beware of tears . . . Though Monsieur Rémond's pedigree was more distinguished than his looks, his opinion of himself was something greater than his fortune. He had a Gallic wit combined with impudence, and a reputation as a bon viveur which had secured him an entrée to London society denied him by the Parisian elect. He was five and forty, short, squat, coarse-featured, with large protruding chocolate-brown eyes and a vanguard of a nose, jutting forward from his face as a shop-sign juts above a door; but of this formidable feature he was inordinately proud, for to him it signified his intellectuality.

The chair, traversing the Oxford Road, came into a narrow lane starred with dog-roses, and crossed a grassy space flanked by tall newly built houses. From behind his unlovely proboscis Rémond gazed up at the cream-painted portals at which his conveyance had halted. An establishment of wealth, but not of elegance. In effect, he decided, the more rich the English, the less ostentatious were they.

"The count, if you please?" he asked of the chairmen, and paid without demur the five shillings demanded. That these animals had cheated him he knew, but one must not dispute before the windows in case one were espied.

Her ladyship's greeting was gracious; Rémond's expansive, with compliments on her appearance. Ravissante! Her letters—"Ah, but your letters, miladi! When first I had the joy of reading these, lent me by my good friend, Monsieur l'Abbé, I was stupefied. What eloquence! What esprit! Épatant!"

She looked upon him kindly. His admiration was voluptuously sweet. Though her physical desires had for long lain dormant she still retained an incurable childish quality that tempted her to contraband adventure. In Hervey she had found, as she believed, all that her spirit sought in loneliness, in dreams . . . And he had failed her. So be it. Life without love offered, even without love returned, was as spiceless as cold beef without mustard.

She led Rémond to talk of her poems; he waxed lyrical. She was, he gesticulated wildly, a genius! He too was a poet, and recited her a chanson strongly reminiscent of Despréaux.

> Que je l'aimais alors! Que je la trouvais belle!
> Mon coeur, vous soupirez au nom de l'infidèle!
> Avez-vous oublié que vous me . . .

The entrance of a footman with the tea-tray, abruptly

terminated Rémond's recitation and the avowal that inevitably would have followed it. While she busied herself with the cups Mary touched upon the topic of the day. Monsieur Rémond had doubtless been in London long enough to take advantage of the rise in South Sea Stock?

Ah! Now this was something, truly, and much to Rémond's taste. He had bought—"As you, madame, have advised me, mais!" he spread his hands, "the risk is comme ma fortune, chancelante. I have—how you say?—flown on my wings to flit over these Seas. I pray le bon Dieu I will fly and not fall in the waves."

"You won't," replied Mary, matter-of-factly, "if you watch the market." And to the servant, "you may go."

He withdrew.

Rémond was jubilant. That this delightful creature should show herself so practical, a woman of affairs, filled him with envy of her husband. What a wife! and what a malheur he had not the good chance to have known her before she had espoused herself with this one there! At which point in his reflections, between intervals of sipping, Rémond choked. His eyes streamed; from those lips that had been about to utter adoration, issued squawks and splutters and a scalding gush of tea.

"Look up," commanded Mary, "and count ten."

"Gug—gug—je vous—ouch! Ouch!" gasped Rémond, between paroxysms. "Je vous demande pardon, madame." He wiped his tears with care for the mascara that bedecked them. This 'tay', then. Name of a name, what species of the urine of a cat did these barbarians, the English, imbibe! "Ça va mieux, miladi, merci, merci." He subsided, shamed.

After which most frightful exhibition it required more than courage to fall upon his knees before the smiling lady and declare, "I am out of myself! I love you madly. Do you not comprehend, chère amie, most divine, I adore you like everything. I am demented." She could well believe it. "Have pity for my douleur." He grabbed her fingers to smother them with kisses. "One might arrange, madame, if you will consider—all will be conducted of the most discreet. I die— I faint with love! The thought of you deprives me of repose."

Detaching her hand whereon the imprint of his lips had

left a trace of carmine, "If you cannot sleep," said Mary, with frigidity, "you should take an opiate."

His theatrical performance, far from breaking her resistance, had strongly reinforced it. She was saved! She had been an utter fool to have listened to the blatherings of this hateful little object with the nose. She said in French, and cruelly, "I find you absurd."

"You find me absurd? In effect, then, I am! Altogether! If to worship this ground where you tread—" he bowed his head to the carpet. His wig, immaculately curled, was plastered thick with powder in the latest Parisian fashion, to enhance the dusky bronze of his skin and throw into bold relief the beetling black of his dyed eyebrows. "If to kiss where your foot has passed is absurd, then I am! For me you are a goddess, excessively unique."

Distastefully she bade him: "Rise, monsieur, don't grovel."

"I will never rise from here again," vowed Rémond sobbing, "unless you assure me you are not all indifferent."

She parried: "If I were indifferent, would I have interested myself in your business affairs?"

"Ah! that beneficence," he cried, "I shall forget, never! How can I repay you, madame, for your——"

"I will be repaid enough," she broke in, briskly, "when you cease to make me these avowals of affection, which I assure you I cannot return."

"Then it is finished!" He leapt to his feet and covered his face. His shoulders heaved with his piteous groans. She was moved to compassion. These French! After all what were they but children? "If there is any other way," she faltered, "in which I can compensate——"

"Non, non! non, non! Ah, non!" violently reiterated Rémond, emerging from behind his hands. "There is no compensation for this stab to my heart. Death would be preferable to life without your love."

"Sir! You are impertinent." And now she spoke in English, coldly, harshly, inconsistently, unjustly, for she knew she had encouraged him enough for this display. "How dare you talk to me of love? You who are of less consequence to me than my African page. He too can amuse me with his antics

261

when he tumbles and sprawls on the carpet. Listen, Rémond, I have only to pull this—" she walked to the bell-rope, "and my servants will eject you from the house."

"Cruelle Aphrodite!" ejaculated Rémond with emotion.

"I am not cruel. I pity you."

"You say! Pity, in your language, is related to love."

"Will you not," she stamped her foot at him, "keep repeating me this word, either in my language or your own. Accept me as a friend, for I am that indeed. Did I not counsel you to buy this Stock, by which you have scooped in a good profit?"

"You rend me with these banalities," he muttered, "I am serious."

"Without doubt. And so am I. You will be well advised, Rémond, to sell out, for I am assured on high authority that the market is about to fall."

"Not possible!" shrieked Rémond. "How have I abused your bounty!"

He was making rapid calculation. If he disposed of these bonds, he would have cleared sufficient to invest again when the Bourse had ceased to stagger.

Her hand was on the bell.

"Madame! Miladi! Mon ange!" Overcome with elation at the prospect of a coup he approached her with outstretched arms. She backed and stood on guard behind a chair. "I leave," he continued, unabashed by her retreat, "for Paris tomorrow. You have offered me friendship. I accept it. I would die for your sake. Will you in return confer on me this favour—that I deposit my small fortune in your hands?"

"Monsieur!" Her tone was steel to cut. He did not flinch.

"Miladi, mon adorée, pardon, pardon! you do not comprehend. You have empowered me with knowledge to sell at a crisis. Do I ask too much of your generosity to remark I have such faith in your judgement that I beg you to replace to my advantage the money I shall gain from the disposal of my stock? I shall not be in London to be advised when it shall be correct to buy. Madame, I am a man of greatest honour, with a temperament above mondaine affairs. It is you who have introduced this subject. Pardon me."

He bowed, and with a lace-edged handkerchief he mopped his face. It was heavily pock-marked. Hysterical laughter surged up in her throat. She stifled it and thought: Only a Frenchman would have the effrontery to ask her in one breath to be his bawd, and in the next to be his banker. But since, as he did not scruple to remind her, she had given him the lead, why blame him if he took it?

"Madame," said Rémond anxiously, "I see you hesitate. Have I caused you an offence?"

"No." She considered, and grudgingly told him, "I will do what I can in your interest, if in return you will give me your promise never again to make me these embêtements."

Such a resolution, he declared, would be his death.

"Rémond, you have died so many deaths on my behalf that one must believe you immortal."

"I love thee, I love thee!" was his sob-impeded murmur.

"Very well then, if you love me—" she extended him her hand; he snatched and seized and kissed it—"you will go."

He went, with agility, secured a passing chair, and was carried to Change Alley where he disposed of his holdings with a margin of nine hundred to the good. A few days later he sent a messenger to Mary with his winnings and renewed entreaties to invest them. Since her recent interview with Rémond she had heard, on further inside information, that there had been no truth in the rumour of a fall in the wavering market. On the contrary, it seemed a rise was imminent. Indeed, her 'high authority' had come from Mr. Pope by way of the Postmaster General, father of Mr. James Craggs. As Rémond had already left for Paris, Mary, compelled to act upon her own initiative, and with folly unimaginable if with misplaced kindness, dumped all his little fortune in the booming South Sea Stock.

Alas for Monsieur Rémond! . . . Never since the Great Plague devastated London had such dire calamity struck at the nation, to bring with it ruin and, in some cases, death to the unwary. Suicides were rife among the beggared thousands who had staked their heritages, fortunes, and all their worldly goods in a burst Bubble.

In one month South Seas dropped to less than half. The goldsmiths and pawnbrokers who had advanced loans to beguiled innocents fled, with the duped vowing vengeance at their heels. Walpole, called in to devise some means of stemming the tide of catastrophe, appealed to the Bank of England to circulate, as security for one year, three million South Sea Bonds. The Bank refused. Then the rage and despair of the multitude was hurled, not only at the perpetrators of a gigantic hoax that had swallowed a nation's savings in a non-existent company, but at those of a fraudulent Government involved. Neither the King nor his two hideous old mistresses, nor his son, nor his son's wife were spared. All stood equally accused of their share in this monstrous deception.

In November King George, recalled from Herrenhausen, landed at Margate with his jaded Duchess, to find the capital in chaos and the Stock down from a thousand to barely a hundred and fifty.

The following February Parliament met to probe the scandal and suffer the invective of the Lords. The most virulent attack, led by that dissolute handsome young rake, the Duke of Wharton, was turned on the Premier, the weakling Lord Stanhope, and the Junior Secretary, Mr. James Craggs, both equally suspect—as was Wharton himself—of blowing the infamous Bubble. So forceful was Wharton's abuse, that when the pallid Lord Treasurer strove to reply he fell down in a fit and expired. His death had been caused by a stroke, it was said; but more likely by the orgy of thirteen hours' solid drinking, held at the house of the Duke of Newcastle on the previous night, to fortify the defence of the guilty.

The sad sudden news of this death, 'so sensibly touched and disturbed' the King, as his gentlemen reported, 'that he could not eat of his supper'. He was not, however, too touched or disturbed to send for Mr. Walpole and hand to him the reins of Government.

Among others on whom cupidity reflected was Postmaster General Craggs. He, sooner than face the bitter accusations of his wretched victims, died of a 'lingering lethargy', according to his doctors—and which was strictly true. He did die of a 'lethargy', self-promoted by an overdose of opium. In the same week his blue-eyed son, James, succumbed to the smallpox, caught from the porter at the house of a lady whom he had been visiting by stealth. That he, one of the most vituperative opposers of Mary Wortley Montagu's 'engrafting', should meet his end thus, was ironical; and to her this demise of her enemy the only cheerful news she had heard since Rémond's departure for Paris.

While tens of ruined thousands ineffectually snarled around those who had bilked them, Mary, left to deal with Rémond and his Stock, thought she had done 'prodigious well' to have sold it again at whatever small profit before it fell to zero; only to find that the buyers had absconded, leaving her with a packet of worthless shares and poor Monsieur Rémond in the soup.

He accepted his misfortune with a laudable indifference. His answering letter assured her his concern was less for his financial loss than for his unrequited love . . . After which he did not write again.

Deeply thankful for his silence, Mary, somewhat tardily, resolved not to meddle any more in his affairs; she had enough to do now with her own. Edward had leased, and afterwards bought, of Sir Godfrey Kneller, Saville House at Twickenham. Persuaded by Pope that country air would greatly benefit her children, Mary urged her husband to accept Kneller's offer at his very reasonable price. For this last year or two she had not seen much of Pope, and she guessed that his interest in her children's health was promoted by his interest in her. Still, the house and its situation in that charming rural resort with a garden that dipped to the river, was a haven of peace from the dirt and smoke of 'this sea-coal city', as she called it. Pope, who had excellent taste in the choice of curtains and the placing of furniture, was constantly beside her with gratuitous advice or the reading of his latest verse; or to delight her with some whisper of a scandal.

Twickenham had latterly become the seat of fashion. The Duke of Wharton was installed—without his Duchess—in the house of the defunct James Craggs. Card-parties, river-parties, masquerades and balls disturbed the sleeping village with sound of music, drunken song, and the roll of coach-wheels back and forth from Town and Hampton Court.

On one of these gala evenings, in the spring of the following year, Mary, in the costume of a shepherdess, with a crook and a toy lamb under her arm, prepared to set forth for the Duke of Wharton's masque to which guests had been invited to attend en pastorale. While she dressed she could hear the strains of flute and viol floating through her window from the water. Dusk had fallen. In her glass the candle-light revealed her as a nymph in rose-pink flowered satin with a coy little hat, strewn with daisies, tipped over one eye. Grace stood by, rhapsodic. "My lady, you look seventeen!"

"And I feel seventy!" Then, as she poised a patch, her small grinning black boy came to the door with a letter, "Just brought, ladee, by de couriah."

With a sinking of her heart Mary recognized the writing. Her fingers trembled as she broke the ornate seal—that, too, she recognized—and read, how that Rémond had discovered her 'tricks', was convinced she retained all his money untouched, and 'would have it again'—underlined—'or he would print every one of her letters.'

"Leave me," she bade the watchful Grace.

"My lady has ill news?"

"Yes—no. Leave me. Go order my chair."

Grace left her, and Mary, with horror increasing, read over the letter again. Here was a to-do! And a happy prelude to a party, heaven help her. What a monster, what a fiend was this Rémond—and what a fool she, to have been led by fulsome flattery to believe that he loved her. Love! Such love as he professed was centred solely in his love of filthy gain. She had been the prey of a scheming low adventurer. But her letters—*what* had she written in her letters, to be flourished—should he carry out his threat—in the faces of her 'friends'? How they would grin—God damn them all!— to see her lowered, and in print! By any bribe or at any cost, this snake must be drawn of his fangs before he bit. . . . Then, hearing her maid at the door, she tucked the letter down between her breasts, dabbed the hare's foot to cheeks that had whitened, and asked for: "My cloak, my mask, my fan." Come what may she must go to the ball and trip it madly with the rest of them, while that hateful paper pricked the flesh beneath her corsets like an asp.

She arrived at Wharton's house to find the Prince there with his retinue from Kew. He led her out to dance a minuet, a signal honour that aroused not a few jealous flutters. She had never been so merry, full of quips to entice, peeping up through the slits of her mask at his ogling, sweat-bedewed face. Whispers, screened by velvet vizards, hissed around her. "See her latest conquest—she aims high." Her ears ached to hear more. Should they link her name with Rémond's in connection with the Bubble, she too would look to burst!

The Prince bowed her to her seat and sought his next choice—another shepherdess, pretty Molly Lepel, his wife's Maid of Honour, euphemistically styled. Mary breathed relief to split her stays . . . Grace had laced them too tight. Her hand strayed to her heart. She had a stitch. Suppose she should die? Yes, and if so what a boon!

She was claimed by her host who whispered against her cool curls, "You have never looked so lovely"—and dragged her from the ballroom to an arbour in the garden. He was drunk. Forcing her down upon a marble bench he crushed her lips against her teeth with his wine-tainted kisses. She fought with him but dared not raise her voice; other couples were dispersed about the lawn.

"Let be! You're soused. I have no wish for you."

Yet he had charm enough when sober to amuse her. The prettiest of fellows and an accomplished voluptuary was Wharton, with an impudent tilt to his nose and a pair of wickedly girlish blue eyes, on account of which Mary nicknamed him 'Sophia'.

"You have no wish for me," he hiccoughed, "nor for none of my kind. You're cold. 'Ods Heart! If I could warm you——"

"But you can't."

"I'm inclined to think—" he stood over her, precariously balanced. The night was full of moon to cast an eerie glow upon his painted cheeks. He was costumed as Hermes with a pleated short white tunic and a pair of wings attached to his heels and his head, fastened either side of his corn-coloured full-bottomed wig. "I'm inclined—" he repeated with solemnity—"to think that Pope is not far wrong in saying you are Sapphic."

"Does he so!" She clenched her fists. "For that I'll kill him."

"Nay, sweet, he'll kill you first—with his pen. It can slash more cruel than any rod. Dear life, lemme protect you."

But when he made as if to kiss again, she aimed the woolly lamb she dangled by its ribbons in his sodden bloated face.

"Go!" she panted. "I am faint."

"Faint!—an' so'm I!" He turned from her, reeling, to lurch his way out before the wine he had taken spilled from him. She heard the splash of it upon the path amid his groans. Disgust and horror bound her frozen to the bench. The night was fragrant, the sky a field of sapphire, star-studded. From where she sat in her dainty dress, with the toy he had wrenched from her hand at her feet, she could see the gleam of fairy-lights reflected in the water, and the drooping willows on the river bank brought to emerald brilliance in the tulip-flare of flambeaux.

The ebb and flow from the ballroom, of guests in every kind of Arcadian fancy, lent a vivacious impermanence to silvered tree-shadows where, posed against yew, box or privet, Daphnis chased a water-sprite, and an overblown Silenus clasped a squealing grape-girdled Bacchante, and the shrill laughter of women mingled with men's voices above the music's lilt . . . Suddenly a shadow, small and crooked in the starshine, crept across the grass. She heard the whisper of her name.

"Madam." A furry-clothed, bedizened little satyr stood before her with furtive mischief a-grin as he made her a leg. What had he seen or what did he know? Or, if he knew nothing, should she confide? . . . 'He will kill you.'

"Pope." She gave him two fingers; he took them, fondling. His eyes—those strangely beautiful, sad eyes—looked deep into hers. And his smile, that hid in its sweetness a haunting of mockery, fled.

"You're in trouble?"

She nodded; her heart swelled. There had never been

another who could so swiftly seize her mood in sympathy to match it.

"I am uneasy. Read this." And from between her breasts she took and handed him the leter.

He fumbled for a tinder-box, carried in a pouch attached to his leathern belt. She glanced down; his absurd little legs were encased in hairy stockings. He crossed his knees, and leaning forward over them held the tiny flame above the paper. She watched him as he read, until, lifting those unfathomable eyes of his where surely a flicker of devilment lurked: "Why fear this frog?" he questioned. "Have you not written letters to me—and to others?"

"I have." She clasped her hands and said intensely, "and there is nothing more personal in those I have written to Rémond than—" she paused—"to any other."

"I can believe it." He nodded, hunching up his shoulders, smiling to himself, acting the part demanded of his out-landish dress; a son of Pan, a goat-foot god. "But this man is far beneath you, and I, my dear, am not."

"Give me the letter."

She held out her hand, not liking his tone, nor that faun's smile of his, as if he shared some secret jest with a familiar. "The letter," she peremptorily repeated. "Please. You must not keep it."

"I keep it? Never!" He sprang to his feet and returned it with a flourish and a bow. "Take it to its treasured hiding-place—" she had an urge to tear that grin from off his mouth—"and forget it. Dance with me."

Dance—with him?

Yet, as if the moonlight and her frantic fear had cast a spell upon her, she was forced against her will to dance—and dance with him again on the star-bemused lawn among those who capered in the wild gay abandon of the jig. His head was scarcely on a level with her chin, his eyes were on her face, and his voice hummed in tune to a pastoral refrain:

'*The pleasures of youth are but flowers of May,*'

Twirl about, two singles, set and turn, change partners, round again; and sweet as a thrush's note above the squeak of flute and horn, Pope sang, unseen,

'Our life's but a vapour, our bodies but clay,
O, let me live well though I live for one day . . .'

Hands across and partners meeting, he to bow and she to
curtsy . . . "I'm fatigued. I must go home."

"You have come here unaccompanied?"

"Yes, my husband is in London."

"With your permission," said Pope, standing on his toes
to offer his arm, "I will be your escort."

"I thank you, but I have my chair."

"Then I will trot beside you."

And not another word, while he hobbled the short distance
between Wharton's house and hers, did he speak till he
handed her out at her door.

A shiver seemed to strike the paling stars; the moon was
hidden and a veiled greyness came . . . "And I will be beside
you always," Pope said softly, "when you call."

She must have been mad! So throughout the wakeful
dawning Mary flayed herself—mad to have shown Pope that
letter. Suppose he should spread it round the clubs that she
had 'tricked' Rémond of his money? Who would believe
him? They might believe worse. Dear God, what to do?
Take her trouble to Edward and leave him to deal with it?
No, never that. He might be tempted to board the next
packet for Calais, coach it to Paris, call out that vermin—
and be slit. Edward was no swordsman. Had he the guts of
a louse, or a man, she could tell him, and devil take the
consequence. She would die of this; and almost did when
Rémond's preliminary offensive was followed by a demand
for the full repayment of his losses, or two thousand pounds
in compensation.

Two thousand . . . She had not that sum in pence. So this
hellish beast, this 'frog', had turned to blackmail. No
mistaking his intent. 'If she refused to comply with his
request he would take the matter further.' To her husband!

She would have to placate him, but how? Were she to sell
her mother's pearls and the few jewels of little worth that
Edward had bestowed on her they would not realize a
quarter the amount.

If she only could remember one word she had written, or

had she kept a copy, her mind would be relieved; yet she was certain she had written nothing compromising: verses, London news, descriptions of her travels in Turkey—and what else? 'That my cursed pen,' she groaned, 'should bring me to this pass.' She had ever been too ready to write letters, though always with a care for polished words and the reservation that they might be read by others. Yet it was damning evidence enough to have invited him to London, and there had been a mort of correspondence to do with the South Seas. A sweet interpretation would be put upon her interest in this reptile's private affairs!

And taking up her 'cursed pen' again, she unburdened herself of her 'misery' to Frances imploring her to approach 'the wretch and make him ashamed of his infamous proceedings . . . of which I heartily wish I had told you long since. I cannot deny I was silly . . . But if people are so silly you'll own 'tis natural for anybody that is good-natured to pity and be glad to serve a person they believe unhappy on their account.'

In this distracted outpour, devoid of any 'polish', Mary is presented in a very different light from the ex-Ambassadress to whose charms, as gossip gave it, His Sublimity, the Sultan, had succumbed; and, in cool defiance of the College of Physicians had rescued with her 'quackery' six felons from the rope. But this was a letter not intended for an audience, and in it and its successors, fear-inspired, Mary leaves an unintentional self-portrait more vital, more convincing, than any other penned in persiflage.

'It came into my head out of a high point of generosity (for which I could wish myself hang'd) to do this creature all the good I possibly could since it was impossible to make them (*sic*) happy in their own way. I advised him very strenuously to sell out of the subscription, and in compliance to my advice he did so. He took leave of me with so many tears and grimaces (which I can't imagine how he could counterfeit) as really moved my compassion . . . He is liar enough to publish that I have borrowd the money from him, though I have a note under his hand in which he desires me to employ it in the Funds . . . Nothing can be clearer than my integrity in this business, but that does not prevent me from being in the utmost terror of the consequences.'

That Frances was unwilling to be drawn into these 'infamous proceedings' is apparent from Mary's next frantic appeal, where her sister is accused of 'unkindness that you have so little care of a business of the last concern to me . . .'

She had taken legal advice and was told she could prosecute. This she dared not do for fear of making her husband 'uneasy' . . . 'He is the only person from whom I would conceal it. For God's sake,' she prays Frances, 'do *something*.' She fears for her health; she carries her 'distemper' about with her 'in an anguish of mind that visibly decays her body', and is 'too melancholy to talk of any other subject. . . .'

Yet not too melancholy to talk of 'heads and ruffles' to be bought at Boileau's, with an added hint that she is sadly in need of new lutestring, which she could have purchased in London but nothing like so good as that obtainable in Paris.

Her chief anxiety, however, and one that largely contributed to her 'visible decay', was how to keep Edward in ignorance of her dealings, not only with Rémond but with the South Sea Bubble. Her husband would not tolerate any form of gambling, and that she should have wasted the money she could have saved from the meagre allowance he doled out for household expenses, would, she guessed, be as painful to him as were Rémond's letters to her.

And still this 'odious monster' wrote demanding reimbursement for his losses or—more threats—he would confront her husband with the truth.

Seeking distraction from her 'anguish', she betook herself to Twickenham where she 'suffered *agonies* every post-day', undiminished by mounting suspense occasioned by Rémond's peculiar silence, until—horror heaped on horror! —he announced he was coming to Town.

Yes! He was crossing the Channel, had landed at Dover, and was on his way, doubtless, to Edward in Cavendish Square. And now that the worst was about to befall, Mary's lost courage returned. She mustered her forces to face what must be, and attack, not as the dastardly Rémond attacked, from the rear, but in bold open fight. 'For I solemnly swear,' she boasted to Frances, 'that if all the credit or money I have in the world can do it'—that she had neither money nor credit did not for one moment deter her—'I will have him used as he deserves.' And since her hints for new commodities had not, apparently, sufficed, she sent 'herewith three guineas to be paid out in lutestring, *plain*. . . .'

Another week crawled by, and still no sight nor sound of Rémond. Her spirits soared with hope renewed. If he intended to pursue his threat and send Edward her letters she would surely, by this time, have known the result. She was on tenterhooks lest her husband should arrive with or without Monsieur Rémond. She could well imagine the scene that would follow, and even went so far as to rehearse it. She was on her knees to him to kill her, if not Rémond, rather than Edward should believe her guilty of taking to herself that detestable man or his money. As for the letters— there was the blind spot. The letters! If only to God she could remember one *word* she had written . . . So on and on, and wretchedly, she paced her room, re-enacting her part of a chaste, maligned Lucretia; until, when Edward did arrive, one early morning in September, her relief at his casual husbandly greeting was so great that she burst into tears.

With unsurprised calm he surveyed her. She was still in her nightshift and a dressing-gown, having been up with the sun to walk in the garden and speak her lines in preparation for the ordeal which she sensed was fast approaching. She looked very young, very small in her sandals without heels to give her height; and her tears had left a smudge where they trickled down her cheeks.

"What's amiss?" asked Edward, coolly. "Are you sick?"

"I am—yes," sobbed Mary. "Sick to the stomach of—" His raised eyebrows queried a heart-beating pause in which she saved herself of rash confession to say: "Oysters. September. In season—" she gabbled—"I ate of a many. I love them but they," she achieved a little laugh, "they don't love me."

"Is that so?"

There was something in his tone, too affable; and in his guarded look, his stiff unbending attitude, one hand behind his back, the other thoughtfully caressing his chin, that dried her tears in a flush-heat of alarm. Faltering, she asked him: "Have you breakfasted?"

273

"Yes," his hesitation was almost imperceptible, "I—halted at Richmond."

"You have rode hard." She glanced at his shoes, white with dust. "'Tis mighty hot today." And going to the window, she opened it.

His eyes strayed to the hearth where the heaped logs burned high. "Hot? No, chill I think, as you, too, seem to find it, though I should not have thought it necessary to have so fierce a fire. Sea-coal costs dear."

"It is not a sea-coal fire. These are logs from the trees that were cut down."

Why did he stand so still—and staring? And what in heaven did he hold behind his back?

"Your daughter," she essayed with false sprightliness, "grows sweetly. I have had all her dresses lowered at the hems. Shall I fetch her to you?"

"No. I have brought you a gift."

"A gift?" Again that surge of relief to break her voice. "How kind!"

And how unusual . . . Then as she saw his stretched smile that showed all his teeth like a grin on the face of a skull, her breath tightened.

"Here," he said, "is what I bring—for your pleasure." And at her feet he flung a packet bound in paper, sealed.

"A pretty way," she panted, "to offer me——"

"—what you must stoop to take."

And with that he turned and left her.

She knelt. Her hands touched blindly; she dared not look to see what he had thrown. Then, as one drowning, she clutched it, lifted it. broke the red seal, Edward's seal, firmly impressed; and within those paper wrappings lay—every one of her letters to Rémond!

A darkness dissolved her as she fingered the first of them. What had she written and what had he read, if he had read any? . . . That last hope was lost; not only had he read but had initialled each with precision: E.W.M.

There, crouched on her knees she stayed, scanning the pages in torment to discover one single sentence to condemn her and found—not a word that could be misconstrued. There were essays in French or her verses in English, some

Town talk of the day and, happily, none of Rémond's speculations. Much, however, of her own; that the least consideration. Yet could she be sure? She believed Edward would more readily forgive her a flirtatious indiscretion than her reckless gambling to lose . . . She must brazen it out. Was she to be brow-beaten for following the lead of the Throne and half the Government?

And while still she knelt, unable to move, nor to steer the tumult of her thoughts to more coherence than this one focal point, that she had her letters safe and could hold them over Rémond to bring him up for trial—(if she dared!) —the door behind her opened.

She scrambled to her feet.

"Well?" His supercilious calm remained intact. "What have you to say?"

The letters lay as she had left them, scattered in her search. His eyes glanced down.

"I have this to say." And she said it with bravado, born of panic. "If you, who have been at pains to read these—" she kicked at the bundle with her toe—"can read into them your own base interpretation, you may do so. There is nothing written here I would conceal."

"I am fully aware of it. Your delight in verbiage was never more apparent. But what—" he fastened upon her a look in which contempt was curiously tinged with supplication— "what," Edward asked, "does he write to you? Is this French-man your—" His head jerked back; a kind of paralysis of speech prevented him from uttering the words that she smilingly said for him.

"My lover?" . . . A wave of exultation overswept her. So he cared! He cared enough to suffer, even as once she would have suffered, to believe him false to her. "My lover? *That* object, that slimy mongrel cur! Do you insult me?"

"Yet," his lips twisted in reply, "you do not scruple to advise 'that slimy mongrel cur' where he should place his investments."

Then he knew! How? These letters had given no hint of a business transaction. Someone had told him, possibly Rémond, more than the truth for her damnification. And with the thought that it were better to confess than to

dissemble, she hurled at him the challenging admission:
"Yes! I *did* advise Rémond on his speculations, to my cost—
as others were doing, and as you might have done, were you
man enough to gamble on a chance."

Since she had surprised him in his momentary weakness
she had regained her equilibrium, to stand upon her rights
and flourish before him proof to dispel the blackening cloud
of suspicion.

"Look!" She ran to her bureau, unlocked it and took from
a drawer the first letter Rémond had written her on his
return to Paris. "This should convince you he is not, nor
never has been to me what degrades you to believe. Read!"
She held it out to him. With no compunction, and remotely,
she observed that his face had a queer mottled pallor. He
shook his head.

"If you're *afraid* to read it," she taunted him, "I will!"

Her little body reared itself. She stood transfigured; her
shoulders beneath her none too spruce chintz morning-gown
were squared, as was her chin. His was sunk in his cravat.
He seemed to shrink; and with an audacity quite incom-
patible with one who 'every post-day suffered anguish' she
read, in French:

'I do not regret the climate nor the social life of England,
but I do regret the conversation of certain persons, and yours
above all, which I have so rarely enjoyed. I know that English
women are incapable of either friendship or of love. I am,
however, less concerned with the madness of the one than
with the sweetness of the other, and am content to love without return.'

"So now you see!" She tossed aside the flimsy foreign
paper. "He wrote that before he had decided to make me
pay his losses. As for these," she pointed to the litter at her
feet, "will you keep them or shall I?"

He shrugged indifference.

"They are yours."

"My dear!" She warmed to him then, and was melted;
impulsively snatched his hand to kiss, and found it cold.
Gently, he freed himself, and as gently said:

"I lied to you——"

She looked up at him in startled apprehension. His eyes

were narrowed; and on an in-drawn breath, "I lied to you," he said again to freeze her, "when I told you I had breakfasted at Richmond. I did not. So if you will excuse me now——"

Into his dressing-room adjoining hers he went, and closed the door between them. The key turned in the lock.

★ 16 ★

THUS, as an axe fells a branch from a tree, in one brief compelling gesture, was Mary severed from the intimacy of her husband's life; her marriage wrecked.

It was not that he suspected nor believed her capable of sinking to an intrigue with a man so far beneath her; it was simply that their years of mutual grievance had ended in the slow death of illusion.

When she could in temperance review the situation, she realized that Edward had resignedly accepted the inevitable. She had failed him as wife; she had cheapened his name; this she granted fairly, since now that the worst had befallen, she could see herself as he must see her in her over-weening vanity and eager thirst for and acceptance of men's homage. The turning of a key symbolized the dissolution, not only of their stillborn love but of all hope for a possible reunion. He was proud; he had been lowered. Her intolerance for his failure to achieve success as politician or Ambassador had wrought its irrevocable injury, to leave upon his heart a scar unhealed.

Sometimes she asked herself, had he seized upon this first opportunity offered to break from her with the same merciless precision with which he had marked and returned all those letters? A poor extenuation for love's murder.

Although since the birth of their daughter they had continued to cohabit, it was abundantly clear that their conjugal relationship had proved unsatisfactory to each; yet they still had lived as man and wife; but now they lived divided.

Pride forbade her to allude to this parting of their ways.

277

Never once did she query that closed door, while within her she applauded his delicacy in the timing of the breach. He could so easily have waited till the night to tell her bluntly that henceforth he had forsworn her bed, which would have been less subtle, if more cruel. But where two ways lay before him, the indirect would be always Edward's choice. And as if in compensation for all that she had lost, Mary returned to the lure of that trivial world she had claimed for her own.

None to see her guessed how that despair and desolation partnered her at balls, at dinners, fêtes; nor that in her lonely nights she created vile fantasies of her husband, driven to seek in sordid adventure, forgetfulness of all that they, once lovers, had cherished and which was now for ever lost.

In that she wronged him. Though the natural consequence of assimilative custom had satisfied his greed for her inflamed by her persistence, his appetite could never be rekindled by purposeless intrigue. And with that widening chasm between them, so, as one accepts a climate, did Mary come to accept the arid conditions of her life and his.

She kept her own counsel; she held her head high to demand of others the respect that from her husband she had forfeited.

Her children, her households in London and Twicken-ham, claimed a great deal of her time. The frugality with which she conducted these establishments gave rise to much critical remark. This did not at all embarrass Mary. Besides that Edward had taught her the value of money, she must make good her catastrophic speculations by saving and stinting wherever she could. Edward had amassed a fortune. Years of thrift had reaped their reward in a hoarding of wealth that, with the death of his father, was to reach the half million mark; but neither he nor Mary cared to spend. She had never wished for nor coveted expensive jewels or clothes. Her coach and her post-chaise were as shabby as her servants' liveries; yet she could afford to go in gowns outmoded, to entertain with markedly unlavish hospitality, and still remain a leader of society. She had set herself a part to play and with amazing aptitude she played it.

Her letters to Frances in Paris at this period are amusingly malicious, pen-pointed to cut at those she called her friends. A round of gaiety submerged her; she hunted the stag in Richmond Park, accompanied by the Prince of Wales, whose open adoration of the lively Lady Mary somewhat compensated for the coolness of the King. His Majesty had never quite forgiven her entry into the enemy's camp, his son's Court, to inoculate his grandchildren at the Princess's desire and in disregard of his own. Lesser men than the Prince were drawn to the unshaded light of Mary's eyes. Chief among these was Mr., now Lord, Hervey, who, since the death of his elder brother, had succeeded to a courtesy title.

In the first months of their marriage, the then Mr. Hervey had on several occasions brought his bride to Mary's house, where to her infinite boredom they were 'perpetually cooing' in her drawing-room. They did not coo there long. Hervey's warm infatuation for his exquisite, if a trifle tepid, little wife, was soon melted in the sun of Lady Mary's riper charms; and although Molly Hervey presented her spouse with a perennial influx of babies, it was not to her he turned for recreation.

Month after month and almost daily, Hervey's chaise, with its flower-wreathed panels, would drive through the Park to the house on the edge of Mary'bone marshes; or he would ride down to Twickenham where Pope, a spy-glass to his eye, watched from behind his starry-blossomed curtains, Lady Mary in her garden receiving visitors to tea; the one tall, thin, immaculate, whose hollow painted cheeks and languid elegance were in striking contrast to the other, Pope's neighbour and pet aversion, Wharton, with his face of a depraved Adonis, and all his Herculean masculinity.

Pope was seldom now invited to the house of his lady, nor approached by her unless to borrow something in a hurry for an unexpected guest; extra cutlery, a pair of sheets—'all my better things are stored in London'—for which he had to ask his widowed mother, who since her husband's death had come to live with him.

As for Mrs. Pope, her crippled son had not, despite his fame, outgrown his petticoats. To her he was still a toddler in the lisping stage, arrested in the flight of time since that unforgotten day when he had been trampled by a savage cow which struck at him with her horns to gore his throat and all but kill him . . . Until that fatal moment he had been sturdy-limbed and plump, a pretty boy whose voice, even before he could speak his words, was so sweet and joyous clear they named him 'the little nightingale'. He could still sing—to rend the heart of his mother. And because that she had left her treasure to a careless nurse, because that he was stunted, crooked, humped, she loved him with a passion shared by her husband, a retired linen-draper, all his life.

And from that linen which had been his father's stock-in-trade, Pope selected a pair of sheets fit for a queen, to offer Lady Mary. These he took in person and the hope he would be asked to stay and dine. He was disappointed. 'Her ladyship,' a footman brought the message, 'thanked Mr. Pope for the loan of the sheets, and regretted much she could not see him. Her ladyship was indisposed.'

So indisposed that half an hour later Pope, from his window, saw her frolicking upon the lawn with Wharton, while Hervey lolled in a chair, and a suit of strawberry plush.

And besides these favoured gentlemen who came to call and stayed to dine where Pope did not, Mary had reaped a harvest of ladies, none in their first bloom, yet all more or less happy to be named her 'dearest friends'.

There was 'poor Mrs. Murray' — Griselda — who had become entangled in a very sad affair. She, while staying in the house of her father, Mr. Baillie, had been awakened in the night to find a masked man leaning over her brandishing a pistol, and threatening instant death to them both if she refused to satisfy his passion.

Her shrieks brought servants running, and her father with a blunderbuss that proved to be unloaded. The intruder, when captured and locked in a stable, was revealed, without his mask, to be one Arthur Gray, an under-footman.

He was brought up for trial and condemned to death with the commutation later of life-long penal servitude. 'Poor Mrs. Murray', rightly named Griselda, found her patience sorely tried by this unhappy misadventure, for, notwithstanding the support of a doting father and a complaisant husband, Gray swore she had conceded him his lustful proposition. In self-defence, therefore, the lady was advised to give evidence against him in the Courts.

Mary, greatly tickled at this *cause célèbre*, made it the subject of a wicked little ballad. Her lurid description of the love-torn footman's jealousy to see his 'great rivals in embroid'ry gay, sate by her side or lead her to the play', is followed by near frenzy when he 'hears the charming tinkle of his lady's morning bell', and hastens to her chamber with her tea. Then:

> *'All my guilt and all my sorrows rise,*
> *I saw the languid softness of your eyes;*
> *I saw the dear disorder of your bed,*
> *Your cheeks all glowing with a tempting red;*
> *Your night-clothes tumbled with resistless grace,*
> *Your flowing hair play'd careless down your face;*
> *Your nightgown fastened with a single pin,*
> *Fancy improved the wondrous charms within. . . .'*

To bring about the fall of Arthur Gray.

It is not surprising this 'Epistle from the Footman in Newgate' was something less facetious to Mrs. Murray's taste than to its author's. There were those who maintained that no woman could have written it, 'and scarce any man', is the verdict of one, 'for if he could paint such sentiments so well he would not have had warmth enough left to . . .'

Exactly.

But all the same Mary did write it, and, moreover, protested, when accused by a justly incensed Mrs. Murray of slander, that nothing in these verses could cast the least aspersion on the lady's character, whose beauty and virtue she extols.

The reply to this artless assurance is not recorded, but may be conjectured from Mary's allusion to 'poor Mrs. Murray, who,' she writes to Frances, 'is at open war to attack me in very Billingsgate language at a masquerade. But without,' she adds wishfully, 'doing me much harm.'

She was mistaken. Griselda might have better excused poor Arthur's attempted violation than Mary's naughty skit at her expense.

Yet despite repeated indiscretions slipped from her pen,

Mary made no effort to restrain it; for in these years of virtual separation from her husband, and while still beneath his roof, she employs herself in writing questionable letters with the obvious intent that they be read by other eyes than those to whom she sends them. None who came within range of that sabre-edged weapon she so gracefully wielded, escaped its spiteful stab. Her enemies were legion; her friends few.

She had of late revived acquaintance with the ageing Dowager Duchess of Marlborough, who, unlike other women, delighted in Mary's sophistical wit.

The passing years had stolen much of the beauty that once had broken the heart of a Queen and held the victor of Blenheim enthralled to the day of his death. Yet the same shrewish temper, the same changeful moods as from a volcano in eruption to a gentle smiling valley, still remained, as did that brilliant golden hair, 'preserved,' confessed the Duchess, 'by the constant use of honey-water'.

She was writing her memoirs and would read passages to Mary, in particular those that dealt with Abigail Hill.

"I'll show the world," her Grace redundantly declaimed, 'how that Maggot, Abigail, a pauper, my own kith whom I rescued from a garret—from a broom!—strove with her evil cunning to crush me. But she cannot crush my pen! This is my dagger—to strike." The Duchess struck at the air with her quill, as if to skewer the eyes of a visionary 'Maggot'. "In that, my dear Mary, you and I are *not* at daggers drawn." Sarah chuckled and took a pastille from a silver box beside her. "This damned wintry weather plays the devil with my chest. You and I are sisters. We have our hatings—by God, we have!—and our likings too. You are one of my chosen. Now tell me"—huddled in her chair by the cheerless hearth, Sarah conspiratorially dropped her voice, "does Hervey point his toe—or his tongue—at the Princess? I'm told he is enamoured, but not surely with that too *too* solid flesh of hers?"

"Or, more seeming," smiled Mary, "with her solid future state."

"Yah!" The Duchess wagged her head. "He's her gentleman-in-waiting. Let him wait! The King'll live another twenty years if he don't burst himself of beer." And with a sidelong glance at Mary, her Grace added: "Still there's no denying Hervey's a rare quiz for all he's but a Jemmy-Jessamy—they say." She prodded Mary with a finger. "You should know!"

"Madam," Mary laughed softly, "this I know. The world is composed of men, women and—Herveys."

"Agad!" Sarah threw back her head, roaring with laughter to show her depleted gums and a loosened yellow fang or two. "Here's a *bon mot* for my book. I'll note it in. Where's my pen? . . . What a girl it is!"

Her Grace had grown jocund in her older age, and much after Mary's own heart. She still attended Court, but despite that George I had brought her out of exile, she openly disparaged 'this pack of parboiled Guelphs' as she called them, and gleefully recounted a tale of a visit she had paid to the nurseries at Leicester House. "The young Prince Frederick—who would then have been around five years old —was so spoiled by that Frau, his mother, he had only to scream and she'd give him the moon——"

"I have always understood," Mary interposed, "that the Prince of Wales is a very stern disciplinarian."

"Stern my ——!" her Grace retorted vulgarly. "Well, and there were we, the Princess and I, striving to comfort the brat who was squalling that he would not, no, he wouldn't and be damned to hell he wouldn't take his physic, when in waddles the Prince. 'Flog him!' cries his Highness. 'Strip him of his hide—dat is how to bring up die junge in de way dey should go. You English—' says the Prince to me with that Guelph thickness in his speech you'd think he had plums in his mouth — Gah! How I abominate these Hanoverians—'Ay,' says he, 'you English is none of you well bred because you were not whipped when you was young.' 'Ho,' thinks I to myself, 'then 'tis certain sure *you* were not whipped when you was young.' And I had the deuce to do to choke my words and not say it flat to his lecherous face, for when all's said he's the heir to the throne."

The Duchess blinked her faded eyes at the fire as if she saw in its feeble flame a resuscitation of her own red-hot youth. "Yes, time revolves to bring in its revenges. I've lived through four—no, what am I about—five, or is it six reigns? I'm forgetful. There was Charles . . . I see him now, riding through the streets of London on that glorious May morning of his Restoration." It mattered nothing to the Duchess that she spoke of a May morning a year before her birth; her age was as elastic as her temper. "Yes, there he rode, the brave lad, with that pugnacious chin of his which, no matter how often he shaved, was blue as his blue-black hair curling down his shoulders almost to his middle—natural too, no periwigs for him. They came later—although 'twas Charles himself who cribbed the periwig from that pox-ridden old punk, Louis, the Sun King of France. *Sun* King!" Unmitigated scorn was in the Duchess's cracked voice. "His sun went down when the smoke of John's cannon went up. And then after Charles came James. Yes, and my John—God bless his angel soul!—was a page in James's Household when he was Duke of York. A fine King he—a Papist King, a runaway, a poltroon—pstst!" The Duchess spat. "So much I think of *him*. Then comes his daughter, a sickly-faced whining stick-in-the-mud-of-the-Hollander's dykes was she, *and* her husband, Orange William. But I'll own, though I abhorred him, he had more sense in one of his ragged toenails than any of his Stuart kin in all their handsome bodies. A weedy, yellow, dwarfish, sneering sort of living corpse, who never had a fair run for his Crown, I'll say. And he—what a difference from his Uncle Charles—was *not* very fond of the girls. A mysogynist, they called him. I called him something else."

Her Grace snickered, took another pastille, and smacked her lips upon it, carefully digging out the remnant that clung to her one remaining molar.

"And last of that lot, after William, who fell off his horse and killed himself, came Anne, on whose silly fat head, believe it or not, I placed the Crown, despite her ingratitude and wickedness to me who loved her. And God alone knows," declared Sarah histrionically, "how truly from my heart I loved that lump of suet. But I forgive her for the wrong she did me, since she was put to't by this hell bitch of a— Did I ever tell you," asked the Duchess, "how my cousin Abigail served me?"

"Yes, madam, often." Mary simply could not bear to hear it all again. Indeed, she had not listened to the Duchess's recital; her attention had been fixed upon the flogging of the Prince; an awkward subject that Mary, after taking her leave of the garrulous old lady, recalled and applied to the parallel vexed problem of her son.

He, now thirteen, had been placed at Westminster School, where, according to his masters, he was indolent, ill-mannered——

"What! My boy, ill-mannered?" Mary interjected, when Edward had read her this report. He was never Edward's boy, always hers. "High-spirited, but indolent—that he's not, I'll swear."

So well she might, but it did not alter facts, nor that later news of the younger Edward gave it he had escaped authority, and fled.

While his horrified father reviewed this transgression with retaliative choler, Mary wept. She visualized her darling set upon by cut-throats, left to die, or lying suicidally at the bottom of the Thames. Her fears, conveyed to her husband, may have caused him to offer, much against his will, a reward of twenty pounds for information of the truant, and treble that amount for his return.

Thus urged, his pursuers had traced him to Oxford, where he had been found in the cloisters of Magdalen and a state of incredible dirt, his shoes worn to ribbons and his suit in rags, eating of a mutton-pie. This, it appeared, he had stolen from an itinerant vendor of such, who, with a score of rowdy undergraduates to cheer him on, had chased but not captured the thief. He had clambered up a wall, jumped down into a nettle-bed and lay there, smarting, till the hunt passed by; then he had climbed up and over again, took to his heels, found a quiet collegiate spot, and had just begun to eat his pie—when he was interrupted.

The price paid by his father for deliverance of the prodigal, brought home in a carrier's cart, may have accounted for the not unrighteous wrath with which the younger Edward had been met.

Strongly offensive to sight and smell, into his father's study he was hustled; and there well and truly he got his deserts.

Outside the door, his mother, hearing the swish of the rod and no sound from her suffering idol, rushed into the room to his rescue and was sternly bidden: "Leave me to deal with—*this*." Another whack. "He returns to Westminster with my orders that he be flogged twice daily for a week."

"You can't!" Mary had made to snatch the rod from Edward's hand. "He'll be raw as an underdone joint and not able to sit."

"Then he must stand," was the inimical reply; and when Mary had turned to comfort the besmirched and silent martyr, she was tersely waved aside again. "This is my affair, not yours."

"It is mine! I'll not have him bullied or beat. He's been a wicked, wicked boy, but he's repentant now. Aren't you, my angel?"

With a scowl and a hand to his buttocks, her angel said: "No."

"No? For shame," weakly admonished his mother.

"The boy is past redemption," his father, with cold intensity, remarked; and stalking to the bell he told the man who answered it, "Take him, wash him, feed him, change his clothes, and order me the chaise."

"You'll not send him back to school tonight?" cried Mary.

"Tonight." On which immense admission her husband closed his lips.

His son opened his; and in a voice that, though still in its childish treble, gave indication, to break his mother's heart, of a deepening distressful croak: "I will not be reduced," he muttered, "to the humble condition of a schoolboy."

It was awful; yet Mary could not but admit that Edward's handling of this deplorable occurrence had proved in the main a success, to subdue the recalcitrant. His masters gave hope of marked improvement. When, as now, he applied himself to study, he could easily outshine his seniors; moreover, his errantry to Oxford had, it seemed, been prompted by his own grandiloquent opinion that he had done with schooling and was qualified to take a University degree.

"In four years' time," his father told him, "you will be sent to Cambridge, to my College. Not to Oxford."

But his son held strong views as to that. Oxford or nowhere was, he maintained, his objective; or he would run away to sea and be a pirate.

'It happens very luckily,' wrote Mary to her 'Sister Mar' in Paris, 'that the discretion and sobriety are on my daughter's side. I am sorry the ugliness is too, for my son grows very handsome.'

This woeful incident crushed Mary so completely that she went into retirement at Twickenham, slowly to recover from the shock of it. She had bought a horse which she deemed no extravagance, having persuaded the susceptible 'Sophia', Duke of Wharton, to part with him at less than bargain price. "He is much superior to any two-legged animal," she told Pope when she met him while exercising her new purchase in the lane outside her house.

Restraining the remark that he was certainly superior to either of the two-legged animals who escorted her on her daily rides, Pope's lavish compliments concerning the lady's equestrian skill were interrupted—"Oh, Pope, I had forgot. There is something I must beg of you. I have guests to stay and would be eternally obliged if you could loan me another pair of sheets. I hate to ask, but you know how it is when persons descend unexpected, for the night."

And with an airy wave of her hand she rode on, and left Mr. Pope bowing and grinning and turning to greet her ladyship's spaniel, presented to her by the Prince of Wales, that ran out at the garden gate to jump up at him with exuberant glee.

"There's a dear lad, a fine fellow." Pope was down beside him on the grass-edged way. "Kiss then, kiss! . . . And when these mangy half-breeds come yelping their spittle-tainted envy of your pedigree—yes, you've a pedigree behind you, lad, which I have not—then you must say, 'I am His Highness's dog at Kew, pray tell me, sirs, whose dog are you?' There, there! Enough—your paws are muddy. Go back. You won't? Well, come with me, and we will share a marrow-bone together. *She'll* not know."

Often when Mary rode out from Twickenham to Richmond Park, accompanied by Hervey or Wharton, sometimes both, Pope, mounted on his scrawny fiddle-headed mare, would meet them and, with exaggerated courtesy, would pass the time of day.

The first time he appeared in the path of his lady and Hervey, to receive from them the briefest of acknowledgements, Pope heard his lordship's lazy drawl: "He should ride that spavined roman-nosed filly of his at Bartholomew's Fair, decked out in a red and yellow coat. Our little brave poet would make the prettiest clown . . ." And Mary's laughing answer. "Yes, but you yourself have said 'tis not the trappings that make fools of men, 'tis the men who are fools in their trappings."

Pope reined in his mare and sitting still, very still, in the saddle, and small, shouted after them: "Ay, so say you! And I'll say 'tis a vile conceit in pompous language, dressed like a clown—or me—in regal purple!"

And digging spurs in his bay mare's flanks he put her to the gallop up a grassy hill-track and rode her, wet and steaming, to her stable.

He found his mother in the kitchen counting over the week's laundry.

"Look here, how your fine Lady Mary returns me this pair of sheets, stained and mucky, after keeping them a month!"

Pope tiptoed to hug her, burrowing his chin in her comfortable shoulder.

"Who's to care? Not I, not you. Foul linen comes clean in the wash." And skipping away from her, he stooped to gather the sheets in his arms.

"Why, what will you do with them, child?" asked his mother; but when he looked back at her with so white, so tense a face, she cried concernedly: "My love, my dear, you're sick, you've rode too far."

"Not far enough," he shrilled at her. "I'll ride till I outride the devil himself. But first—to tub this dirty linen and hang it on the line!"

Thereafter, every day for weeks, Pope made a point of meeting Mary when she rode out with Hervey or Mrs. Molly Skerret, her only friend among all others named as such. This friendship between herself and Mrs. Skerret, first the mistress then the wife of Robert Walpole, was covertly watched by the Premier's schoolboy son, Horace; and he, from his earliest Eton days having seen his adored mother slighted, supplanted by a rival, has left a record for our keeping, to Mary's discredit, of malice unexampled even from the pen of that incomparable scribe, who mingles his ink with gall.

Molly Skerret was staying at Saville House when news came to Mary that the Duke of Kingston had been taken with a seizure. She rushed to Town post-haste, but not in time to see the last of her father alive.

As she stood alone in the hush of the dim curtained room gazing down at that heavy waxen face on the pillow, transfixed in the majesty of death, the years slipped from her and she saw him as she had seen him on that distant summer night, standing at an open doorway in the candleshine to welcome her. *'Make a bold entrance, sweet, an you love me.'* Yes, she had loved him then; she loved him still, had never ceased to love him, or maybe the father-image she had sought in worship of another to whom she had rendered her soul . . . Her soul! Did this Thing upon the bed with its sagging jaw upheld by a bandage possess a soul? Words, she mused, man-made in fear of the hereafter; man's self-protection against the unknown. For what are we but dust-specks in the infinite compass of the universe? O, but life, she cried within her, is too pitifully short, and some day soon, or not so soon, she too would come to this—this ghastly silence, this inertia, a shrouded shape upon a bed. Of what use to live since one must die, unless to be drawn back to that pure boundless Source within whose sight a thousand years are but as yesterday?

She sank upon her knees. Her desolation deepened into sorrow; not for him whose cumbrous spirit, straining at the leash, had escaped across the threshold of eternity, but for the unsolved mystery of life itself.

The sound of hysterical sobbing brought her in a hurry to her feet.

The little Duchess, draped in black, vastly becoming to her rose and golden prettiness, tottered into that quiet room supported by Aunt Cheyne.

"Evie! Evie!" The 'Fair Isabella' flung herself weeping upon the prostrate form. "Don't leave me, take me with you—to the grave!"

"We've had this all the morning," muttered Evelyn, who followed on the heels of her aunt and her step-mother. "Between intervals—that is to say—of interviewing modistes and painting her face. And not a tear shed, mark you."

"God's will be done," intoned the equally tearless Lady Cheyne. "My poor beloved brother has flown to a higher, a happier realm—let us hope. Evelyn, at what o'clock did the attorney tell you he would come? 'Tis past two now. I cannot stay much longer."

"Ah, me!" sobbed the Duchess, "I know how it will go—every penny to my poor dead darling's grandson. Do I care? Gladly would I see myself beggared to bring my loved one back again."

"You won't see yourself beggared," snapped Evelyn. "You and yours are well endowed. You've seen well enough to that."

"Hearken to this cruel unfeeling toad!" appealed the Duchess, abandoning grief to fury. "In my hour of need she dares accuse——"

"I did not accuse. I merely stated," Evelyn calmly interposed, "a blatant fact."

Mary left them to it, but she did not leave them long. On the arrival of the family lawyer, a conclave, over which Aunt Cheyne presided, was called, and Mary summoned to attend it. With what appeared to her to be unconscionable haste, the Will was read. Whereupon the stricken Duchess showed herself sufficiently recovered to protest against 'the miserable addition of two thousand a year to her jointure'. She was convinced her 'dear dead' had been unfairly influenced to leave her such inadequate provision. 'She and I,' Mary later reported to Frances, 'were in an actual *scold* when our father departed. Nevertheless her good Grace remains a passable rich widow, and is already presented by the Town with a variety of young husbands.'

Much to her astonishment, Mary, who had been threatened with nothing but a shilling from her father, received, as did each of her sisters, the sum of six thousand pounds. The residue of the Duke's estate went to his heir, William's son.

This increase in Mary's financial position from a dependant on her husband to a woman of moderate means, eased her way considerably toward that pursuit of pleasure with which she drugged the ache of an unsatisfied existence. Her letters to Frances, during the next year or two, exhibit a gaiety, palpably forced, to conceal her concern at her sister's ill-health. According to friends who had met her in Paris, Frances had developed an increasing melancholia. She would sit for hours silent, or swing to the other extreme and chatter incessantly all about nothing— or all about Mar.

Throughout their married life Frances had been harrowed by the ever present fear that her husband's adherence to the Royal exile would eventually bring him to the block. On this not unlikely contingency she brooded until it became an obsession. Mary, who remembered old Nurse's head-shakings at the tantrums and hysterical outbursts of Frances, was much disquieted at these reports. Nor did her sister's letters reassure her. They were full of her hypochondriacal ills, her insomnia, or, if she slept, of her fearful nightmares. Then, within a few months of their father's death, came another. Evelyn had died in childbirth.

'We are now but two in the world,' Mary wrote; and adds, spicing sympathy with some impatience, 'I am very sorry for your ill-health, but hope it is so entirely passed that you by this time have forgot it . . . 'Tis only the spleen that gives you these ideas. As for me, having nothing to say, I say nothing.' Whereupon, and contradictorily, she has much to say 'of ridiculous things happening which I cannot help (as far as in me lies, dear sister) sharing all with you.'

Not quite all, however. The one most 'ridiculous thing' yet to happen could never with Frances be shared.

*   *   *

During the months that followed these family bereavements, Mary, in dutiful black, was seen much about the Court of the Princess of Wales. London had never been more gay, notwithstanding the King's speech from the Throne which conveyed ominous portent of war. When, in 1726,

Prussia seceded from the Treaty of Hanover for no other reason than that the young Prince Frederick, eldest son of the Prince of Wales, had flatly refused to marry the Emperor's daughter, the disturbed conditions in Europe, resultant on this deliberate slight, reacted most unfavourably in Britain.

Stocks were falling, trade was at a standstill; men hurried to Change Alley to sell out their holdings in the Funds. Diplomats gloomily anticipated secret alliances between Austria and Spain; and when the King told Parliament that information had come to him of Spain's attempt to revive Popish plots in the cause of the Pretender, the House rose in a ferment. Disaster loomed ahead; the Spanish Ambassador had been recalled from London; the Ambassador for Britain from Madrid, and war was imminent.

News that the Spaniards had seized a British merchant-man threw the country in a tumult. Gibraltar was menaced; the Rock besieged.

With the coolest indifference the garrison surveyed the too optimistic invaders. Secure behind their fortress, and supported by Sir Charles Wager's fleet, slipping past armed galleons to bring up supplies, the British turned their full force of cannon on the swarming Spaniards. Reduced to less than half their numbers by disease, desertion, and that relentless banging from the Rock, the Spaniards gave up—and gave in.

Mary's 'Sophia', Duke of Wharton, leader of the Hell-Fire Club, who, to everyone's amaze, had proclaimed himself a Jacobite and received the Order of the Garter from the Stuart King in Paris, went over to the enemy. Other of his rowdy fellow-members, to whom a good fight was better than women or wine, joined forces with the Duke to strike a blow for the 'Pretender'. Most of them were killed, but Wharton came off lightly with the loss of a big toe. He lost also Mary's friendship by his exploits.

No sooner had Walpole brought this farcical war to a strategic conclusion than the King, fretted sick with the worry of it, took himself to Herrenhausen for a holiday.

A solemn-eyed pale youngster, son of the Prime Minister, saw the King the night before he sailed. When His Majesty came down to supper, one of the ladies attendant on the

Schulenberg, who now enjoyed a semi-royal state, brought Walpole's boy to an ante-chamber. There the ten-year-old Horace knelt and kissed the King's hand for the first and last time in his life.

Impatient to be home in his beloved Hanover, the King went on ahead, leaving his Minister, Lord Townshend, and his mistress, to follow at their leisure in the rear. On June 8 he was at Delden and up with the dawn and on his way again, urging all possible speed.

Rattling along the vine-bordered roads of his Fatherland, the King, excitedly peering through the windows of his coach, was taken, of a sudden, with a fit.

The coach halted; horrified attendants hastened to his aid. There, on the leathern-padded seat, with his tongue lolling out, his eyes starting from their sockets, sat the King who had never thought, never wished to be King of Great Britain and Ireland.

At his last gasp he managed to articulate, "On . . . On to Osnabrück!"

He lived long enough to die in the room where he was born.

"And this," said Duchess Sarah when, with Mary, 'very well diverted', she viewed from the windows of Marlborough House, the Coronation procession leave St. James's, "makes the seventh I've seen crowned."

*　　　*　　　*

The death of George I brought about considerable changes in Court circles, not altogether to Mary's delight. Hervey, who as Vice-Chamberlain succeeded Lord Harrington, was much in request by the Queen at the Palace, and seldom now at Twickenham with Mary.

Throughout that Coronation year, she, back and forth from Town, was greatly bothered by the antics of her 'young rogue, the most ungovernable little rake that ever played truant'.

He had played it again, and this time could not be so easily traced. To add to her troubles came ill-omened tidings from Paris.

Frances was reported to be mentally deranged.

Nor was that the worst of it, though bad enough. Mary, determined to have her sister in her care, no matter how serious her state, was baulked by the Earl of Mar's brother, Lord Grange, who had smuggled the ailing Frances to England with the intention of taking her North, where he could keep her under his control. Mar's estates had been forfeited and sold for thirty-six thousand pounds, which Grange had hoped to grab; clearly the last person on earth to whom Mary would entrust her stricken sister.

Grange, a promiscuous adulterer, had a superfluous wife whom he kept imprisoned on the island of St. Kilda, and on the excuse that she had betrayed certain Jacobite secrets which might have got him and his brother Mar hanged. Tales of cruelty to his captive lady had come to Mary's ears and convinced her that she would sooner see her sister dead than in the care of Grange.

In these straits she called on Hervey to intercede with Walpole that she might be given sole custody of Frances. But Grange, who had learned of her purpose, was already posting on his way to Scotland with the wretched Frances shrieking at his side. Her cries for help, her poor distraught face at the carriage window, served to save her; for the sheriff's men, who by order of the Premier were spurring hell for leather North along the King's Highway, caught up with and halted, at pistol-point, the chaise whence issued those maniacal yells, and 'Procured on the false affidavit of her sister, Lady Mary,' thus Grange's version of the episode, 'the arrest of the Countess of Mar'.

Brought back to London, Frances was delivered up to Mary who nursed her, guarded her, suffered with her, prayed that she might die. But Frances, in her moon-distorted world, refused to die; she would sit for hours, staring; or would stand, never speaking, her great haunted eyes fixed on visions, her ears strained for voices that none save she could hear; or she would sing a wailing tuneless tune of: 'Misery misery *mee*, and a dying duck sang in the willows a-weep, O . . . misery, misery me-*eee*!'

In her grieved disturbance for her sister's case, which

medical opinion pronounced to be incurable, Mary's first anxiety concerning her 'young rogue' had considerably lessened. But as time hurried on with no result from unceasing inquiry, she inclined to think herself the victim of some relentless fate.

"I sure must be one of the damned," she confided to Hervey, "for my life, since I was born, has gone awry to such degree that all persons and things I love and want most I seem to lose. I clutch at shadows. Yet I still hope I am only in purgatory, and that after whining and grunting a number of years I shall be snatched up and taken to some happier sphere."

They were out riding together on one of those too rare occasions when Hervey could escape from his Court duties. It was a gusty March morning in the New Year, 1728, with Spring's breath in the air and her touch upon the spreading oaks of Richmond, and on the rusted bracken where sweet new greening fronds unfurled to brush knee-high their horses as they passed.

"What happier sphere," asked Hervey, "could you desire more than this? I would rather live in these dear times, in this dear land, than any other. And though there be much of mud and mire in our paths, we can step across it and tread in cleaner ways."

He edged his horse alongside hers, and, shifting his riding-crop from his right to his left hand, laid it for an instant on her rein.

"Pull in; let us walk them for a while. Why dwell on misfortune when you can have no greater good fortune than to give and be given—in friendship?"

Friendship!

A sigh fluttered through her. Always he must harp upon that word and none warmer.

"You have never known the sorrows and cares of a mother, or," she laughed a little, "of a wife."

"That is so, and not my fault. I'd have made," he said drily, "a good wife for a man . . . or for you. But listen, sweet," his voice and eyes caressed her, "though you may think it odd in me, I have known care and sorrow too. We do not speak of that."

295

"We speak of nothing," she flashed at him. "You will always talk—and *talk*—in riddles. I know less of you, not more, as life wears on."

"Yet you should know," he stared between his horse's ears, "that my mind is never naked except when it walks and talks—with yours. Shall we gallop now? This lad of mine is chafing to be off. I'll race you up this hill-rise."

But when they reached the top of it Mary saw, with a twinge of alarm, how an egg-shell pallor showed beneath the rouge upon those frail hollowed cheeks. Unfathomable creature, less like a man than the ghost of one there in the saddle.

He left her at her door and turned his horse's head to London. She went slowly in to be met with joyful news.

Her son was found!

Edward had sent a brief note from Cavendish Square to tell her that their truant was safely housed—"and I'll warrant he's beat to a jelly, the poor little brute!" So she laughed and cried together to an equally overjoyed Grace.

With a heart full of prayerful thanksgiving she gave orders to have the chaise take her to London at once, when the footman detained her.

"My lady, Mr. Pope has called. He is waiting below. His message, he bids me say, is urgent."

Thinking to spare him five minutes before the chaise was brought round, she went down to the parlour. In her black velvet habit and braided cocked hat, with its white feather for half-mourning, she was like a bewitching boy.

"Pope!" She ran to him. "Have you heard? He's found —my son is found, brought back. He's safe! Dear God, I'm happy."

As she pulled off her hat a tumble of curls fell about her shoulders. She was nearing forty and she looked fourteen.

"I too am happy in your happiness."

His hands were holding hers; she let them stay. He bent his head and kissed her fingers. 'My dear, though I come on a pretext of urgency, and though urgent always is my need— my hope—to see, to speak with you——"

She tore her hands away. An unpardonable trick to force his presence on her by a ruse! "If this matter that has

296

brought you here is merely for a sight of me, I beg you, Pope, consider. I am off to Town directly—to my son."

"And who brought him back to you?" asked Pope with a smile of provocative significance.

"That I have yet to discover."

"Shall I tell you?"

"How? How can *you*—" there was faint insolence in the stressed pronoun—"tell me who brought him?"

"None better," he said carelessly, "than I, who have made it my business to send my paid scouts here there and everywhere, combing the country!"

"No!"

Disbelief, indignation that he should dare to take so much upon himself, struggled with her eager curiosity. "But why should you do this for me—for us?"

"For you," he quietly corrected. "Do you remember my promise?"

"What promise?"

As though they were stilettos, his eyes probed her while he answered:

"That I would be beside you when you called. For there is between us, Mary—" never before had he dared address her by her name—"a curious affinity as of an invisible cord strung from one to the other, and I have a curious notion that if this link were severed I, or both of us, would bleed internally."

"Pope," taking up her hat and gloves she assumed a businesslike air, "time will not wait. My chaise is ordered. I must go."

"You will not go. You will hear me." He came nearer, gazing up at her with that smile, half indulgent, half quizzical, as to a child. "I have this to tell you, Mary, that your boy was found—at Blackwall."

"Blackwall!" She paused on her way to the door. "But that's down by the river."

"Yes, where he has been these three months, hobnobbing it with fisher-folk and sailormen and wherrymen."

"God in heaven!" breathed Mary, "is this the truth, or another of your highly flavoured fabrications?"

"No fabrication, though high—or more correctly

I should say—*ill*-flavoured, and redolent of fish scales."

"What!"

"Your son," he said, "has earned himself a living, crying mackerel, fresh whiting and eels all alive-o, from Billingsgate to Blackwall, where he lodged in a seamen's hostel."

"I can't—I won't—" began Mary wildly, "believe——"

"That I would invent such a tale?"

"No, that—yes!" Incredulity gave way to buoyant reason. "Yes! 'tis likely—more than likely—that he would have hid himself in some such hole. When he was a baby on the shores of the Bosphorus he had a longing for the sea. The Golden Horn—that lovely harbour overlooked by our windows at Pera—had always for him an immense fascination. I should have thought of that. We have spent a mint of money advertising him in all the news-sheets. Pope," her tone softened, "how came you to send your searchers after him?"

The corners of his mouth curved quaintly.

"Well, 'tis simple enough for one who sups at taverns, and though I make it no habit to frequent the town haunts of clubmen, I have scavengered among houndish journalists who are ever at the ready to put their noses to a news-scent, whether it be false or fair."

"That you," her voice quavered, "should do this for me! I cannot thank you, but God will bless you for it."

"I do not ask God's blessing nor your thanks to give you happiness. And that, by the application of a little commonsense, I am overjoyed to have secured. Let us speak no more of it. There is something else I wish to say."

"Of him—of my young vagabond?"

She was beautifully animated now.

"Not of him."

Pope came nearer till he stood almost touching her, his arms hanging loose at his sides, his face enigmatic. She looked down at him with vague discomfort stirring. Was he about to ask that she defray the expenses incurred by his activities on her son's behalf?

"I have waited," said he, to scatter that thought, "I've waited—how long have I known you—fourteen years?—to tell you this. I would not have you think I take advantage of any service I can render you, nor would I wish it known that I have interfered in the finding of your boy. Forget it, but remember—beyond forgiveness, beyond all understanding, beyond all hope, I love you, and must love you till I die."

If he had left her then; or if he had not followed his soft-toned declaration by striking an attitude, aping the man, who was not as other men; or if she had not seen and been revolted by his imperious desire, she might have suppressed the surge of her laughter sprung from the stored hysteria of weeks; but she could not. She was helpless against the torrent of giggles that rushed from her like the rattling of rain upon a window-glass.

"I can't—I daren't listen! I must not. You said—forget—" She was choking out her words, idiotically, to save herself and him.

He caught her hands and gripped them in his bony little fingers.

"You shall," he shouted, "hear me. Though I am but a droll from a fair—yes, and though today I have discarded my red and yellow trappings—you *shall* hear me!"

His words had struck some dormant memory to stir it; yet she could not stay her laughter.

"Stop! It is too—too utterly ridiculous! You——"

"Yes, I!" And his sudden shriek of laughter now capped hers. It was horrible. His face, ashen white, had no merriment. His voice rose high and higher as with mouth distorted, gibbering, "Yes!" he screamed at her, "I am ridiculous—a tumbling dwarf in cap and bells! But even—hah-*yah*—" he gave a yelp like a dog that has inadvertently been trodden on—"even a dwarf, a subhuman monstrosity, can love its mistress and come fawning for her favour. Speak up, my queen!" He recaptured her hands, and made a play of clapping them together. "You're lovely and you're hateful. Your lashless eyes are hateful. Your body that I want and would tear to pieces with my love—if I could have it—is hateful. Take me to it, take me. I offer you mine, ludicrous, misshapen thought it is, for you to fondle. Hi-*hee*!" Again that mirth-tormented yelp. "*That* makes you laugh, yes? Even as I did laugh when you flung your dirty linen back in my face, unwashed. You're dirty. Dirty!" His lips were drawn back in a snarl. His spittle ran over his chin. "Do you

wash? Your nails—" he turned her hands, they were none
too clean. "Ah! I see your nails are in mourning too."

She wrenched away from him; her breath shuddered in
her throat, and the storm of her laughter sank.

There fell a silence between them; no sound except her
hurried breathing, no words spoken until, in a voice of
harsh melancholy to startle that petrified stillness:

"You have too much wit for me," he said; and dropping
on his knees, he raised the hem of her habit to kiss. *"Vale,
Madonna. Indomitable Sappho. This is the silly season, as
they say."

He struggled to his feet, walked with his halting gait to the
door and, swinging round upon her, he elaborately bowed.

"Peace be with you, and between us—let peace for ever
die."

Like a mad thing he ran out of that house and back to his
own, never stopping to air his feeble lungs. His mother
watched him stumble up the steps; but when, shocked by
his pallor and the wild unseeing look in his eyes, she would
have followed him, he waved her off.

"I am in my labour pains. Leave me to my work."

He locked himself into his study.

His mother sent him up a tray with cold meats and a
bottle of wine. He left it untouched. He was writing; and
wrote long into the night, and all the next day, and the next.

★ 17 ★

MARY HAD more to concern her in the ensuing weeks than
Pope's singular behaviour or her own reaction to it. Now
that her fears for the fate of her son were assuaged, she
strongly supported her husband's unrelenting view of
Edward's second bid for freedom. On his return in a state
of parlous filth, with no explanation to offer for his truancy
other than that he loathed his school, he was promptly
removed from it and placed in the care of a tutor. This

decision had been made in no agreement with the younger Edward's wishes. The gentleman chosen to act as his warder was one eminently fitted to cope with refractory pupils. The Reverend Mr. Fisher, in full accordance with his employer's creed, held the miserable Edward virtually enchained, slept in his room, kept strictest watch on his studies and his movements, and did not spare the rod on the slightest provocation.

When the upheaval caused by Edward's disappearance had eventually died down, and when Mary did upon occasion revert to that appalling incident at Twickenham, she was bound to admit herself at fault. Yet the circumstances offered some excuse. She had been overwrought, as was only natural after months of unceasing anxiety, to hear such happy tidings of her runaway. But was that, she argued, sufficient cause for her deplorable lack of control? To laugh at a cripple! She burned with shame to recall it—even though it was not at him—God forbid!—she had laughed, but at the irony of life that should have cast at her feet one in the full pride and power of his genius, whose weakly frame had not the manhood to support it. All in her that was woman must instinctively revolt against the abnormal; nor could she believe that the 'love' he professed for her was genuine. He had never loved her. He had no doubt been flattered by her letters, her admiration for his consummate art, and by her patronage. Yes, he had held her interest; but to hold her heart would have meant more to Pope, an inveterate snob and always super-conscious of his undistinguished origin, than all the eulogies heaped on him by the literary world . . . So let it pass. He would recover from his temper and come running, as he promised, when she called.

As for this cock-and-bull story of his search for Edward, she must take one half of it, the smaller half, with a very large pinch of salt. In so far as it went it was true enough that he, an habitué of Button's, would possibly have heard how some or other waterman, accustomed to ferrying the Quality, had seen her young scapegrace crying fish—Good Heavens!—down at Blackwall. His accent alone, if not his bearing, would have stamped the boy untuned—or at least 'twas to be hoped—to the habits and vernacular of Billingsgate. Indeed, her husband had remarked how that the rough but seemingly discerning fellow who had brought their son home to Cavendish Square had said he had only to hear the young gentleman speak to know he was better born than he appeared to be.

So much for that. Let Pope, if he must, place her under obligation to himself for a tale that was already round the clubs the very night the boy had been dragged back to his father. Pope, it was evident, had snatched the opportunity to take all credit of it to himself and to importunate her with his most ill-timed avowal, in the morning. She would likely hear no more of that unfortunate affair, since he had given her no further indication he remembered it.

Weeks went by, and months, and when still no allusion, either from direct or indirect sources arose to remind her of what was best forgotten, Mary ceased to think of it. And then . . . suddenly, among a collection of *Miscellanies,* the joint work of Swift and Pope, appeared a ballad addressed: 'To a Lady who fastens her Lampoons on her Acquaintances'.

This, with the warning: "You have a powerful enemy here," had been sent to her by Molly Skerret.

It began in the merriest style to tell of a sober yeoman of Yorkshire'—the significance of the locality is unmistakable—whose wife, having hatched more chicks than she could rear, seized upon a capon, made it very drunk, and clapped the surplus brood beneath its wings.

Having read thus far, Mary inclined to the belief that Molly had started an unnecessary hare. Mrs. Skerret, hypersensitive of her position as Robert Walpole's mistress, was ever on the watch for enemies and libels. The concluding couplet, however, revealed the good wife's identity beyond all doubt, for:

> 'Such, Lady Mary, are your tricks,
> But since you hatch, pray own your chicks.'

A vicious little squib fired at the lady who 'anonymously lampoons her acquaintances'. Yet Mary thought it wiser to ignore the 'Wasp of Twit'nam', than in retaliation to invite a further sting.

Thereafter, for a while, he ceased to buzz around her

name. He was engaged in a furious attack upon his fellow penmen and the literary critics, among whom a certain facetious Mr. Dennis had written:

'He is neither poet nor versifier, but only an eternal rhymer . . . A little incorrigible creature that, like the Frog in the fable, swells and is angry because he is not allowed to be as great as an ox.'

No more lenient than he had been to Mary for her laughter was Pope to Mr. Dennis, or any other of his kind who derided him for his deformity, his religion as a Papist, or his tremendous gift, when, with murderous insolence, he flung down the gage to challenge his offenders in that sublime and lofty satire, the *Dunciad*.

The world of letters, the social world of Mary, the coffee-houses, taverns, clubs, and those trashy scribblers of Grub Street, the 'Dunces' whom he stamped beneath his foot, talked of nothing but his wicked ridicule of persons known or not known to him; of individuals in the abstract, or of life at large.

Artfully, to guard himself from libel, Pope persuaded three peers to undertake the publication of this, his greatest work; the easygoing, rather foolish Bathurst, the magnificent Burlington, the good-natured Oxford, son of Harley, the 'mystery man' of Anne's reign, were only too delighted to launch the first edition.

It was a masterly move. Not a man of the 'Dunces' who writhed beneath the thongs with which he lashed them, would dare to bring an action against three peers of the realm, though they might against 'poor little Pope'.

He was not poor, he was rich. Money rolled in from the *Dunciad*. All were avid to read the 'Wasp's' abuse of his neighbours. Steele was spared, he was dying; but Pope would never have struck at Steele, his friend. And in that shower of poison-tipped shafts he let fly, to fall where they would on the small or the great, his second dart at Mary ricocheted aside with the merest grazing of her skin.

> '*When hapless Monsieur much complains at Paris*
> *Of wrongs from Duchesses and Lady Maries.*'

Surely not one in a hundred would recognize that reference

to Rémond; and when not one in a hundred did, Pope sharpened his quill to drive it home up to the hilt in his note to the *Dunciad's* second edition.

'The passage is thought to allude to a famous lady who cheated a French wit of £5,000 in the South Sea year. But the author meant it generally of all bragging travellers, and of all *whores* and *cheats* under the name of ladies.'

And in these lines is all the venom, all the jealousy, the hurt and the hate he had fostered, waiting for this moment when he who had been spurned could reap his bitter vengeance, to draw blood.

That the Rémond affair, long since buried, should by this foul assault be disinterred for all to see and gloat upon was the dirtiest reprisal for imaginary grievance . . . Up and down her room in fever-heated fury, Mary raged; and without pausing to reflect upon the consequence, she counter-attacked in a 'Pop upon Pope', based on the rumour that the poet had been set upon and thrashed in Ham Walks by two of his satirized victims.

Few believed Mary's denial that she was not the author of 'Pop', and particularly when another assault, in the form of 'One Epistle to Mr. Alexander Pope', was flung at him and his associates, Swift and the Jacobite doctor, Arbuthnot.

To him Mary wrote protesting her innocence in that she had no acquaintance with, and was an utter stranger to, Dr. Swift, 'and even to his person which I never saw to my knowledge'. The unspeakable Pope, she was convinced, had determined to 'blast her reputation'; and after expressing the amiable hope that she would live to see him hanged on a gibbet, she ventures to subscribe herself, 'with an uncommon warmth', the doctor's 'Friend'.

Whether or not the kindly Arbuthnot had any faith in Mary's warmth or friendship, he certainly endeavoured to bring about a peace between the two—with no success. For Pope this sport of Mary-baiting had a sadistic fascination. While he ruthlessly pilloried those of his fellows who did not scruple to jeer at his misshapen body, she, whose laughter still rang in his ears to kill the glory of his verse, was his chief target.

Year in, year out, the flaming arrows flew to strike at her, nor to spare any one of her intimate circle. He had a name for each. Wharton is 'Clodio', 'the scorn and wonder of his days'. Hervey is 'Sporus', 'Lord Fanny', 'Adonis', 'Narcissus', who, 'tho' not with genius fired, is by schoolboys quoted and by girls admired'. Molly Skerret is 'Phryne'; Mary 'Sappho': a vile implication.

It was 'Sappho' and 'Phryne' who together 'raised a monstrous sum because they feared a man would cost a plum'. Here the wicked little tyrant shows a calculated cunning in his method of attack. There is nothing outrageously offensive in a jocular allusion to a partnership between ladies of fashion who demanded from admirers a substantial return for favours given. But his aim, none the less, is unerring. At first he deliberately shoots beyond his mark before he hits the bull's-eye in those blistering lines addressed to a 'furious Sappho', whose 'fate' is: 'Pox'd by her love and libelled by her hate'.

Like some malignant fungus spread the growth of poetic injustice; nor did the impeccable Edward escape Pope's pollution. He is pinioned as 'Shylock', 'Avidion', 'Gripus', 'the miser' who will sell a gift of game or fruit for the money, 'yellow dirt', that is his passion.

And yet . . .

> 'As e'en in hell there must be still
> One giant-vice so excellently ill
> That all beside, one pities. not abhors;
> As who knows Sappho smiles at other whores.'

She stood alone; deserted. Pope's virus had done its evil worst. Even those whose secret lives were by no means unimpeachable looked askance at and avoided Lady Mary. There must be some foundation for the great Master Poet's insistence, or why, if she were guiltless of these dreadful imputations, did she not defend herself?

She did.

Driven at last to desperation she appealed to Hervey, not her husband: a fatal error this. Disgusted though he was by the horrific notoriety which by her friendship with one so 'despicable' she had brought upon herself and him, Edward would not have scrupled to drag the noisome case into open Court and to its end; for, as Edward saw it, forensic reprisal was the one course of action to take. Mary, however, preferred to fight Pope with his own weapons and on his own ground, clad in shoddy imitative armour.

In his *Imitation of the First Satire of the Second Book of Horace* Pope had launched his most virulent offensive; and with Hervey's aid, Mary concocted a set of verses that for sheer malevolence equal any Pope has slung at her. And there they halt. Beside the thunder of his execrations, her retort is the hooting grimace of an urchin, a mouthful of spit at a cripple.

> *'Unwhip't, unblanketed, unkick'd, unslain,*
> *That wretched little carcase you retain,*
> *The reason is, not that the world wants eyes,*
> *But thou'rt so mean, they see and they despise . . .*
> *Like the first bold assassin's be thy lot,*
> *Ne'er by thy guilt forgiven or forgot;*
> *But as thou hat'st, be hated by mankind,*
> *And with the emblem of thy crooked mind*
> *Mark'd on thy back, like Cain, by God's own hand,*
> *Wander, like him, accursed through the land.'*

An unworthy poor revenge was this, to rend him in his weakness; and if for an instant his 'wretched little carcase' doubled at the blow, he was up again and on his toes to hurl his caustic mockery at him who of them all he most detested; he, who in his elegance and beauty had won what Pope had lost, the love of a woman he so desperately wanted, and that might have been his were he clean-limbed and not a travesty—'mark'd by God's own hand'.

And at Hervey, in wave upon wave of corrosive contempt, Pope pours his immortal defiance.

> *'Let Sporus tremble!—What? that thing of silk,*
> *Sporus, that mere white curd of ass's milk?*
> *Satire or sense, alas! can Sporus feel?*
> *Who breaks a butterfly upon a wheel? . . .*
> *Amphibious thing! That acting either part,*
> *The trifling head, or the corrupted heart,*
> *Fop at the toilet, flatterer at the board,*
> *Now trips a lady and now struts a lord . . .*

Beauty that shocks you, parts that none can trust,
Wit that can creep, and pride that licks the dust."

There could be no reply to it; nor would Hervey have demeaned himself to do so. "It is beneath me," he said, "to enter into paper-war with one so contemptible as he."

But Mary, whose reputation, as she had foretold, had been 'blasted' by this 'paper-war' until no shred of it remained, did not agree with Hervey's lofty attitude. Pope's attack had left him and his status unaffected, even though the 'Wasp', with renewed ferocity, returned to sting again. In a letter of surpassing impudence he offers Hervey a gratuitous apology, explanation, what you will, for the epithet 'Lord Fanny'.

'Fanny, my lord, is the plain English for *Fannius* . . . A foolish critic and enemy of Horace, extremely fond of both his poetry and his person . . . Moreover of a delicate or effeminate complexion . . . So much for Fanny, my lord.'

His excuse 'in regard to the Right Honourable Lady, your lordship's friend', is fraught with pure malice. He was 'far from designing a person of her condition by a name so derogatory to her as that of *Sappho*, a name prostituted to every infamous creature that ever wrote verse or novels'. . . .

The rubbing of salt in an open wound; but while Hervey had seemed to ignore the smart of it, Mary inwardly, painfully bled. Her position in Society had suffered from Pope's slanders. The Queen, with whom she had latterly stood in high favour, now received her with chill; she was conscious of whispers, of hostile stares, as she passed through the Drawing-Room. Even Hervey, from behind the Queen's throne, returned a smileless bow to her bob. She allowed he had cause for resentment, since foul insinuation had plastered his name upon hers. Of them all, Edward alone stood beside her, but with disapproval stiff in every joint of him. He had made it clear that only for their daughter's sake did he withhold drastic action against Pope—'for the same reason,' he added in careful afterthought, 'that I refrain from taking action to terminate this pretence of a union between us.'

It was out! All the hoarded enmity, his sickened love, his

rancour, were in those measured words, and in his eyes that held no pity; only an aching weariness as of one who has too long and uncomplainingly endured some cankerous obscure disease.

And as if closed shutters had opened on a room of death, Mary, in that revealing moment, saw herself as he must see her ... She, and she alone, was responsible for this destruction of their marriage. She had overstepped the bounds of those 'Proprieties' by which he lived, the gods by which he swore, and to whom he would have had her be his sacrificial offering. She, who was his chattel, had disastrously attempted to infringe upon his rights; the rights of Man.

He could not, nor never would, be persuaded to acknowledge her individual liberties as woman that, in order to ensure his male paramount superiority, must stay for ever leashed within the confines of a legalized concubinage. He could not hear how, in her forceful predominance, she had sounded the first call to arms in that two hundred years' war to be fought between the sexes to its triumphant end in the cause of feminine enfranchisement.

But Mary knew; dimly, deep within her, she divined that the name which he had given her and to which she had brought disgrace and obloquy, would be upheld and honoured through the centuries to come.

She had one consolation left her in the fallen structure of her life . . . 'A small damsel who at present is everything I like, but alas! she is as yet in a white frock. At fourteen she may run away with the butler.'

* * *

Ten years had gone by since Mary had written that to her 'Sister Mar' in Paris; and now, although, like her mother, the 'damsel' was still small, she no longer wore white frocks nor had she run away with the butler.

She had none of her mother's beauty, but much of her mother's wayward will that, blent with her father's 'discretion and sobriety', resulted in a salutary tincture. She was snub-nosed, dimpled, with demure grey eyes full of latent humour, mild-mannered, gently spoken — and she was seventeen.

They had named her Mary, and they called her 'Anne' after her whom in feature, more than either of her parents, she resembled.

A mutual love for this child of Mary and Edward was the one firmly forged link in the slackening chain of their marriage. Their son was entirely lost to them. He had gone his own way to lead his own life, and to wed with a woman twice his age picked up in a stew at Oporto.

To her 'small damsel', therefore, Mary turned to lavish all the love her life had missed.

Anne's first appearance in Society, much to Mary's satisfaction and something to her wonder, had proved an unqualified success. A train of admirers flocked to the house in Covent Garden that Edward had bought with a thousand or two of the fortune left him by his father. Mary was encouraged to plan an ambitious future for her daughter. Her portion would be fabulous. Inherently mean though he was, Mary knew her husband could deny nothing to Anne, who, she decided, must marry a Duke. There were Dukes in plenty to be had for the asking and the daughter of a millionaire.

So Mary proposed, but God—or a young man from Scotland—disposed of this happy illusion.

A fearfully earnest, estimable youth was the sandy-haired, brawny Lord Bute, whose sole interest, since he had succeeded to his earldom, had been centred in his island home and farming, until . . .

It was at a Birthday Night Ball at the Palace that John Bute met his fate, and fell head over ears in love at first sight; an alarming experience.

Of Miss Wortley Montague it has been noted that 'the ugliness was all on her side': as gross a libel as any Pope has cast upon her mother. Miss Wortley Montagu was anything but ugly, and to the Earl of Bute's impassioned eyes endowed with the graces of Hebe. He hung upon her words, that, though few as her mother's were many, rang in his ears, accustomed to the rude Gaelic accent of the North, like the sound of a heavenly choir. What she said mattered little to the captivated Bute; what he said to her, on that first occasion of their meeting, mattered much.

Might he be permitted to attend Miss Wortley Montagu at her father's house?

Yes, Miss Wortley Montagu thought . . . perhaps he might.

"Perhaps tomorrow?"

"Perhaps . . ." there may have been some pretty palpitations, "yes, tomorrow."

Tomorrow and tomorrow; a succession of tomorrows unfolded before them, each day a golden bead to count upon a secret thread of happiness . . . Oh, dear! And how long, fluttered 'Miss', before he spoke to Father? They met in the Ring, at the Play, at a revival of the *Beggar's Opera*, when Miss Mary, in a box beside Mamma, and Lord Bute, opposite in solitary state, were carried in spirit 'Over the hills and far away', to walk in Elysian fields.

"This Bute," said Mary after some few weeks of it, "is paying court to Anne."

She had come upon her husband in his library to tell him so. Perched on a ladder, digging out a volume on political economy, Edward turned so sharply that he all but toppled down.

"Have a care!" cried Mary. "Do you want to break your neck?"

She steadied the steps until he had descended with a book beneath his arm and his hands beneath his nose; he was myopic.

"Do the housemaids," he inquired, "never dust these shelves?"

"They should, but I am sure I don't know. I cannot be for ever running after them up ladders."

Edward held his peace.

Glancing aside at her it struck him she was ageless. The years had dealt more kindly with Mary than with him. Though her eyes harboured shadows and her skin had the ivory tint of mellowed parchment, her figure was that of a girl. He caught sight of himself in a mirror; his face had thinned, his cheekbones protruded, his shoulders stooped a little. In accordance with the fashion of the day his wig was white, as the cropped hair beneath it.

"I was speaking of your daughter," Mary said.

"Yes. What of her?"

"Send me patience!" cried his wife. "Have I not told you? This Bute is courting Anne. He is always at her heels, and although I allow them no chance to meet alone I strongly suspect clandestine assignations."

"Has he money?"

"None at all, I believe. But I don't complain of that. She will have a handsome settlement."

"She will not have a shilling till I die," said Edward, sharp.

"We will not talk of dying. She will, of course, have her portion. That is, providing she marries one whom I—we—choose for her. I wish only to bring to your notice, for the present, that if you are willing to permit your daughter to wed with an impoverished Scotsman, who can offer her no better home than a dilapidated castle on an island in the middle of the sea, I am not."

Edward stared, and said, severely: "When, or if, the young man should speak to me of his intentions, it will be time enough to discuss the matter. I know nothing against him, providing he can keep her. He comes of good stock. And pray send a maid to dust these books. They are filthy."

He took himself off.

Since it was evident her husband did not share her disapproval of Anne's swain, Mary called her daughter to her and bluntly spoke her mind.

"This Bute, who dances attendance on you daily—with flowers—don't deny it!" as Anne, turning red and pale, opened her lips and shut them quick—"which I'll wager," pursued Mary, "he can ill-afford—has he declared himself, my dear?"

"No, Mamma," Anne said, meekly, casting down her eyes.

"Hah! So he *has* declared himself. Answer me."

Anne was dumb.

"Has he?" persisted Mary. "Don't stand there like a deaf-mute, girl. I am asking you a question."

"Well, no," Anne swallowed, "I can't say he has *spoken*, but I think—Oh, Mamma!" The face she turned upon her mother was radiant with blushes. "I know he loves me almost as much as I love him."

"Indeed."

Mary folded her lips and her hands, with a prayer in her heart. God, I want only her happiness but never—no never —with Bute! Her sister Frances had married a Scot and what came of it? Tragedy. All Scotsmen, Mary sweepingly asserted, were Jacobites, and therein danger lay. Besides, she was too young to take the first. I, said Mary, had to wait. Pity me, I did! And, rising from her chair, "I will send this Bute," she told her daughter, "on his business. He has shown himself no proper gentleman to make his addresses to you before first approaching your father. Moreover, he's a numskull—one can see that in a glance. I don't have to hear him speak." She walked to her bureau and sat. "I am writing to tell your young gentleman that henceforth he must cease his attentions, of which neither I nor your Papa approve."

Mary paused; she had heard a loud breathing behind her, and turned to find Anne at her elbow.

"You can't. You shan't!"

A silence pregnant as with gathering storm followed this unparalleled outburst. That her gentle, mild-mannered daughter should so far forget herself as to utter the unutterable, was a rude but not a paralysing shock. Mary summoned her forces.

" 'Can't'—'shan't'—to me? Do you wish to have me slap you?" she asked, awfully.

"I don't care." Anne's body was shaking, her lower lip bulging, her words tumbling out of her. "Do what you will— *kill* me if you must, but you can't kill my love for him. You can't!"

"What's this?" For an instant Mary's eyelids closed as if against the impact of a blow; and on that momentary weakening Anne swooped to seize her advantage.

"You wouldn't be so cruel, Mamma, as to—o," and she was weeping, "write to John."

Oho! thought Mary, so it's 'John', and 'Anne', no doubt, and Lord knows what besides.

"Come, child," she urged briskly, "don't be foolish. A grown girl to cry? I'm surprised at you. Leave me now. I wish to be alone."

"I won't leave you. I won't!" Rocked in a tumult of emotion, Anne sprang at her mother, her eyes wild, her small breasts heaving. "I'll *not* give him up! You can't make me. 'Tis true he hasn't actually spoken of marriage, but he has spoken of his love. Yesterday. In Bond Street."

"In Bond Street?" echoed Mary, limp.

"Yes. You sent me out with Grace to buy ribbands for my night-shifts. And he was there. And so I sent Grace back to buy more ribbands. And then," sobbed Anne, "he said that he adored me."

"A very interesting attachment," articulated Mary. "And what else did he say?"

"Nothing else," blubbered Anne. "But 'twas I told him —*begged* him—not to go to my father. Not until I could speak to Papa first. I knew I couldn't speak to you. But Papa is not so hard. You're hard." The storm was up again and raging. "You're cruel. You have ideas. You hate the Scots. 'Tis unreasonable—*wicked* to hate him for a Scot because of Uncle Mar. I know. You think I'm a fool. A bread-and-butter fool. You think everyone's a fool except yourself."

At the enormity of this unprecedented impudence from one who was the soul of 'discretion and sobriety', Mary sat confounded; but only for a moment. Gathering her fallen dignity about her she rose to make reply.

"I am immeasurably shocked. How dare you speak so to your mother?"

"I shall speak so, and I can!" was Anne's graceless response to that; and though great tears were splashing down her cheeks, the defiance and the temper stayed. Truly the girl is translated, Mary soothed herself to think; and was wretchedly aware of her own defencelessness against such seismic convulsion.

"I *can*!" yelled Anne, reiterative and stamping. "You've ruled me all my life, but you can't rule me for ever. My brother ran away from you. He was stronger than me—than I. It's always what *you* want. Never what *we* want. And I know what *I* want—and that's to marry John. You eloped with my father," cried Anne, terribly. "Yes, you did. You can't deny it. Everybody knows it. Grace told me you did. She helped you. And my Uncle Kingston helped you. But

I've no one to help me. And if you and Papa—" screamed Anne with rising passion, "won't give your consent to my marrying John, then as true as I'm alive I shall marry him without it!"

She dashed from the room, banging the door to shake it off its hinges. Her steps pattered in the hall; Mary heard her bounding up the stairs, and then the slamming of another door above.

With a queer empty sensation as if all the breath in her body had left it and the blood in her veins had ceased to flow, Mary found herself whispering weakly, "Who would ever have dreamed that the child had it in her?"

Had *what* in her? The spirit that her mother recognized and inwardly, despite dismay, applauded. Yes, ecod! And so it should be. This 'bread-and-butter fool' of hers had proved herself a chip of her own block; yet if war must be declared, I know, said Mary, with a private little smile, who will win.

And crossing to the bell she rang for Grace.

"Pack Miss Wortley Montagu's baggage and order the coach to be ready to leave before sundown. I am sending my daughter to Yorkshire. Tonight."

And to Yorkshire that night did Anne go, but not to stay; to outrace the moorland winds along the Great North Road, post-speeding it to Gretna with—John Bute.

So in one moment of recurrence, of history retold, the unpredictable had happened. Youth, secure in its arrogant purblind conviction that life and all life's laws were created solely for itself, had entered the lists against Age to give tongue, and with shrill triumphant battle-cry had burst open the doors of the citadel to deal its bitter blow—though not its death-blow. Never! While shaken to the depths of her heart's core by this cataclysmic upheaval that had over-turned her hitherto assured autocracy, Mary did not fall before it; she faced, with Spartan courage, her humiliation.

She had nursed beneath her roof an unsuspected and ungovernable spirit, a savage young vixen in the guise of a personal mouse; which was indeed dreadful enough, but that Anne, docile, pliant, her pride and her hope, should have turned to lacerate her by an act of such irrevocable cruelty was past all power of credence.

Anne had gone! And with what unimaginable subterfuge and cunning, guarded, not by the dotingly indulgent Grace, but by a pair of trusted servants, William and Mary, who had been sternly enjoined never for one instant to relax their charge. And then . . . O, monstrous! The elaborate deceit, the note conveyed, God alone knew how, to the lodging of her lover to inform him of this crisis, to induce him to follow and carry her off, within three days of her departure, from the inn at Boroughbridge. The immense, incalculable shame of it!

To exacerbate her further Edward evinced a philosophic tolerance to this horror thrust upon them.

"Youth," he said, "must have its way—full circle."

Full circle! Nemesis! Blood of her blood had reverted to Nature's inexorable call, to sow, in one moment's imbecility, seeds of unending remorse.

So Mary in the aftermath of revolution may have reasoned; and, as in the shattered remnants of her pride, she may have hoped. If she could have looked into the future it might have salved her wound to know that her child's stolen marriage would be fulfilled in joy and motherhood complete, denied to her. It might have gratified her also could she have foretold that 'this Bute', to whom his young wife with unfailing regularity bore eleven children, would rise to lead the country as First Lord of the Treasury, Prime Minister of England, in the reign of George the Third.

But Mary was no oracle to prophesy the fate of her unrepentant girl beyond the price—at what a cost!—that she herself had paid for her impetuosity; nor would she raise a hand to call her back.

*　　　*　　　*

The fierce high tides of twelve long troubled years had passed into the stream of middle life, when Mary declared her resolve.

Out of a blue sky and on a summer's morning in 1739, she shot her bolt. "The wanderlust," she told her husband, "is upon me, as every so often, like a tertian fever, it comes, and there is no better remedy than to let it run its course."

"To kill", a slow ironic smile dragged the corners of his mouth, "or to cure?"

"If there be any cure," her smile bitter-sweetly answered his, "for that special malaise of the heart that I believe is always the accompaniment to fever."

An involuntary spasm crossed his face; and as if to hide it he stroked his chin and gently coughed into his hand.

"We have both," he said sententiously, "shared our disappointments. Our son—" a tremor gripped his voice to halt it; and something broke within her.

"Edward!" She went to him, her eyes alight and shining with the hope that throbbed through the whisper, "can we not share what may be left to us of all that once was ours? . . . If we could!"

He stood motionless, his querulous white eyebrows drawn together on a swift intake of breath; and had he spoken then, the wintered ashes of their lives might have been rekindled to a semblance of the flame that had long ago consumed them. Yet though he seemed to struggle with words unuttered, as one who has been dumb and finds lost speech returning, his lips were closed; and from her eyes the glow had vanished.

"But I see," her smile stayed, "that we cannot."

It was scarcely a matter of general interest that Lady Mary intended to travel abroad. The days when her doings were in everybody's mouth belonged to the past. She, formerly notorious, famed for her beauty and daring and the numerous scandals attached to her name by that very naughty Mr. Pope, was regarded by the younger generation as a relic from an age remote from theirs; an oddity, a curio, a tiresome sharp-tongued old person. None was concerned to hear that Lady Mary's doctor had ordered her to Italy to avoid an English winter—so bad for her bronchitis.

This polite fiction was maintained between Edward and herself, even to the length of an understanding that he would join her later.

To a traveller of Mary's hardened experience the prospect of a journey to the Continent, accompanied by only two servants, offered no intimidation. She might be away a year or two, or ten, or merely a few months, and would go or stay when or where the spirit moved her.

Methodically she made her preparations; Venice was her goal, then Florence, Rome; and after, if so minded, she would explore the South of France. Edward raised no obstacle; indeed he urged her for her health's sake not to delay her departure till the autumn, but to leave in mid-summer. As soon as his business to do with his Yorkshire estates had been dealt with, he would endeavour to meet her in Italy and spend the winter in the sun.

There were no farewell scenes. At the last minute, Edward, who had seemed to develop a cold, was persuaded by his wife not to drive with her to Dover. She would write to him from Dartford on the road. He must nurse that nasty rheum. She had ordered him a hot foot-bath of mustard water. Grace, left behind to run the house in her lady's absence, would see to his wants.

Nothing could have been more wifely. He was touched, and wrote a letter to her to be left at the Dover post-house, urging her to hire a boat and not to take the packet. He would be more content to know that she had crossed to France in 'private comfort' than in a public vessel.

She followed his advice, at a cost to herself of five guineas, a prudent outlay, 'for otherwise I must have gone in the night,' so ran her scribbled note from Dover. 'The wind is fair, and I hope to be in Calais in the morning.'

But those fair winds rose to a gale, to send the barque rocking over high seas under a haggard grey sky.

"Storm always follows me," she told the skipper, "on my travels."

He suggested she should go below; they were in for a blustering voyage. She laughed in his face. "There's nothing I like more than a rough passage."

Yet as the staunch little ship ploughed through the Channel's angry waters, a silvery light slid out of the clouds to crest the nearing coast of France with the promise of sun before nightfall. . . .

. . . And that light was all about her when she woke at taper-time.

" 'Give me, great God', I said, ' a little farm, in summer shady and in winter . . .' But there is no winter where I've lived so long, and where God gave to me my farm."

Her eyelids lifted; she saw her daughter there beside her, heard her tears.

"Why do you sigh?" From that wisp of a body the quavering voice welled up with gathered strength to say, "I am not sad. That I am here with you again is as much a miracle as any in the Golden Legend."

There were movements in the shadowed room, and murmurs; a portly shape outlined against the dark uncurtained window. "You may go," she told the doctor, "I wish to be alone with Lady Bute."

The boards creaked to his step; the door closed, and in those filmed old eyes sprang a gleam as of a burnt candle's last flicker.

"These poke-nose physicians," she said. "I've had a taste of 'em, and I've beat them at their own game, too!" A chirp of a chuckle was followed by the words, "They've made good use of my story in a nutshell in the five and twenty years I've been abroad . . . How London's changed! This Third George is also a farmer, they say. There's been a fine to-do over the birth of his son, and that'll be another George, the Fourth . . . Give me a draught. My mouth's dry. No, not that man's physic, 'tis bitter as hell. A sip o' the cognac I brought with me from France."

Her daughter filled a phial and held it to her lips. She grew garrulous on brandy to speak of her long exile. Her daughter let her talk, as often now, when 'that man's' despised physic had narcotized the pain so bravely borne, she would talk and tell of those sun-filled days that crowded round her, growing ever nearer, more distinct, until the past became the present and there was no life but memory.

Her farm in Italy, at Gottolengo . . . It had a wooded garden running down to the river, and there she used to fish, a fine large trout something similar to, and as good to

318

eat as any salmon. Her garden was a vineyard. She brewed her own wines. "I'd have sent you a pipe but that the Customs would have charged you too high for it."

Every morning she rose at six o' the clock, inspected her dairy, her bees, she kept bees, and took a turn among her poultry. She had two hundred hens, geese, ducks, turkeys; peacocks too, for roasting . . . "And," she smiled, "I was happy." She had only two regrets. "The one, that I came home too late to see your father"—she had never seen him since the day she parted from him—"and the other, that you've never seen my farm."

Yes, and she made friends with two old priests; and each evening she would play at Whisk with them, or watch the dancing on the green . . . "Where partners lose themselves to find themselves and meet again, hands given," her voice sank; her smile deepened, "when the jig is done."

COOMBE HILL. *October 1952—December 1953.*

319

AUTHORITIES CONSULTED

Letters of Lady Mary Wortley Montagu. W. Moy Thomas, with introductory anecdotes by her grand-daughter, Lady Louisa Stuart, 1861.

Letters and Works, Lady Mary Wortley Montagu. Edited by Lord Wharncliffe, 1837.

Lady Mary Wortley Montagu and her Times. George Paston, 1907.

The Admirable Lady Mary. Lewis Gibbs, 1949.

Sir Richard Steele. Willard Connely, 1934.

Anecdotes. Rev. Joseph Spence, 1858.

Works and Life of Pope. Rev. Whitwell Elwin and W. J. Courthope, 1889.

Pope, the Leslie Stephen Lecture. Lytton Strachey, 1925.

Addison. Edited by W. J. Courthope, 1884.

The Four Georges. W. M. Thackeray.

Lord Hervey's Memoirs. Romney Sedgwick, 1952.

Memoirs of the Reign of George II. John, Lord Hervey, edited by John Wilson Croker from the original manuscript at Ickworth.

The London Spy. Ned Ward, with introduction by Ralph Straus.

Lord Hervey and his friends. Edited by the Earl of Ilchester, 1950.

Georgian England. H. E. Richardson, 1931.

A Constitutional King, George I. Sir W. M. Imbert-Terry, 1927.

Critical Review (on the Embassy letters). Smollett.

The Harem. N. M. Penzer, 1936.

Constantinople. A. Von Millingen, 1906.

National Dictionary of Biography, Gentleman's Magazine, Spectator, Tatler, etc.

*Made and printed in Great Britain
for The Companion Book Club (Odhams Press Ltd.)
by Odhams (Watford) Limited, Watford, Herts
S.1055.ZT*